Algebra 2 Connections
Version 3.0

Managing Editors

Judy Kysh
San Francisco State University
San Francisco, CA

Evra Baldinger
Phillip and Sala Burton Academic High School
San Francisco, CA

Contributing Editors

Karen Arth
Central High School East
Fresno, CA

Mark Atkinson
North Salem High School
Salem, OR

Carlos Cabana
San Lorenzo High School
San Lorenzo, CA

John Cooper
Del Oro High School
Loomis, CA

Elizabeth Coyner
Christian Brothers High School
Sacramento, CA

Dolores Dean
Holy Family High School
Broomfield, CO

Ernest Derrera
Roosevelt High School
Johnston, CO

Leslie Dietiker
Michigan State University
East Lansing, MI

Bob Petersen
Rosemont High School
Sacramento, CA

Norm Prokup
The College Preparatory School
Oakland, CA

Barbara Shreve
San Lorenzo High School
San Lorenzo, CA

Estelle Woodbury
San Lorenzo High School
San Lorenzo, CA

Karen Wootton
Odenton, MD

Illustrator

Kevin Coffey
San Francisco, CA

Technical Managers

Bethany Armstrong
Davis, CA

Sarah Maile
Sacramento, CA

Aubrie Maze
Berkeley, CA

Technical Assistants

Daniel Chan
Evan Clark
Elizabeth Fong
Rebecca Harlow
Carolyn Kooi

Brian Chow
Marcos Rojas
Eric Sadur
Tiffany Trujillo

Program Directors

Leslie Dietiker
Michigan State University
East Lansing, MI

Brian Hoey
Christian Brothers High School
Sacramento, CA

Judy Kysh, Ph.D.
Departments of Education and Mathematics
San Francisco State University

Tom Sallee, Ph.D.
Department of Mathematics
University of California, Davis

Contributing Editors to the Parent Guide

Brian Hoey
CPM Educational Program
Sacramento, CA

Sarah Maile
CPM Educational Program
Sacramento, CA

Bob Petersen
Rosemont High School
Sacramento, CA

Karen Wootton
CPM Educational Program
Odenton, MD

Technical Manager

Sarah Maile
CPM Educational Program
Sacramento, CA

3 4 5 6 7 8 9   12 11 10 09   Version 3.0

Printed in the United States of America   ISBN-13: 978-1-931287-97-5

A Note to Students:

Welcome to Algebra 2! In this course, you will deepen and extend your knowledge of algebra to build a powerful set of mathematical tools for solving problems. Algebra is a way of thinking: a way of investing new situations, discovering relationships and figuring out strategies to apply to problems. You will apply your algebraic tools to a variety of situations and use them to draw and support your conclusions. Learning to think this way is useful both in mathematical contexts and in other courses, and in life beyond school.

In meeting the challenges of Algebra 2, you will not be working alone. During this course you will collaborate with other students as a member of a study team. Working in a team means speaking up and interacting with others. You will explain your ideas, listen to what others have to say, and ask questions if there is something you do not understand. In algebra, a single problem can often be solved more than one way. You will see problems in different ways than your teammates do. Each of you has something to contribute while you work on the lessons in this course.

Together, your team will complete problems and activities that will help you discover new mathematical ideas and methods. Your teacher will support you as you work, but will not take away your opportunity to think and investigate for yourself. The ideas in the course will be revisited several times and connected to other topics. If something is not clear to you the first time you work with it, keep track of it, but don't worry – you will have more chances to build your understanding as the course continues.

Learning math this way has a significant advantage: as long as you actively participate, make sure everyone in your study team is involved, and ask good questions, you will find yourself understanding mathematics at a deeper level than ever before. By the end of this course, you will have a powerful understanding of properties and principles of functions. You will see how these properties and principles connect with each other so that you can use them together to model real life situations. With your teammates you will meet mathematical challenges you would not have known how to approach before.

We wish you well and are confident that you will enjoy learning Algebra 2!

Sincerely,

The CPM Team

Algebra 2 Connections
Table of Contents
Student Edition

Chapter 8 Trigonometric Functions

Chapter 9   Polynomial Functions

CHAPTER 8   Trigonometric Functions

This chapter begins with an experiment that will generate a new curve called a cyclic function. You will then explore the relationship between right-triangle trigonometry and this new curve. You will be introduced to a new representation that is useful for the study of cyclic functions: a unit circle. You will also learn how to use radians instead of degress to describe angles.

In the second section of this chapter, you will transform cyclic functions and find general equations for them. You will also learn about a new property that is charactaeristic of cyclic functions called a period. Then you will write equations for the curve that you generated in the experiment at the beginning of the chapter.

Guiding Questions

Think about these questions throughout this chapter:

What is the connection?

What does it mean?

How can I transform it?

What representations can I use?

In this chapter, you will learn:

> To recognize and create multiple representations of the functions $y = \sin\theta$ and $y = \cos\theta$.

> How to graph functions of the family whose parents are $y = \sin x$ and $y = \cos x$.

> The relationships between a unit circle and a graph of a cyclic function.

> How to use radians instead of degrees to measure lengths of arcs and angles.

Chapter Outline

Section 8.1   In this section, you will use your understanding of the trigonometric ratios in right triangles to build understanding of three new functions. You will also learn to use a new unit to measure angles.

Section 8.2   In this section, you will apply your expertise with transforming parent graphs to develop general equations for cyclic or trigonometric functions. You will also learn about a property particular to cyclic functions called a period.

8.1.1 What cyclic relationships can I model?

Introduction to Cyclic Models

In this chapter, you will learn about a new family of functions that are very useful for describing relationships that are **cyclic** (have repeating cycles), like the height of the ocean as the tides fluctuate between high and low or the distance of a swinging pendulum from its center point.

8-1. EMERGENCY!

Nurse Nina rushes through the hospital with one hand on her clipboard and the other pulling a portable blood stand. The bags of blood swinging from the stand are needed in the emergency room (E.R.) *'stat'* for three patients in severe need. She is so intent on delivering the blood in time that she does not notice that one of the bags has a small hole in it and is dripping on the floor behind her. As she reaches the E.R., she is horrified to see a small pool of blood beginning to form on the floor. Looking down the corridor from where she came, she sees the trail of blood that dripped and notices that it forms a very interesting pattern.

What shape do you think the trail of blood created?

Your task: Use the materials and instructions provided by your teacher to re-create the pattern that the nurse saw on the hallway floor behind her. Make as many observations as you can about the shape you see and how that shape relates to what was happening to the bag of blood. Be sure to keep track of all the details. Be prepared to explain your observations to the class. (Note: Complete directions for conducting this experiment are on the next page.)

Directions for the Pendulum Experiment (Problem 8-1)

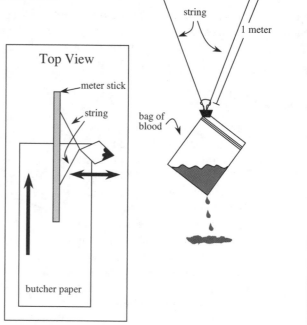

Find a space in the classroom where there is room to work. You may need to move your table or desks out of the way.

Set up your pendulum by attaching your bag of liquid to a meter stick using string, as shown at right.

Assign the following tasks:

- One student holds the meter stick from which the pendulum swings.

- One student holds the bag, releases it when ready, and then stops it when it reaches the end of the paper.

- Two students hold the butcher paper, one at each end, and slide it *at a constant rate* underneath the swinging pendulum. Be sure to slide the paper parallel to the meter stick and perpendicular to the swing of the pendulum, as shown in the diagram at right.

Tips for a successful experiment:

- The student holding the meter stick should hold the places where the string attaches. Otherwise, the string has a tendency to slide toward the center of the meter stick.

- Use as much of the string as you can so that your pendulum is as long as possible.

- When you are ready, have your teacher cut a *very* small hole in the corner of the bag. The student holding the bag should pinch this hole closed until the pendulum begins swinging.

- Be sure to slide the butcher paper under the pendulum *at a constant rate*.

- As you pull the bag up to start the pendulum swinging, hold it taut from the bottom corner so that the bag remains in line with the string (see diagram at right).

- Have an extra bag ready to place the dripping bag into when the experiment is complete.

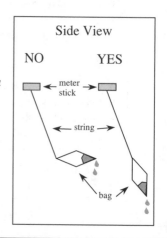

8-2. Now you will make predictions about a new curve.

a. With your team, design your own curve similar to the one already created. Decide exactly how you want it to look. How long do you want each cycle? How tall do you want it to be? Where do you want it to be on your paper? Where do you want it to start? Once you have decided on your new curve, make a sketch of it on your paper.

b. Predict how you could conduct an experiment to get exactly the curve you have described. How fast should you move the paper? Where would you start it? How high would you start your pendulum? Be prepared to share your predictions and their **justifications** with the class.

8-3. Draw a sketch of one of the shapes the class created with the drips from the swinging pendulum in Lesson 8.1.1.

a. Sketch what the shape would look like if the bag were pulled out farther before it was let go.

b. Sketch what the shape would look like if the paper underneath the pendulum traveled faster.

8-4. Karin was working on graphing the function $f(x) = \frac{2}{x-3}$. She made a table (shown below), but she is not sure how to graph the values in the table. Show Karin how to make her graph and tell her everything you know about her function.

x	-3	-2	-1	0	1	2	3	4	5	6	7	8	9
$f(x)$	$-\frac{1}{3}$	$-\frac{2}{5}$	$-\frac{1}{2}$	$-\frac{2}{3}$	-1	-2	*	2	1	$\frac{2}{3}$	$\frac{1}{2}$	$\frac{2}{5}$	$\frac{1}{3}$

*undefined

8-5.   In each of the following triangles, find the length of the side labeled x.

a.

28 feet

b.

150 cm

c.

47 meters

38°

8-6.   Copy the triangles at right and label the missing side lengths.

8-7.   Find the equation of the parabola that passes through the points $(0, 0)$, $(3, 9)$, and $(6, 0)$.

8-8.   Solve and check your solution: $2\sqrt{21-x} - \sqrt{3x-6} = 5$.

8-9.   Find the inverse functions for the functions given below.

a. $f(x) = \sqrt[3]{4x-1}$ b. $g(x) = \log_7 x$

8-10.   Find the x- and y-intercepts of $y - 7 = 3^{(x+4)}$.

8-11.   Change $x^2 - 2x + y^2 - 29 = 0$ to graphing form then sketch the graph and label the important points.

8.1.2 How can I graph it?

Graphing the Sine Function

Today you will use what you know about right-triangle relationships and about graphing functions to **investigate** a new function.

8-12. *"HURRY!!! Let's get there before the line gets too long!"* shouts Antonio to his best friend René as they race to get on *The Screamer*, the newest attraction at the local amusement park.

"It's only been open for one day, and already everyone is saying it's the scariest ride at the park!" exclaims Antonio. *"I hear they really had to rush to get it done in time for summer."*

Antonio whistles as he screeches to a halt in front of the huge sign that says, *"Welcome to The Screamer, the Scariest Ride on Earth."* The picture below it shows an enormous wheel that represents *The Screamer*, with its radius of 100 feet. Half of the wheel is below ground level, in a very dark, murky pit with water at the bottom. As *The Screamer* rotates at dizzying speeds, riders fly up into the air before plunging downward through blasts of freezing air, hair-raising screams, and sticky spider webs into the pit where they splash through the dark, eerie water on their way back above ground.

René and Antonio wait impatiently to get on the ride, watching passengers load and unload. New passengers get on and strap themselves in as others emerge from the pit looking queasy. The ride rotates 15° to load and unload the next set of riders. As René straps himself in, he remembers Antonio's ominous words: *"I hear they really had to rush to get it done in time for summer."*

Sure enough, just as the ride plunges René and Antonio into the greasy water, they hear the piercing scream of metal twisting. Sparks fly and the pit fills with smoke as the ride grinds to a halt. To escape, all of the passengers must climb vertically to ground level from wherever they got stuck, either up from the pit or down from dizzying heights.

Problem continues on next page. →

8-12. *Problem continued from previous page.*

notch to turn

Your task: Find a function that describes the distance each passenger must climb in order to escape from the broken ride, *The Screamer*.

To help you gather data, your teacher will provide you with the materials to build a model of this situation. Layer your transparency circle on top of your cardboard circle and insert a toothpick to act as an axle. Then slide the circles into the slit in your cardboard box, as shown in the diagram at right.

a. Use the transparent One Unit Ruler to measure the escape heights on the model for at least 16 different possible seat positions. The seat could be in the pit, high in the air, or right at ground level. Remember that this position depends on the angle of the ride's rotation when it broke down. The radius of the model wheel will be referred to as one unit. That is, a model height of one unit corresponds to an actual height of 100 feet on the ride, so an actual height of 80 feet on the ride will be represented by a measured height of 0.8 units on the model. Record your data in a table like the one shown below. Leave room for additional columns.

Degree of Rotation from 0° (Platform)	Measured Height $(0 \le y \le 1)$	Actual Height Above (or Below) Platform	

b. Graph your data on a large graph.

c. Suppose you were asked to add 20 more data points to your table. What shortcuts could you use to reduce the amount of work?

8-13. What function can you use to model the situation in problem 8-12? To help you figure it out, sketch the right triangle shown in the diagram at right.

a. With your team, write an equation and use it to calculate the height of the triangle. Does the escape height you calculated seem reasonable compared to the data you collected in problem 8-12?

b. Write an equation representing the escape height $h(\theta)$ for *any* passenger, for any angle of rotation of *The Screamer*. (Note that the angle is represented by the Greek letter theta, which looks like this: θ.)

Problem continues on next page. →

8-13.   *Problem continued from previous page.*

    c.   Enter the data from the first two columns of your table into your grapher. Adjust the viewing window so you can see all of the data. Then graph $h(\theta)$ on top of the data. How well does $h(\theta)$ fit your data?

    d.   Adjust the viewing window so that you can see more of the graph of $h(\theta)$. Describe the behavior of the graph as θ gets larger. Does this make sense? Why or why not?

    e.   Use the 'table' function of your calculator to find its calculated values for $h(\theta)$. Add another column to your table from problem 8-12, label it with the equation you found for $h(\theta)$, and enter these values, rounding off to the nearest hundredth. How do the calculated values compare with your measured ones?

8-14.   René and Antonio finally make it home from the amusement park unhurt, but in need of a shower. As soon as they have cleaned up, they go over to a friend's house to share their scary experience on *The Screamer*. They draw a picture of the Ferris wheel and five of the seats, located at 15°, 30°, 45°, 60°, and 75° (shown at right and on the resource page provided by your teacher).

    a.   Label each triangle with its *calculated* height. You can use your data from problem 8-12. If you do not have data for all of these angles, return to the 'table' function on your grapher. Plot these heights at their angle location on the coordinate system to the right of the circle. You will be plotting points in the form (x = angle in degrees, y = height).

    b.   Draw five new triangles that are congruent to the first five, but that are located in the second quadrant. Label these with their angle measures (from 0°) and heights. Use the angle measures and heights to plot five new points on the graph that correspond to these five new points on the circle.

    c.   Continue this process by drawing triangles in the third and fourth quadrants. You should have a total of twenty triangles drawn and twenty points plotted. Then label the points where the circle intersects the x- and y-axes with their angle measures and heights and then add points for them to the graph as well. Sketch a smooth curve through the points.

    d.   Discuss with your team all of the relationships you can find among the points on the circle and between your unit circle and the graph. Be prepared to share your ideas with the class.

METHODS AND MEANINGS

Special Right-Triangle Relationships

As you may recall from geometry, there are certain right triangles whose sides have special relationships that make certain calculations easier. One such triangle is half of an equilateral triangle and is known as a **30° – 60° – 90° triangle**, named after the degree measures of its angles.

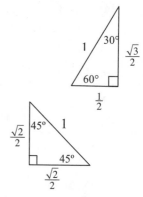

The other special triangle is half of a square and is known as the **45° – 45° – 90° triangle**. Both triangles are shown at right.

━━━━━ Review & Preview ━━━━━

8-15.   Copy the triangles at right.

a.   Label the missing sides with their *exact* lengths. That is, leave your answers in radical form.

b.   The 30° – 60° – 90° triangle is sometimes called a half-equilateral. Draw a picture to illustrate this, and explain how that fact can be used to help label the missing sides in part (a).

8-16.   Find the measure of angle *A* in the diagram at right.

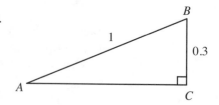

8-17.   This is a Checkpoint problem for completing the square and finding the vertex of a parabola.

Complete the square to change the equation $y = 2x^2 - 4x + 5$ to graphing form, identify the vertex of the parabola, and sketch its graph.

If you needed help completing the square to change this equation to graphing form and identify the vertex, then you need more practice. Review the Checkpoint 14 materials and try the practice problems. Also, consider getting help outside of class time. From this point on, you will be expected to complete the square and identify the point (h, k) for equations such as these quickly and accurately.

8-18.   Leadfoot Lilly was driving 80 miles per hour when she passed a parked highway patrol car. By the time she was half a mile past the spot where the patrol car was parked, the officer was driving after her at 100 miles per hour. If these rates remain constant, how long will it take the officer to catch up to Lilly? Write and solve an equation to represent this situation.

8-19.   Evaluate each expression without using a calculator or changing the form of the expression.

a. $\log(1)$ b. $\log(10^3)$

c. $10^{\log(4)}$ d. $10^{3\log(4)}$

8-20.   Complete the table of values for $f(x) = \frac{x^2 + 4x - 5}{x - 1}$.

x	-2	-1	0	1	2	3
y						

a.   Graph the points in the table. What kind of function does it appear to be? Why is it not correct to connect all of the dots?

b.   Look for a simple pattern for the values in the table. What appears to be the relationship between x and y? Calculate $f(0.9)$ and $f(1.1)$ and add the points to your graph. Is there an asymptote at $x = 1$? If you are unsure, calculate $f(0.99)$ and $f(1.01)$ as well.

c.   Simplify the formula for $f(x)$. What do you think the complete graph looks like?

8-21.   In 1998, Terre Haute, Indiana had a population of 72,000 people. In 2000, the population had dropped to 70,379. City officials expect the population to level off eventually at 60,000.

   a.   What kind of function would best model the population over time?

   b.   Write an equation that would model the changing population over time.

8-22.   A semi-circular tunnel is 26 feet high at its highest point. A road 48 feet wide is centered under the tunnel. Bruce needs to move a house on a trailer through the tunnel. The load is 22 feet wide and 24 feet high. Will he make it? Use a diagram to help **justify** your reasoning completely.

8-23.   Find the value of x.

   a.

   b.

8-24.   Solve the system of equations shown at right.

$$x + y + z = 40$$
$$y = x - 5$$
$$x = 2z$$

8-25.   What is the domain of the entire graph of $h(\theta) = \sin\theta$? **Justify** your reasoning.

8-26.   Antonio's friend Jessica was also on *The Screamer* when it broke. Her seat was 65 feet above the ground. What was her seat's angle of rotation? Is there more than one possibility?

8-27.   Hilda was working on her homework. She completed the square to change $y = 3x^2 - 24x + 55$ to graphing form in order to identify the vertex of the parabola. She did the work at right and identified the vertex to be $(4, 39)$.

$$y = 3x^2 - 24x + 55$$
$$y = 3(x^2 - 8x) + 55$$
$$y = 3(x^2 - 8x + 16) + 55 - 16$$
$$y = 3(x - 4)^2 + 39$$

When she got back to class and checked her answers, she discovered that the vertex she found is incorrect, but she cannot find her mistake. Examine Hilda's work and explain to her what she did wrong. Then show her how to complete the square correctly and identify the vertex.

8-28.   Consider the system of equations at right. $x^2 + y^2 = 25$

      a.   Solve the system graphically. $y = x^2 + 3$

      b.   Now solve the system algebraically. In this case, which variable is easier to solve for first? Do it. Now try to solve for the other variable first. What caused you to get stuck?

8-29.   Mr. Keis wrote the following problem on the board and told his class, "*No calculators please. Simplify. You have sixty seconds!*"

$$\left(\tfrac{13^{12}}{14^{23}}\right)\left(\tfrac{27^{3}}{13^{11}}\right)\left(\tfrac{2^{10}}{27^{4}}\right)\left(\tfrac{14^{22}}{13}\right)\left(\tfrac{27}{2^{9}}\right)$$

Time yourself and simplify the expression. Did you meet the challenge?

8-30.   Graph the system at right. $1 + x - y \geq 3x - 2y - 4$

$$y < 2x^2 + 1$$

8-31.   Solve each of the following equations and check your solutions.

      a. $\dfrac{1}{x} + \dfrac{5}{4x} = \dfrac{1}{x+1}$ Challenge: $\dfrac{1}{1-x} + \dfrac{1}{1+\sqrt{x}} = \dfrac{1}{1-\sqrt{x}}$

8-32.   A function $W(x)$ is sketched at right.

      a.   Make your own copy of the graph, and then sketch the graph of the inverse of $W(x)$.

      b.   Is the inverse a function? Explain.

8-33.   Mary has an antique marble collection containing 40 marbles. She has five more red marbles than blue and twice as many red as green marbles. Write a system of equations and use matrices to find the number of each color of marble.

8.1.3 How are circles and sine graphs connected?

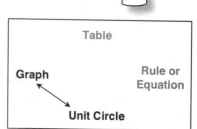

Unit Circle $\leftrightarrow$ Graph

Throughout this course, you have used multiple representations (table, graph, equation, and situation) to solve problems, **investigate** functions, and **justify** conclusions. In Lesson 8.1.2 you found that a unit circle is one representation of a sine function. Today you will **investigate** the connections between the unit circle and the graph, as you build a deeper understanding of the sine function.

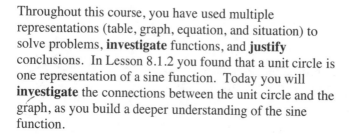

8-34.   Draw a circle on your paper. Draw a triangle that could represent René and Antonio's position on the wheel when *The Screamer* came to a sudden stop. Be sure to choose a different angle position from any of those you drew in problem 8-14.

   a.   Label the triangle with its height and its angle measure (from $0°$).

   b.   Did any other riders have to climb the same distance to get to safety (up *or* down) as René and Antonio did? If so, draw the corresponding triangles and label them completely.

   c.   What is the relationship between these triangles? Work with your team to **generalize** a method for finding all of the other corresponding angles when you are given just one angle.

8-35.   In problem 8-34, you used a unit circle to find the height of a seat on *The Screamer*. Could you use your graph of $y = \sin\theta$ instead to find the height?

   a.   Use the Lesson 8.1.3 Resource Page (a sine calculator) provided by your teacher to find the height of a seat that had rotated $130°$ from the starting platform.

   b.   Are there any other seats at exactly the same height? If so, indicate them on your sine calculator.

   c.   How can you use the symmetry of the graph to calculate which angles correspond to seats with the same height? Discuss this with your team and be prepared to share your **strategies** with the class.

   d.   For each of the following angles, use the sine calculator from the resource page to find the height at that angle and to find another angle with the same height. Then sketch a small unit circle, draw in each pair of angles, and label the heights.

   i. $80°$ *ii.* $200°$ *iii.* $310°$

8-36.   With your team, discuss the ways in which a unit circle and the graph of $s(\theta) = \sin\theta$ are connected. Be prepared to share your ideas with the class. Then record your ideas in a Learning Log. Use diagrams, arrows, and other math tools to help demonstrate your ideas. Label this entry "Unit Circle $\leftrightarrow$ Graph for $s(\theta) = \sin\theta$" and label it with today's date.

8-37.   Sketch a graph of the first two cycles of $s(\theta) = \sin\theta$. Then label your graph to show the following positions of a passenger on *The Screamer*.

   a.   The passenger gets on initially.

   b.   The passenger reaches the bottom of the water pit.

   c.   The passenger is halfway between the highest point of *The Screamer* and the ground level.

8-38.   Each of the points on the graph at right represents the position of a rider on *The Screamer*. Draw a diagram of each rider's position on a unit circle and describe where the rider is.

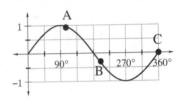

8-39.   While trying to measure the height of a tree, Julie noticed that a 3.5-foot post had a 4.25-foot shadow. If the tree's shadow is 100 feet long, how tall is the tree?

8-40.   Suppose you were to bend two whole sheets of $8\frac{1}{2}$-by-11 paper to form two cylinders (a tall, skinny one and a short, wide one). The volume of a cylinder can be calculated using the formula $V = (base\ area)(height)$ or $V = \pi r^2 h$.

   a.   Do the two cylinders have the same volume? **Justify** your answer.

   b.   Is the result different if you start with $8\frac{1}{2}$-by-$8\frac{1}{2}$ paper?

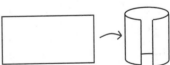

8-41.   Find the x- and y-intercepts of the quadratic function $y = 3x^2 + 6x + 1$.

8-42.   Write the quadratic function in problem 8-41 in graphing form and sketch its graph.

8-43.   Solve $|x + 5| = |x| - 5$ by graphing. Express your solution algebraically.

8-44.   Solve $\log_2 x = 2^x$ using any method.

8-45.   Maria Elena is collecting college pennants. She has five fewer pennants from Washington campuses than from California campuses and twice as many pennants from California campuses as from Pennsylvania campuses. She has 40 pennants in her collection. Write a system of equations to find the number of Pennants from each state.

8.1.4 How can I graph cosine?

Graphing and Interpreting the Cosine Function

In this lesson, you will use your knowledge of right triangles again—this time to develop your understanding of another cyclic function.

8-46.   Work with your team to find the coordinates of point P on the unit circle shown at right. Is there more than one way to find point P? Be prepared to share your **strategies** with the class.

8-47.   Now **generalize** what you found in problem 8-46 to write the coordinates of point Q on the unit circle shown at left.

8-48.   What can a sine value tell you about a point on a circle? What about a cosine value?

8-49.   If you know the sine of an angle in a unit circle, can you find its cosine? How? Work with your team to find a **strategy** and be prepared to share it with the class.

8-50.   Obtain a copy of the Lesson 8.1.4A Resource Page from your teacher. To graph the cosine function you will follow the same process as you did for the graph of the sine function in problem 8-14, but use the horizontal distance (or base of the triangle) instead of the height.

   a.   Label the length of the base of each triangle in the unit circle. Plot these lengths at their angle location on the coordinate system to the right of the circle. You will be plotting points in the form (angle in degrees, base).

   b.   Draw five new triangles that are congruent to the first five, but that are located in the second quadrant. Label the angle measure (from 0°) and the base for each triangle. Add five new corresponding points to the graph.

   c.   Continue this process by drawing triangles in the third and fourth quadrants. You should have a total of twenty triangles drawn and twenty points plotted. Then find the four points where the circle crosses the axes and label them with both their angle measures and their horizontal distances from the origin. Add points for these to the graph on the right as well. Finally, sketch a smooth curve through the points.

   d.   Compare this graph to the sine graph you got from graphing heights in problem 8-14. How are the two graphs similar? How are they different?

8-51.   Remember the scary Ferris wheel, *The Screamer*? LaRasha does! She was riding *The Screamer*, sitting 27 horizontal feet away from the central support pole, when the ride stopped. What was her seat's angle of rotation? Is there more than one possibility? **Justify** your answer using as many representations as you can.

8-52.   UNIT CIRCLE ↔ GRAPH

In problem 8-51, did you use a graph of $y = \cos\theta$ to find lengths of bases of triangles?

   a.   Use the Lesson 8.1.4B Resource Page (a cosine-calculator graph) provided by your teacher to find the length of the base of a triangle formed by a seat on *The Screamer* that had rotated 130° from the starting platform.

   b.   Are there any other triangles with the same base? If so, mark their corresponding points on your cosine calculator.

   c.   How can you use the symmetry of the cosine-calculator graph to calculate the angle location of seats on *The Screamer* that have the same base? Is your method different than the one you used to find the heights?

8-53.　Find the coordinates of points P and Q on the unit circle at right.

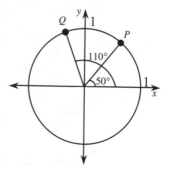

8-54.　The measure of $\angle ROS$ in $\triangle ROS$ below is 60°.

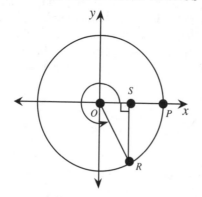

a.　The curved arrow represents the rotation of $\overline{OR}$, beginning from the positive x-axis. Through how many degrees has $\overline{OR}$ rotated?

b.　If $OR = 1$, what are the *exact* length of OS and SR?

c.　What are the *exact* coordinates of point R?

8-55.　What angle in the first quadrant could you reference to help you find the sine and cosine of each of the following angles?

a.　330°　　　b.　120°　　　c.　113°　　　d.　203°

8-56.　At right is a sequence of doodles and some numbers to go with them.

 180　 120　 90　 72

a.　Draw the next two doodles and state the numbers to go with them.

b.　What number would go with the 99th doodle? With the nth doodle?

8-57.　Solve $\frac{1}{1-\sqrt{x}} = 1 + \frac{\sqrt{x}}{1-\sqrt{x}}$.

8-58.　Solve $(\frac{1}{8})^{(2x-3)} = (\frac{1}{2})^{(x+2)}$.

8-59.   Sketch a graph of each equation below.

   a. $y = -2(x-2)^2 + 3$

   b. $y = (x-1)^3 + 3$

8-60.   Solve $3^x + 5 = x^2 - 5$ using any method.

8-61.   Rip-Off Rentals charges $25 per day plus 50¢ per mile to rent a mid-sized car. Your teacher will rent you his or her family sedan and charge you only 3¢ if you drive one mile, 6¢ if you drive two miles, 12¢ if you drive three, 24¢ for four, and so on.

   a.   Write a rule that will give you the cost to rent each car.

   b.   If you plan to rent the car for a two-day road trip, which is the better deal if you drive 10 miles? 20 miles? 100 miles?

8-62.   Refer back to your solutions from problems 8-24, 8-33, and 8-45. Explain how these problems are related.

8-63.   Shinna was riding *The Screamer* when it broke down. Her seat was 53 horizontal feet from the central support pole. What was her seat's angle of rotation? How can you tell?

8-64.   Sketch a unit circle. In your circle, sketch in an angle that has:

   a.   A positive cosine and a negative sine.

   b.   A sine of −1.

   c.   A negative cosine and a negative sine.

   d.   A cosine of about −0.9 and a sine of about 0.4.

   e.   Could an angle have a sine equal to 0.9 and cosine equal to 0.8? Give an angle or explain why not.

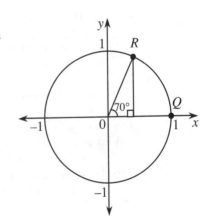

8-65.   A 70° angle is drawn for you in the unit circle at right.

   a.   Approximate the coordinates of point R.

   b.   How could you represent the *exact* coordinates of point R?

8-66.   Daniel sketched the graphs at right for $y = \sin\theta$ and $y = \cos\theta$.

Unfortunately, he forgot to label the graphs, and now he cannot remember which graph goes with which equation. Explain to Daniel how he can tell (and remember!) which graph is $y = \sin\theta$ and which is $y = \cos\theta$.

8-67.   Consider the system of equations $y = \cos x$ and $y = -1$.

   a.   Is it possible to solve this system by substitution? By the Elimination Method? By graphing?

   b.   List at least five possible solutions.

   c.   Consider the list of solutions you wrote in part (b) as a sequence and write a rule to represent *all* possible solutions.

8-68.   This problem is a checkpoint for writing and solving exponential equations.

When rabbits were first brought to Australia, they had no natural enemies. There were about 80,000 rabbits in 1866. Two years later, in 1868, the population had grown to over 2,400,000!

   a.   Why would an exponential equation be a better model for this situation than a linear one? Would a sine function be better or worse? Why?

   b.   Write an exponential equation for the number of rabbits t years after 1866.

   c.   How many rabbits do you predict would have been present in 1871?

   d.   According to your model, in what year was the first pair of rabbits introduced into Australia? Is this reasonable?

   e.   Actually, 24 rabbits were introduced in 1859, so the model is not perfect, but is close. Is your exponential model useful for predicting how many rabbits there are now? Explain.

   f.   Check your answers to parts (a) through (e) by referring to the Checkpoint 15 materials at the back of your book.

If you needed help to complete any part of this problem, then you need more practice writing and solving exponential equations to solve problems. Review the Checkpoint 15 materials and try the practice problems. Also, consider getting help outside of class time. From this point on, you will be expected to write and solve exponential equations to solve problems quickly and accurately.

8-69.   Solve each equation.

a. $\frac{3}{x+1} = \frac{4}{x}$ b. $\frac{3}{x+1} + \frac{4}{x} = 2$

c. $\frac{3}{x+2} + 5 = \frac{3}{x+2}$

d.   Explain why part (c) has no solution.

8-70.   Write the equation of any line parallel to $3x - y = 2$. Then write the equation of a parabola that intersects your line but does *not* intersect the graph of $3x - y = 0$.

8-71.   A $5' \times 4' \times 3'$ box is made for the purpose of storage. What is the longest pole that can fit inside the box?

8-72.   While working on their homework on sequences, Davis was suddenly stumped!

"This problem doesn't make sense!" he exclaimed. Tess was working on her homework as well.

"What's the problem?" she asked.

"This problem is about a SEQUENCE, $t(n) = 9n - 2$, but it is asking whether or not it is a function. How can a sequence be a function?"

"Well of course a sequence is a function!" said Tess.

Who is right? Should Davis be confused, or is Tess correct? Explain completely.

8.1.5 How else can I measure angles?

Defining a Radian

Whose idea was it to measure angles in degrees? And why are there 360° in a full turn? This decision actually dates back almost 4000 years! Degrees were created by the Babylonians, an ancient people who lived in the region that is now Iraq. The Babylonians also based their number system, called a sexigesimal system, on sixty.

Although you are familiar with measuring angles in degrees, this is not the only way to measure angles, nor is it necessarily the most useful. Today you will learn a different unit for measuring angles called a **radian**. Using radians instead of degrees is actually the standard across mathematics! When you take calculus, you will learn why radians are used in math more often than degrees.

8-73. What word are you reminded of when you hear the word **radian**? Discuss this with your team and make a conjecture about how this might relate to a way to measure angles. Be prepared to share your ideas with the class.

8-74. HOW TO MAKE A RADIAN

Imagine wrapping the radius of a circle around the circle. The angle formed at the center of the circle that corresponds to the arc that is one radius long has a measure of exactly one **radian**.

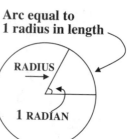

Your teacher will provide each member of your team with a differently sized circular object and some scissors.

a. Trace your circular object onto a sheet of paper and carefully cut out the circle. Fold the paper circle in half and then in half again so that it is in the shape of a quarter circle, as in the diagram at right. How can you see the radius of your circular object in this new folded shape?

b. Place your circular object onto another sheet of paper and trace it again, only this time leave the circular object in place. Roll (or wrap) a straight edge of your folded circle around your circular object and mark one radius length on the traced circle. Then mark another radius length that begins where the first one ended. Continue marking radius lengths until you have gone around the entire circle.

c. Remove the circular object from your paper. On your traced circle, connect each radius mark to the center, creating central angles. Each angle you see, formed by an arc with a length of one radius, measures one **radian**. Label each of the radius lengths and each angle that measures one full **radian**. Write a short description of how you constructed an angle with measure one radian.

8-75.   Assume the radius of a circle is one unit.

   a.   What is the area of the circle? What is its circumference?

   b.   How many radii would it take to wrap completely around the circle? Express
        your answer as a decimal approximation *and* as an exact value.

   c.   Does the size of the circle matter? That is, does the number of radii it takes to
        wrap around the circle change as the radius of the circle gets larger or smaller?
        Why does this make sense?

   d.   Exactly how many radians are in 360°? In 90°?

   e.   How is a radian related to a radius? Explain your understanding
        of this relationship in your Learning Log. Use diagrams to
        support your explanation. Title this entry "Radians" and label it
        with today's date.

8-76.   Parts (a) through (g) below describe angles. Draw each angle on its own unit circle.

   a.   1 degree   b.   1 radian   c. π radians   d. $\frac{\pi}{2}$ radians

   e. $\frac{\pi}{4}$ radians   f. $\frac{\pi}{3}$ radians   g. $\frac{\pi}{6}$ radians

8-77.   Find your sine-calculator from Lesson 8.1.3. Use your new understanding of radians to
         convert the units on the θ axis from degrees to radians. Be prepared to share your
         conversion **strategies** with the class.

METHODS AND MEANINGS

Radians

MATH NOTES

A **radian** is defined as an angular measure
such that an arc length of one radius on a
circle of radius one produces an angle with
measure one radian. It can also be thought of as
the ratio of an arc length to the radius of the
corresponding circle.

Arc equal to
1 radius in length

RADIUS

1 RADIAN

The circumference of a complete circle is
$2\pi r$ units, so the corresponding radian
measure is $\frac{2\pi r}{r} = 2\pi$. Thus, there are 2π radians in a complete circle.

8-78.   Your scientific or graphing calculator can function in both degrees and radians. See if you can figure out how to put your calculator in radian mode and then how to switch it back to degree mode. On most scientific calculators, a small "DEG" or "RAD" shows on the screen to let you know which mode you are in.

   a.   With your calculator in degree mode, find sin 60° and record your answer. Then switch to radian mode and find $\sin \frac{\pi}{3}$. Did you get the same answer? Explain why your answers should be the same or different.

   b.   Find $\sin \frac{\pi}{4}$. Which angles, measured in degrees, would have the same sine as $\sin \frac{\pi}{4}$?

8-79.   Calculate each of the following values. Express your answers exactly and as decimal approximations.

   a. $\sin(\frac{\pi}{4})$ b. $\sin(\frac{2\pi}{3})$

8-80.   Colleen and Jolleen both used their calculators to find sin 30°. Colleen got $\sin 30° = -0.9880316241$, but Jolleen got $\sin 30° = 0.5$. Is one of their calculators broken, or is something else going on? Why did they get different answers?

8-81.   Recall the strategies developed in class for converting degrees to radians. How could you reverse that? Convert each of the following angle measures. Be sure to show all of your work.

   a. π radians to degrees   b. 3π radians to degrees

   c.   30 degrees to radians   d. $\frac{\pi}{4}$ radians to degrees

   e.   225 degrees to radians   f. $\frac{3\pi}{2}$ radians to degrees

8-82.   Greg was working on his homework. $y = 2x^2 - 6x + 2$
He completed the square to change
$y = 2x^2 - 6x + 2$ to graphing form and $y = 2(x^2 - 3x) + 2$
identify the vertex of the parabola. He did $y = 2(x^2 - 3x + \frac{9}{4}) + 2 - \frac{9}{4}$
the work at right and identified the vertex
to be $(\frac{3}{2}, -\frac{1}{4})$. When he got back to class $y = 2(x - \frac{3}{2})^2 - \frac{1}{4}$
and checked his answers, he discovered that his vertex was wrong, but he cannot find
his mistake. Examine Greg's work and explain to him where the mistake occured.
Then show him how to correct the mistake and state the vertex.

8-83.   Change each of the following equations to graphing form and then, without graphing,
identify the vertex and axis of symmetry for each.

a. $y = 3x^2 - 18x + 26$ b. $y = 3x^2 - 4x - 11$

8-84.   Solve each of the following equations for x.

a. $171 = 3(5^x)$ b. $171y = 3(x^5)$

8-85.   Sketch a graph of $x^2 + y^2 = 100$.

a.   Is it a function?

b.   What are its domain and range?

c.   Draw a central angle that measures $\frac{2\pi}{3}$ radians. If you remove this wedge of the
circle, how much area remains?

8-86.   Find the equation for the inverse of the function $f(x) = 2\sqrt{\frac{(x-3)}{4}} + 1$. Sketch the graph
of both the original and the inverse.

8.1.6 What do I know about a unit circle?

Building a Unit Circle

In this lesson, you will further develop your understanding of the unit circle and how useful it can be. By the end of the lesson, you should be able to answer the questions below.

> What can the unit circle help me understand about an angle?

> What does my information about angles in the first quadrant tell me about angles in other quadrants?

8-87.   There are some angles for which you know the *exact values* of sine and cosine. In other words, you can find the exact sine and cosine without using a calculator. Work with your team to find as many such angles (expressed in radians) as you can.

8-88.   Now you will build a unit circle. Obtain the Lesson 8.1.6 Resource Page from your teacher. There are points shown at $\frac{\pi}{12}, \frac{\pi}{6}, \frac{\pi}{4}, \frac{\pi}{3}, \frac{5\pi}{12}, \frac{7\pi}{12}, \frac{2\pi}{3}, \frac{3\pi}{4}, \frac{5\pi}{6}$, and $\frac{11\pi}{12}$ units along the circle, starting from the positive x-axis.

   a.   Find and label the exact coordinates, in (x, y) form, for three of the points shown in the *first quadrant*.

   b.   Mark *all* other points in the unit circle for which you can find *exact* coordinates. Not all of them are shown. Label each of these points with its angle of rotation (in radians) and its coordinates.

   c.   If you have not done so already, label each angle with its corresponding radian measure.

8-89.   Draw a new unit circle, label a point that corresponds to a rotation of $\frac{\pi}{12}$, and put your calculator in radian mode.

   a.   What are the coordinates of this point, correct to two decimal places?

   b.   Use the information you found in part (a) to determine each of the following values: (Hint: Drawing each angle on the unit circle will be very helpful.)

   i. $\sin(-\frac{\pi}{12})$ *ii.* $\cos\frac{13\pi}{12}$ *iii.*   Challenge: $\cos\frac{7\pi}{12}$

8-90.   For angle α in the first quadrant, $\cos\alpha = \frac{8}{17}$. Use that information to find each of the following values without using a calculator. Be prepared to share your **strategies** with the class.

a. $\sin\alpha$

b. $\sin(\pi + \alpha)$

c. $\cos(2\pi - \alpha)$

METHODS AND MEANINGS

MATH NOTES

Reference Angle

For every angle of rotation, there is an angle in the first quadrant ($0 \le \theta \le 90°$) whose cosine and sine have the same absolute values as the cosine and sine of the original angle. This first-quadrant angle is called the **reference angle**.

For example, the angles $51°$, $129°$, $231°$, and $309°$ (pictured at right) all share the reference angle of $51°$.

Review & Preview

8-91.   Calculate the value of each expression below. Each measure is given in radians.

a. $\sin(4)$ b. $\sin(\frac{4\pi}{3})$

8-92.   Find the exact values of the angles that are solutions to the equation $\sin(\theta) = 0.5$. Express your solutions in radians.

8-93.   You have seen that you can calculate values of the sine function using right triangles formed by a radius of the unit circle. Values of θ that result in $30° - 60° - 90°$ or $45° - 45° - 90°$ triangles are used frequently on exercises and tests because their sines and cosines can be found exactly, without using a calculator. You should learn to recognize these values quickly and easily. The same is true for values of $\cos\theta$ and $\sin\theta$ that correspond to the x- and y-intercepts of the unit circle.

The central angles that correspond to these "special" values of x are $30°, 45°, 60°, 90°,$ $120°, 135°, 150°, 180°, 210°, 225°, 240°, 270°, 300°, 315°,$ and $330°.$ What these angles have in common is that they are all multiples of $30°$ or $45°$, and some of them are also multiples of $60°$ or $90°$.

Copy and complete a table like the one below for all special angles between $0°$ and $360°$.

Degrees	0	30	45	60	90	120		
Radians	0	$\frac{\pi}{6}$						

8-94.   Draw a picture of an angle that measures 6 radians.

a.   Approximately how many degrees is this?

b.   Using only your picture, estimate the sine of 6 radians.

8-95.   Evaluate each expression without using a calculator or changing the form of the expression.

a. $\log(10)$

b. $\log(\sqrt{10})$

c. $\log(0)$

d. $10^{(2/3)\log(27)}$

8-96.   What interest rate (compounded annually) would you need to earn in order to double your investment in 15 years?

8-97.   Phana's garden is 2 meters wide and 5 meters long. She puts a walkway of uniform width around her garden. If the area of the walkway is 30 square meters, what are the outer dimensions of the walkway? Drawing a diagram will help you solve this problem.

8-98.   Solve each of the following equations.

a. $2(x-1)^2 = 18$

b. $2^x + 3 = 10$

8.1.7 What is tangent?

The Tangent Function

In the past several lessons, you have used your understanding of the sine and cosine ratios to develop and interpret the functions $s(\theta) = \sin\theta$ and $c(\theta) = \cos\theta$. In this lesson, you will expand your understanding by exploring the tangent ratio and graphing the function $t(\theta) = \tan\theta$.

8-99.   Jamal was working on his homework when he had a brilliant realization. He was drawing a triangle in a unit circle to estimate the sine of $\frac{\pi}{10}$, when he realized that this triangle is the same kind of triangle that he draws when he wants to find the slope of a line.

   a.   How could you express the slope of the radius in terms of sine and cosine?

   b.   Is there any other way you can use a trigonometric ratio to represent the slope? Discuss this with your team.

8-100.   THE TANGENT FUNCTION

   Obtain the Lesson 8.1.7 Resource Page from your teacher. Use your knowledge of sine, cosine, and tangent to create a graph of the tangent function. Conduct a full **investigation** of the tangent function. Be prepared to share summary statements with the class.

Discussion Points

Does every angle have a tangent value?

How is the tangent graph similar to or different from the sine and cosine graphs?

Why does the tangent graph have asymptotes?

Further Guidance

8-101.   For each triangle in the first quadrant of the unit circle on your resource page, label the sine and cosine.

a.   Use your knowledge of tangent to complete a table like the one below. Start with the exact values for the sine and cosine.

θ	$\sin\theta$	$\cos\theta$	$\tan\theta$ (exact)	$\tan\theta$ (approximate to nearest 0.01)
$\frac{\pi}{6}$	$\frac{1}{2}$	$\frac{\sqrt{3}}{2}$	$\frac{1}{\sqrt{3}}$	
$\frac{\pi}{4}$	$\frac{\sqrt{2}}{2}$	$\frac{\sqrt{2}}{2}$		
$\frac{\pi}{3}$	$\frac{\sqrt{3}}{2}$	$\frac{1}{2}$		

b.   Plot the tangent values on the graph to the right of the unit circle.

c.   Draw five new triangles that are congruent to the first five, but that are located in the second quadrant. Add values for these new angles to your table and your graph.

d.   Continue this process by drawing triangles in the third and fourth quadrants. You should have a total of twenty triangles drawn and twenty angle values accounted for on your graph. If you have not done so already, add data to your table and points to your graph corresponding to the intercepts of the unit circle.

8-102.   **Investigate** the tangent graph by analyzing the following questions:

a.   Describe the domain and range of the tangent function.

b.   Describe any special points or asymptotes.

c.   Does it have symmetry? Describe any symmetry you see in the graph.

d.   How is the graph of $t(\theta) = \tan\theta$ different from the graphs of $s(\theta) = \sin\theta$ and $c(\theta) = \cos\theta$?

───────────   *Further Guidance*   ───────────
section ends here.

8-103.   Draw a new unit circle and label a point that corresponds to a rotation of $\frac{\pi}{6}$ radians.

a.   What are the coordinates of this point? Use exact values.

b.   Use this information to find each of the following values without a calculator. (Hint: Drawing each angle on the unit circle will be very helpful.)

i: $\tan(\frac{7\pi}{6})$ ii: $\cos(\frac{13\pi}{6})$ iii: $\tan(\frac{2\pi}{3})$

METHODS AND MEANINGS

Sine, Cosine, and Tangent

MATH NOTES

For any real number θ, the **sine of θ**, denoted $\sin \theta$, is the y-coordinate of the point on the unit circle reached by a rotation of θ radians from **standard position** (counter-clockwise starting from the positive x-axis).

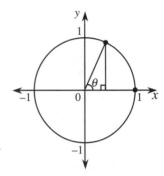

The **cosine of θ**, denoted $\cos \theta$, is the x-coordinate of the point on the unit circle reached by a rotation of θ radians from standard position.

The **tangent of θ**, denoted by $\tan \theta$, is the slope of the terminal ray of an angle (the radius) formed by a rotation of θ radians in standard position.

Review & Preview

8-104.   What central angle, measured in degrees, corresponds to a distance around the unit circle of $\frac{7\pi}{3}$?

   a.   What other angles will take you to the same point on the circle?

   b.   Make a sketch of the unit circle showing the resulting right triangle.

   c.   Find $\sin(\frac{7\pi}{3})$, $\cos(\frac{7\pi}{3})$, and $\tan(\frac{7\pi}{3})$ exactly.

8-105.   Evaluate each of the following trig expressions without using a calculator.

   a. $\sin(180°)$ b. $\sin(360°)$ c. $\sin(-90°)$

   d. $\sin(510°)$ e. $\cos(90°)$ f. $\tan(-90°)$

8-106.   How do you convert from degrees to radians and from radians to degrees? Explain and **justify** your method completely.

8-107. Convert each of the following angle measures. Give exact answers

    a. $\frac{7\pi}{6}$ radians to degrees   b. $\frac{5\pi}{3}$ radians to degrees

    c.   45 degrees to radians   d. $100°$ to radians

    e. $810°$ to radians   f. $\frac{7\pi}{2}$ radians to degrees

8-108. Simplify each of the following expressions, leaving only positive exponents in your answer.

    a. $(x^3y^{-2})^{-4}$ b. $-3x^2(6xy - 2x^3y^2z)$

8-109. Sketch a graph of $f(x) = \frac{1}{2}(x+1)^3$. Then sketch its inverse and write the equation of the inverse.

8-110. Rewrite $f(x) = 2x^2 - 16x + 34$ in graphing form.

8-111. The temperature of a pizza after it has been delivered depends on how long it has been sitting on the family-room table.

    a.   Sketch a reasonable graph of this situation. Be sure to label the axes.

    b.   Should your graph have an asymptote? Why or why not?

8-112. Solve for x: $\frac{1}{ax} + \frac{1}{b} = \frac{1}{x}$

8.2.1 How can I transform a sine graph?

Transformations of $y = \sin x$

In Chapter 4, you developed expertise in **investigating** functions and transforming parent graphs. In this section, you will **investigate** families of cyclic functions and their transformations. By the end of this section, you will be able to graph any sine or cosine equation and write the equation of any sine or cosine graph.

8-113.　As you have seen with many functions in this and other courses, x is generally used to represent an input and y is used to represent the corresponding output. By this convention, sinusoidal functions should be written $y = \sin x$, $y = \cos x$, and $y = \tan x$. But beware! Something funny is happening.

With your team, examine the unit circle and the three graphs below. What do x and y represent in the unit circle? What do they represent in each of the graphs? Discuss this with your team and be prepared to share your ideas with the class.

a.

b.

c.

d.

8-114.　With your team, you will apply your knowledge about transforming graphs of functions to transform the graphs of $y = \sin x$ and $y = \cos x$ and find their general equations.

Your task: As a team, **investigate** $y = \sin x$ and $y = \cos x$ completely. You should make graphs, find the domain and range, and label any important points or asymptotes. Then make a sketch and write an equation to demonstrate each transformation of the sine or cosine function you can find. Finally, find a general equation for a sine and a cosine function. Be prepared to share your summary statements with the class.

What can we change in a cyclic graph?

Which points are important to label?

How can we apply the transformations we use with other functions?

Are there any new transformations that are special to the sine function?

Further Guidance

8-115.   Sketch a graph of at least one cycle of $y = \sin x$. Label the intercepts. Then work with your team to complete parts (a) through (c) below.

    a.   Write an equation for each part below and sketch a graph of a function that has a parent graph of $y = \sin x$, but is:

        i.   Shifted 3 units up.   *ii.*   Reflected across the *x*-axis.

        iii. Shifted 2 units to the right.   *iv.* Vertically stretched.

        i.

        iii.

    b.   Which points are most important to label in a periodic function? Why?

    c.   Write a general equation for the family of functions with a parent graph of $y = \sin x$.

*Further Guidance
section ends here.*

8-116.   Imagine the graph $y = \sin(x)$ shifted up one unit.

a.   Sketch what it would look like.

b.   What do you have to change in the equation $y = \sin x$ to move the graph *up* one unit? Write the new equation.

c.   What are the intercepts of your new equation? Label them with their coordinates on the graph.

d.   When you listed intercepts in part (c), did you list more than one x-intercept? Should you have?

8-117.   The graph at right was made by shifting the first cycle of $y = \sin x$ to the left.

a.   How many units to the left was it shifted?

b.   Figure out how to change the equation of $y = \sin x$ so that the graph of the new equation will look like the one in part (a). If you do not have a graphing calculator at home, sketch the graph and check your answer when you get to class.

8-118.   Which of the situations below (if any) is best modeled by a cyclic function? Explain your reasoning.

a.   The number of students in each year's graduating class.

b.   Your hunger level throughout the day.

c.   The high-tide level at a point along the coast.

8-119.   The CPM Amusement Park has decided to imitate *The Screamer* but wants to make it even better. Their ride will consist of a circular track with a radius of 100 feet, and the center of the circle will be 50 feet under ground. Passengers will board at the highest point, so they will begin with a blood-curdling drop. Write a function that relates the angle traveled *from the starting point* to the height of the rider above or below the ground.

8-120.   Should $y = \sin x$ and $y = \cos x$ both be parent graphs, or is one the parent of the other? Give reasons for your decision.

8-121.   Evaluate each of the following expressions exactly.

   a. $\tan \frac{2\pi}{3}$

   b. $\tan \frac{7\pi}{6}$

8-122.   David Longshot is known for his long golf drives. Today he hit the ball 250 yards. He estimated that the ball reached a maximum height of 15 yards. Find a quadratic equation that would model the path of the golf ball.

8.2.2 What is missing?

One More Parameter for a Cyclic Function

In this lesson, you will study one more transformation that is unique to cyclic functions. You will also extend your understanding of these functions to include those with input values that do not correspond to angles.

8-123.   Does the general equation $y = a\sin(x - h) + k$ allow for every possible transformation of the graph of $y = \sin x$? Are there any transformations possible *other than* the ones produced by varying values of a, h, and k? Look back at the graphs you made for the swinging bag of blood in the first lesson of this chapter. Discuss this with your team and be prepared to share your conjectures with the class.

8-124.   THE RADAR SCREEN

   Brianna is an air traffic controller. Every day she watches the radar line (like a radius of a circle) go around her screen time after time. On one particularly slow travel day, Brianna noticed that it takes 2 seconds for the radar line to travel through an angle of $\frac{\pi}{6}$ radians. She decided to make a graph in which the *input* is time and the *output* is the distance from the outward end of the radar line to the horizontal axis.

   Your task: Following the input and output specifications above, make a table and graph for Brianna's radar.

Discussion Points

How can we calculate the outputs?

How is this graph different from other similar graphs we have made?

How long does it take to complete one full cycle on the radar screen?
How can we see that on the graph?

8-125.   Now that you have seen that it is possible to have a sine graph with a cycle length that is not 2π, work with your team to make conjectures about how you could change your general equation to allow for this new transformation.

a.   In the general equation $y = a\sin(x-h)+k$, the quantities a, h, and k are called **parameters**. Where could a new parameter fit into the equation?

b.   Use your graphing calculator to test the result of putting this new parameter into your general equation. Once you have found the place for the new parameter, **investigate** how it works. What happens when it gets larger? What happens when it gets smaller?

c.   Write a general equation for a sine function that includes the new parameter you discovered.

8-126.   Which of the following have a period of 2π? Which do not? How can you tell? If the period is not 2π, what is it?

a.

b.   A pendulum takes 3 seconds to complete one cycle.

c. $y = \sin\theta$

d.   A radar line takes 1 second to travel through 1 radian.

8-127.   Find an equation for each graph below.

a.

b.

c.

d.

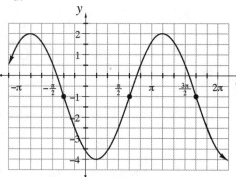

8-128.   Claudia graphed $y = \cos\theta$ and $y = \cos(\theta + 360°)$ on the same set of axes. She did not see any difference in their graphs at all. Why not?

8-129.   This is a checkpoint for solving equations and inequalities involving absolute value.

 Solve each absolute value equation or inequality below.

a. $2|2x+3|=10$ b. $|3x-5|>13$

c. $-|x+3|<10$

d.   Check your answers by referring to the Checkpoint 16 materials located at the back of your book.

If you needed help to solve these equations and inequalities correctly, then you need more practice solving equations and inequalities with absolute value. Review the Checkpoint 16 materials and try the practice problems. Also, consider getting help outside of class time. From this point on, you will be expected to solve equations and inequalities such as these quickly and accurately.

8-130.   Find the x- and y-intercepts of the graphs of each of the following equations.

a. $y=2x^3-10x^2-x$ b. $y+2=\log_3(x-1)$

8-131.   The average cost of movie tickets is $9.50. If the cost is increasing 4% per year, in how many years will the cost double?

8-132.   Change each equation to graphing form. For each equation, find the domain and range and determine if it is a function.

a. $y=-2x^2-x+13$ b. $y=-3x^2-6x+12$

8-133.   Too Tall Thomas has put Rodney's book bag on the snack-shack roof. Rodney goes to borrow a ladder from the school custodian. The tallest ladder available is 10 feet long and the roof is 9 feet from the ground. Rodney places the ladder's tip at the edge of the roof. The ladder is unsafe if the angle it makes with the ground is more than 60°. Is this a safe situation? **Justify** your conclusion.

8-134.   Deniz's computer is infected with a virus that will erase information from her hard drive. It will erase information slowly at first, but as time goes on, the rate at which information is erased will increase. In t minutes after the virus starts erasing information, $5{,}000{,}000(\frac{1}{2})^t$ bytes of information remain on the hard drive.

a.   Before the virus starts erasing, how many bytes of information are on Deniz's hard drive?

b.   After how many minutes will there be 1000 bytes of information left on the drive?

c.   When will the hard drive be completely erased?

8-135.   Graph $f(x) = |x - 6| - 4$.

a.   Explain how you can graph this without making an $x \to y$ table, but using parent graphs.

b.   Graph $g(x) = \left| |x - 6| - 4 \right|$. Explain how you can graph $g(x)$ without making an $x \to y$ table by using your earlier graph.

8-136.   Find the value of x in each triangle.

a.

b.

8.2.3 What is the period of a function?

Period of a Cyclic Function

In Lesson 8.2.2, you found a place for a new parameter in the general form of a trigonometric equation and discovered that it must have something to do with the period. By the end of this lesson, you will have the tools you need to find the equation for any sine or cosine graph and will be able to graph any sine or cosine equation. In other words, you will learn the equation ↔ graph connection. The following questions can help your team stay focused on the purpose of this lesson.

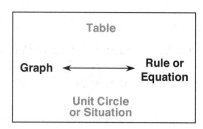

How can we write the equation for any sine or cosine graph?

How can we graph any sine or cosine function?

8-137.   Find the period for each of the following situations:

a.   The input is the angle θ in the unit circle, and the output is the cosine of θ.

b.   The input is time, and the output is the average daily temperature in New York.

c.   The input is the distance Nurse Nina has traveled along the hallway, and the output is the distance of bloody drips from the center-line of the hallway.

8-138. Put your graphing calculator in radian mode. Set the domain and range of the viewing window so that you would see just one complete cycle of $y = \sin x$. What is the domain for one cycle? Range?

a. Graph $y = \sin x$, $y = \sin(0.5x)$, $y = \sin(2x)$, $y = \sin(3x)$, and $y = \sin(5x)$. Make a sketch and answer the following questions for each equation.

   i. How many cycles of each graph appear on the screen?

   ii. What is the amplitude (height) of each graph?

   iii. What is the period of each graph?

   iv. Is each equation a function?

b. Make a conjecture about the graph of $y = \sin(bx)$ with respect to each of the questions (*i*), (*ii*), (*iii*), and (*iv*) above. If you cannot make a conjecture yet, try more examples.

c. Create at least three of your own examples to check your conjectures. Be sure to include sketches of your graphs.

d. What is the relationship between the period of a sine graph and the value of *b* in its equation?

8-139. Take the graph you made by swinging a pendulum in Lesson 8.1.1. Decide where to draw *x*- and *y*-axes and find the equation of your graph. Is there more than one possible equation? Be prepared to share your **strategies** with the class.

8-140. *Without* using a graphing calculator, describe each of the following functions by stating the amplitude, period, and vertical and horizontal shifts. Then sketch the graph of each function. *After* you have completed each graph, check your sketch with the graphing calculator and correct and explain any errors.

a. $y = \sin 2(x - \frac{\pi}{6})$ b. $y = 3 + \sin(\frac{1}{3}x)$

c. $y = 3\sin(4x)$ d. $y = \sin \frac{1}{2}(x + 1)$

e. $y = -\sin 3(x - \frac{\pi}{3})$ f. $y = -1 + \sin(2x - \frac{\pi}{2})$

8-141.   Farah and Thu were working on writing the
         equation of a sine function for the graph at right.
         They figured out that the amplitude is 3, the
         horizontal shift is $\frac{\pi}{4}$ and the vertical shift is –2.
         They can see that the period is π, but they disagree
         on the equation. Farah has written
         $f(x) = 3\sin 2(x - \frac{\pi}{4}) - 2$ and Thu has written
         $f(x) = 3\sin(2x - \frac{\pi}{4}) - 2$.

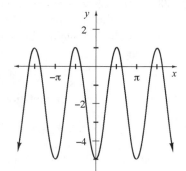

   a.   Whose equation is correct? How can you be
         sure?

   b.   Graph the incorrect equation and explain how it is different from the original
         graph.

8-142.   Look back at the general equation you wrote for the family of sine functions in
         problem 8-114. Now that you have figured out how period affects the equation, work
         with your team to add a new parameter (call it b) that allows your general equation to
         account for any transformation of the sine function, including changes in the length of
         each cycle. Be prepared to share your general equation with the class.

8-143.   Based on your explorations in class, complete parts (a) through (c) below.

   a.   Describe what the graph of $y = 3\sin(\frac{1}{2}x)$ will look like compared to the graph
         of $y = \sin x$.

   b.   Sketch both graphs on the same set of axes.

   c.   Explain the similarities and differences between the two graphs.

8-144.   What is the period of $y = \sin(2\pi x)$? How do you know?

8-145.   Sketch the graph of each equation below.

   a. $y = \sin(2\pi x)$ b. $y = 3\sin(\pi x)$

   c. $y = 2\sin(2\pi x) + 1$

8-146.   Match each equation with the appropriate graph. Do this without using a graphing calculator.

   a. $y = \sin(x + \frac{\pi}{2})$ b. $y = \sin(2x)$

   c. $y = 2\sin(\frac{x}{2})$ d. $y = \sin(x) - 3$

   e. $y = -\sin[2(x - \frac{\pi}{8})]$

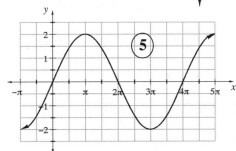

8-147. Ceirin's teacher promised a quiz for the next day, so Ceirin called Adel to review what they had done in class. *"Suppose I have y = sin 2x,"* said Ceirin, *"what will its graph look like?"*

"It will be horizontally compressed by a factor of 2," replied Adel, *"so the period must be π."*

"Okay, now let's say I want to shift it one unit to the right. Do I just subtract 1 from x, like always?"

"I think so," said Adel, *"but let's check on the graphing calculator."* They proceeded to check on their calculators. After a few moments they both spoke at the same time.

"Rats," said Ceirin, *"it isn't right."*

"Cool," said Adel, *"it works."*

When they arrived at school the next morning, they compared the equations they had put in their graphing calculators while they talked on the phone. One had $y = \sin 2x - 1$, while the other had $y = \sin 2(x - 1)$.

Which equation was correct? Did they both subtract 1 from x? Explain. Describe the rule for shifting a graph one unit to the right in a way that avoids this confusion.

8-148. George was solving the equation $(2x - 1)(x + 3) = 4$ and he got the solutions $x = \frac{1}{2}$ and $x = -3$. Jeffrey came along and said, *"You made a big mistake! You set each factor equal to zero, but it's not equal to zero, it's equal to 4. So you have to set each factor equal to 4 and then solve."* Who is correct? Show George and Jeffrey how to solve this equation. To be sure that you are correct, check your solutions.

8-149. Complete the square to change $3x^2 + 6x + 3y^2 - 9y < 36$ to graphing form. Identify key points. Find the domain and range. Sketch the graph.

8-150. Simplify each expression without using a calculator.

a. $25^{-1/2}$

b. $(\frac{1}{27})^{-1/3}$

]c. $9^{3/2}$

d. $16^{-3/4}$

8-151. Consider the equation $f(x) = 3(x + 4)^2 - 8$.

a. Find an equation of a function $g(x)$ such that $f(x)$ and $g(x)$ intersect in only one point.

b. Find an equation of a function $h(x)$ such that $f(x)$ and $h(x)$ intersect in no points.

$8.2.4$ What are the connections?

Graph $\leftrightarrow$ Equation

In the past few lessons, you have been developing the understanding necessary to graph a cyclic equation without making a table and to write an equation from a cyclic graph. In today's lesson, you will strengthen your understanding of the connections between a cyclic equation and its graph. By the end of this lesson, you will be able to answer the following questions:

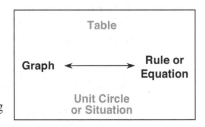

Does it matter if we use sine or cosine?

What do we need to know to make a complete graph or write an equation?

8-152. What do you need to know about the sine or cosine functions to be able to graph them or write their equations? Talk with your team and write a list of all of the attributes of a sine or cosine function that you need to know in order to write an equation and graph it.

8-153. CREATE-A-CURVE

Split your team into partners. With your partner, you will create your own sine or cosine function, write its equation, and draw its graph. Be sure to keep your equation and graph a secret! Start by choosing whether you will work with a sine or a cosine function.

a. Half the distance from the highest point to the lowest point is called the **amplitude**. You can also think of amplitude as the vertical stretch. What is the amplitude of your function?

b. How far to the left or right of the y-axis will your graph begin? In other words, what will be the **horizontal shift** of your function?

c. How much above or below the x-axis will the center of your graph be? In other words, what will be the **vertical shift** of your function?

d. What will the **period** of your function be?

e. What will the **orientation** of your graph in relation to $y = \sin x$ or $y = \cos x$ be? Is it the same or is it flipped?

f. Now that you have decided on all of the attributes for your function, write its equation.

8-154. Copy the equation for your curve from problem 8-153 on a clean sheet of paper. Trade papers with another pair of students.

a. Sketch a graph of the equation you received from the other pair of students.

b. When you are finished with your graph, give it back to the other pair so that they can check the accuracy of your graph.

8-155. When you look at a graph and prepare to write an equation for it, does it matter if you choose sine or cosine? Which will work best?

With your team, find *at least four* different equations for the graph at right. Be prepared to share your equations with the class.

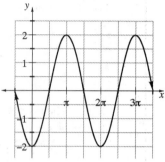

a. Does it matter if you choose sine or cosine?

b. Which of your equations do you prefer? Why?

8-156. Sarita was watching her little sister bounce on a trampoline and she decided to take some data, so she started her stopwatch. Half a second later, her sister reached the highest point, 15 feet above the ground! When the stopwatch read 1.4 seconds, Sarita's sister was at the lowest point, stretching the trampoline down to just one foot above the ground. Find a cyclic equation that models the height of Sarita's sister over time if she continues to bounce in the same way.

8-157. LEARNING LOG

In your Learning Log, write your ideas about the target questions for this lesson: *Does it matter if I use sine or cosine? What do I need to know to make a complete graph or write an equation?* Title this entry "Cyclic Equations and Graphs" and label it with today's date.

METHODS AND MEANINGS

General Equation for Sine Functions

The **general equation** for the **sine function** is $y = a\sin[b(x-h)] + k$.

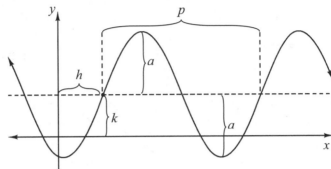

The **amplitude** (half of the distance between the highest and the lowest points) is a.

The **period** is the length of one cycle. It is labeled p on the graph.

The number of cycles in 2π is b.

The **horizontal shift** is h.

The **vertical shift** is k.

Review & Preview

8-158.   Susan knew how to shift $y = \sin x$ to get the graph at right, but she wondered if it would be possible to get the same graph by shifting $y = \cos x$.

a.   Is it possible to write a cosine function for this graph?

b.   If you think it is possible, find an equation that does it. If you think it is impossible, explain why.

c.   Adlai said, *"I can get that graph* without *shifting to the right or left."* What equation did he write?

8-159.   In the function $y = 4\sin(6x)$, how many cycles of sine are there from 0 to 2π? How long is each cycle (i.e., what is the period)?

8-160. Write the equation of a cyclic function that has an amplitude of 7 and a period of 8π. Sketch its graph.

8-161. Sketch a graph of each of the following trigonometric functions.

    a. $y = \sin(0.5(x - \pi))$ b. $y = 10\sin(3x) - 2$

    c. $y = 5\cos(x + \frac{\pi}{4})$ d. $y = \cos(2(x - \frac{\pi}{4}))$

8-162. Find the exact value for each of the following trig expressions. For parts (g) and (h), assume that $0 \le \theta \le 2\pi$.

    a. $\cos(\frac{3\pi}{4}) =$ b. $\tan(\frac{4\pi}{3}) =$ c. $\sin(\frac{11\pi}{6}) =$ d. $\sin(\frac{3\pi}{4}) =$

    e. $\tan(\frac{5\pi}{4}) =$ f. $\tan(\frac{17\pi}{6}) =$ g. $\tan(\theta) = 1$ h. $\tan(\theta) = -1$

8-163. Use the Zero Product Property to solve each equation in parts (a) and (b) below.

    a. $x(2x + 1)(3x - 5) = 0$ b. $(x - 3)(x - 2) = 12$

    c.   Write an equation and show how you can use the Zero Product Property to solve it.

8-164. Find a quadratic equation whose graph has each of the following characteristics:

    a.   No x-intercepts and a negative y-intercept.

    b.   One x-intercept and a positive y-intercept.

    c.   Two x-intercepts and a negative y-intercept.

8-165. A two-bedroom house in Seattle was worth $400,000 in 2005. If it appreciates at a rate of 3.5% each year:

    a.   How much will it be worth in 2015?

    b.   When will it be worth $800,000?

    c.   In Jacksonville, houses are depreciating at 2% per year. If a house is worth $200,000 now, how much value will it have lost in 10 years?

Chapter 8 Closure What have I learned?

Reflection and Synthesis

The activities below offer you a chance to reflect on what you have learned in this chapter. As you work, look for concepts that you feel very comfortable with, ideas that you would like to learn more about, and topics you need more help with. Look for connections between ideas as well as connections with material you learned previously.

①   TEAM BRAINSTORM

With your team, brainstorm a list for each of the following three categories. Be as detailed as you can. How long can you make your list? Challenge yourselves. Be prepared to share your team's ideas with the class.

Topics: What have you studied in this chapter? What ideas and words were important in what you learned? Remember to be as detailed as you can.

The Web: Which connections on the multiple-representations web have you learned about for cyclic functions? Which are strongest and most useful? Which are less useful for you?

Connections: How are the topics, ideas, and words that you learned in previous courses connected to the new ideas in this chapter? Again, make your list as long as you can.

② MAKING CONNECTIONS

Below is a list of the vocabulary used in this chapter. Make sure that you are familiar with all of these words and know what they mean. Refer to the glossary or index for any words that you do not yet understand.

amplitude	angle	asymptotes
cosine	cyclic function	parameter
pendulum	period	radian
reference angle	sine	tangent
trigonometric functions	unit circle	

Make a concept map showing all of the connections you can find among the key words and ideas listed above. To show a connection between two words, draw a line between them and explain the connection, as shown in the example below. A word can be connected to any other word as long as you can **justify** the connection. For each key word or idea, provide a sketch of an example.

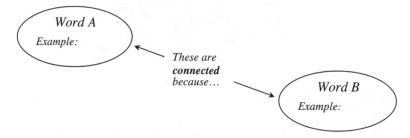

Your teacher may provide you with vocabulary cards to help you get started. If you use the cards to plan your concept map, be sure either to re-draw your concept map on your paper or to glue the vocabulary cards to a poster with all of the connections explained for others to see and understand.

While you are making your map, your team may think of related words or ideas that are not listed above. Be sure to include these ideas on your concept map.

③   GROWTH OVER TIME

This section gives you an opportunity to show growth in understanding of key mathematical ideas over time as you complete this course.

Part 1: On a separate sheet of paper, explain everything that you know about $f(x) = 2^x - 3$. Be sure to include everything you have learned since the last time you did this problem, and do not leave out anything you included in your earlier attempts.

Part 2: Compare your three responses to this "Growth Over Time" problem. Write an evaluation of your growth based on your responses. Consider each of the following questions as you write your answer.

- What new concepts did you include the second time you did the problem? In what ways was your response better than your first attempt?

- How was your final version different from the first two? What new ideas did you include?

- Did you omit anything in the final version that you used in one of the earlier versions? Why did you omit it?

- Rate your three attempts by making three bars like the ones below and shading each bar to represent how much you knew on each attempt.

First Attempt:	
Second Attempt:	
Final Attempt:	

- Is there anything you want to add to your current version? If so, add it and keep this version for future reference.

④   SUMMARIZING MY UNDERSTANDING

This section gives you an opportunity to show what you know about certain math topics or ideas.

With your team, make a list of the **big ideas** of this chapter. Discuss the important ideas of the chapter and try to agree on a short list of no more than five big ideas. Be prepared to share your list in a whole class discussion. When the class has reached agreement on a list, continue with parts (a) and (b) below.

a.   Write your own description of each big idea.

b.   For each big idea, provide one or two representative example problems. Solve each problem completely, using multiple representations, if applicable.

Your teacher may give you a "GO" page to work on (or you can download this from www.cpm.org). "GO" stands for "Graphic Organizer," a tool you can use to organize your thoughts and communicate your ideas clearly.

⑤   WHAT HAVE I LEARNED?

This section will help you evaluate which types of problems you feel comfortable with and which you need more help with. This section will appear at the end of every chapter to help you check your understanding. Even if your teacher does not assign this section, it is a good idea to try these problems and find out for yourself what you know and what you need to work on.

Solve each problem as completely as you can. The table at the end of this closure section has answers to these problems. It also tells you where you can find additional help and practice on similar problems.

CL 8-166. Describe how you can tell the difference between the graphs of $y = \sin x$ and $y = \cos x$. Be sure to **justify** your ideas.

CL 8-167. Convert the following angles to radians.

     a. $225°$ b. $75°$ c. $-15°$ d. $330°$

CL 8-168. Sketch each of the following angles in its own unit circle.

     a.   An angle that has a positive cosine and a negative sine.

     b.   All angles that have a sine of 0.5.

     c.   An angle that measures $\frac{4\pi}{3}$ radians. Find its exact sine.

     d.   An angle with a negative cosine and a positive tangent.

CL 8-169. Without using a calculator, give the exact value of each expression.

     a. $\sin 60°$ b. $\cos 180°$ c. $\tan 225°$

     d. $\sin \frac{\pi}{4}$ e. $\cos \frac{2\pi}{3}$ f. $\tan \frac{3\pi}{2}$

CL 8-170. If an angle between 0 and 2π radians has a sine of -0.5, what is its cosine? How do you know?

CL 8-171. Find the exact values of x and y in the drawings below.

a.

b.

CL 8-172. For each equation determine the amplitude, period, locator point and sketch part of the graph.

a. $y = 3\cos(2x)$

b. $y = \tan(x - \frac{\pi}{2})$

CL 8-173. Write an equation for each of the following graphs. If you have a graphing calculator, use it to check your equation (be sure to set your window to match the picture).

a.

b.

c.

d.

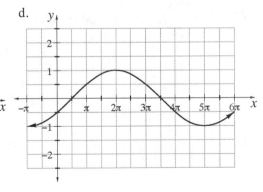

CL 8-174. Rewrite each equation below in graphing form and sketch its graph. Then state the domain and range and whether or not it is a function.

a. $y = 3x^2 + 30x - 2$

b. $x^2 + y^2 - 6x + 4y + 4 = 0$

CL 8-175. Solve each equation to the nearest thousandth.

a. $2 \cdot 3^x = 40.8$

b. $3x^4 = 27$

c. $\log_5(2x + 1) = 3$

d. $\log(x) + \log(2x) = 5$

CL 8-176. Find an equation for an exponential function that passes through the points $(1, 22)$ and $(3, 20.125)$ and has a horizontal asymptote at $y = 20$.

CL 8-177. Check your answers using the table at the end of this section. Which problems do you feel confident about? Which problems were hard? Have you worked on problems like these in previous chapters math classes? Sort the problems into three groups: the ones you are confident you can do, the ones you need more practice with, and the ones you need further help to understand.

⑥   HOW AM I THINKING?

This course focuses on five different **Ways of Thinking**: **justifying**, **generalizing**, **choosing a strategy**, **investigating**, and **reversing thinking**. These are some of the ways in which you think while trying to make sense of a concept or attempting to solve a problem (even outside of math class). During this chapter, you have probably used each Way of Thinking multiple times without even realizing it!

Review each of the five Ways of Thinking described in the closure sections of Chapters 1 through 5. Then choose three of these Ways of Thinking that you remember using while working on this chapter. Show and explain where and how you used each one. Describe why thinking in this way helped you solve a particular problem or understand something new. Be sure to include examples to demonstrate your thinking.

Answers and Support for Closure Activity #5
What Have I Learned?

Problem	Solutions	Need Help?	More Practice
CL 8-166.	The graph of $y = \cos x$ has a y-intercept of 1 because $\cos 0 = 1$ and the base of the triangle at 0 degrees in the unit circle is 1 unit long. The graph of $y = \sin x$ has a y-intercept of 0 because $\sin 0 = 0$ and the height of the triangle at 0 degrees in the unit circle is 0 units.	Lessons 8.1.2, 8.1.3, and 8.1.4 Math Notes box in Lesson 8.1.7 Learning Log entry from problem 8-157	Problems 8-14, 8-37, 8-48, 8-49, 8-50, 8-51, 8-53, 8-63, 8-64, 8-66, and 8-114
CL 8-167.	a. $\frac{5\pi}{4}$ b. $\frac{5\pi}{12}$ c. $-\frac{\pi}{12}$ d. $\frac{11\pi}{6}$	Lesson 8.1.5	Problems 8-78, 8-81, 8-93, 8-106, 8-107
CL 8-168.	a. b. c. $\sin\frac{4\pi}{3} = -\frac{\sqrt{3}}{2}$ d.	Lessons 8.1.3 and 8.1.6 Math Notes box in Lesson 8.1.5	Problems 8-64, 8-76, 8-104
CL 8-169.	a. $\frac{\sqrt{3}}{2}$ b. -1 c. 1 d. $\frac{\sqrt{2}}{2}$ e. $-\frac{1}{2}$ f. undefined	Lessons 8.1.5 and 8.1.6	Problems 8-79, 8-91, 8-104, 8-105, 8-121, and 8-162
CL 8-170.	$\frac{\sqrt{3}}{2}$ or $-\frac{\sqrt{3}}{2}$; If the sine is negative, the angle must lie in the 3rd or 4th quadrant and 0.5 is one leg of a 30°-60°-90° triangle.	Lessons 8.1.3, 8.1.4, and 8.1.6 Math Notes box in Lesson 8.1.7	Problem 8-35, 8-52, 8-64, 8-78, 8-104

Problem	Solutions	Need Help?	More Practice

CL 8-171.   a. $x = 5\sqrt{2}$, $y = 5\sqrt{2}$

b. $x = 60°$, $y = 30°$

Math Notes box
in Lesson 8.1.2

Problems 8-6, 8-15

CL 8-172.   a. Locator: $(0, 3)$, Amplitude: 3,
Period: π

b. Locator: $(\frac{\pi}{2}, 0)$, Period: π,
There is no amplitude

Lessons 8.1.2,
8.1.7, 8.2.1, 8.2.3,
and 8.2.4

Problems 8-115,
8-127, 8-140, 8-143,
8-145, 8-146 8-153,
8-159, and 8-161

CL 8-173.   a. $y = \sin x$, $y = \sin(x + \frac{\pi}{2})$ or
$y = -\sin(x - \frac{\pi}{2})$

b. $y = -3 - \sin x$,

c. $y = 5 \sin 4x$,

d. $y = \sin \frac{1}{3}(x - \frac{\pi}{2})$

Lessons 8.2.1,
8.2.2, 8.2.3, and
8.2.4

Math Notes box
in Lesson 8.2.4,

Learning Log
entry from
problem 8-157

Problems 8-127, 8-141,
8-146, 8-155, 8-161

CL 8-174.   a. $y = 3(x - 5)^2 - 2$,
$-\infty < x < \infty$, $y \geq -2$;
it is a function.

b. $(x - 3)^2 + (y + 2)^2 = 9$,
$0 \leq x \leq 6$,
$-5 \leq y \leq 1$;
it is not a
function.

Lessons 4.1.3,
4.3.1, and 4.3.2

Math Notes box
in Lesson 4.2.2

Checkpoint 14

Problems 4-38, 4-71,
4-108, 4-121, 4-132,
4-135, 4-137, 4-146,
4-149, 5-66, 5-72,
6-52, 7-84, 7-158,
7-175, 8-17, 8-42,
8-110, 8-132, 8-149

Problem	Solutions		Need Help?	More Practice
CL 8-175.	a. 2.745 c. 62	b. ≈ 1.732 d. 223.607	Lessons 7.2.1 and 7.2.2	Problems 7-111, 7-133, 7-139, 7-140, 7-223, CL 7-230,8-19 and 8-84
CL 8-176.	$y = 8(\frac{1}{4})^x + 20$		Lesson 7.2.3 Checkpoint 15	Problems 7-125, 7-127, 7-164, CL 7-232, 8-21, 8-68, and 8-134

POLYNOMIALS

9

RIDE the world's FIRST UNDERGROUND ROLLERCOASTER!

CHAPTER 9

In this chapter you expand your knowledge of families of functions to include polynomial functions. As you **investigate** the equation ↔ graph connection for polynomials, you will learn how to search for factors (which can help you find *x*-intercepts) and how to use division to find additional factors.

When you **investigate** the graphs of polynomials and systems involving polynomials, you will see many that appear not to intersect. As you **investigate** these systems further, you will learn about imaginary and complex numbers.

In the last section of the chapter, you will apply your knowledge of polynomials to model some of the attractions at a county fair.

Guiding Questions

Think about these questions throughout this chapter:

How can I model this situation?

How can I find the other solutions?

How can I graph it?

What is an imaginary number?

In this chapter you will learn:

> How to sketch complete graphs of polynomial functions.

> How to divide one polynomial expression by another.

> How to solve some equations you could not solve earlier by expanding the set of numbers you use.

> What imaginary and complex numbers are, their properties, and how they are related to graphs that do not have real intersections.

> How to find solutions for factorable polynomial equations of one variable.

> How to write polynomial equations given their graphs and how to use polynomial functions to represent some situations.

Chapter Outline

Section 9.1 You will **investigate** polynomial functions and learn how to sketch them without using a graphing calculator. You will also learn how to find polynomial equations from their graphs.

Section 9.2 Here you will be introduced to a number system called *complex numbers*. You will see how these numbers relate to quadratic equations that have no real solutions and to the roots of other polynomial equations.

Section 9.3 In this section, you will learn how to divide polynomials by applying your knowledge of generic rectangles and factoring. You will solve equations using polynomial division to factor polynomials.

9.1.1 How can I predict the graph?

Sketching Graphs of Polynomial Functions

In previous courses and chapters, you learned how to graph many types of functions, including lines and parabolas. Today you will work with your team to apply what you know to more complicated **polynomial** equations. Just as quadratic polynomial equations can be written in standard or factored form, other polynomial equations can be written in standard or factored form. For example, $y = x^4 - 4x^3 - 3x^2 + 10x + 8$ is in standard form, and it can be written in factored form as $y = (x+1)^2(x-2)(x-4)$.

During this lesson, you will develop techniques for sketching the graph of a polynomial function from its equation, and you will **justify** why those techniques work.

9-1. The Mathamericaland Carnival Company has decided to build a new roller coaster to use at this year's county fair. The new coaster will have a very special feature: part of the ride will be underground. The designers will use polynomial functions to describe different pieces of the track. Part of the design is shown at right. Your task is to guess a possible equation to represent the track and test it on your graphing calculator. To help get an idea of what to try, start by checking the graphs of the equations given below. Think about how the graphs are the same and how they are different.

$y = x(x-2)$

$y = (x-2)^2$

$y = x(x-2)(x-3)$

Your task: Use the information you found by graphing the above equations to help you make guesses about the equation that would produce the graph of the roller coaster. Once you have found a graph that has a shape close to this one, try zooming in or changing the viewing window on your graphing calculator to see the details better. Keep track of what you tried and the equations you find that fit most accurately.

9-2.   POLYNOMIAL FUNCTION INVESTIGATION

In this **investigation**, you will determine which information in a
polynomial equation can help you sketch its graph.

Your task: With your team, create summary statements explaining the
relationship between a polynomial equation and its graph. To accomplish this task,
first divide up the equations listed below so each team member is responsible for two
or three of them. Make a complete graph of each of your functions. Whenever
possible, start by making a sketch of your graph without using a graphing calculator.
Then, as a team, share your observations including your responses to the "Discussion
Points." Choose two or three equations that can be used to represent all of your
findings. You can choose them from the list below, or you can create new ones as a
team.

The form of your presentation to the class can be on a poster, transparencies or as a
PowerPoint™ presentation. Whichever format your teacher decides, make sure you
include complete graphs and summary statements that are well **justified**.

$$P_1(x) = (x-2)(x+5)^2$$ $$P_2(x) = 2(x-2)(x+2)(x-3)$$

$$P_3(x) = x^4 - 21x^2 + 20x$$ $$P_4(x) = (x+3)^2(x+1)(x-1)(x-5)$$

$$P_5(x) = -0.1x(x+4)^3$$ $$P_6(x) = x^4 - 9x^2$$

$$P_7(x) = 0.2x(x+1)(x-3)(x+4)$$ $$P_8(x) = x^4 - 4x^3 - 3x^2 + 10x + 8$$

Discussion Points

What can we predict from looking at the equation of a polynomial?
Why does this make sense?

Which form of a polynomial equation is most useful for making a graph?
What information does it give?

How can we use the equation to help predict what a useful window might be?

Which examples are most helpful in finding the connections between
the equation and the graph?

How does changing the exponent on one of the factors change the graph?

9-3.   As a team, examine the first polynomial $P_1(x) = (x-2)(x+5)^2$.

   a.   What family of functions is it a member of? How do you know? Based on its equation, sketch the shape of its graph.

   b.   Now use your graphing calculator to graph $P_1(x)$. Label the x-intercepts. How are the x-intercepts related to the equation? "Reading" from left to right along the x-axis, describe the graph before the first x-intercept, between x-intercepts, and after the last x-intercept.

9-4.   Continuing as a team, examine the equation $P_2(x) = 2(x-2)(x+2)(x-3)$.

   a.   How many distinct (different) factors are there? How many x-intercepts would you predict for its graph? Draw the graph and label the x-intercepts. How is this graph similar to or different from the graph of $P_1(x)$?

   b.   Does the factor 2 have any effect on the x-intercepts? On the shape of the graph? On the y-intercepts? How would the graph change if the factor 2 were changed to be a factor -2?

9-5   What is different about $P_3(x) = x^4 - 21x^2 + 20x$? What x-intercept(s) can you determine from the equation, before graphing with the calculator? Explain how you know. Use the graph to figure out exactly what the other intercepts are. Explain how you can prove that your answers are exact.

9-6.   With your team, divide up the work to **investigate** $P_4(x)$ through $P_8(x)$ and continue your **investigation**, referring back to the "your task" statement and the discussion points in problem 9-2.

——————   *Further Guidance*   ——————
                section ends here.

9-7.   Based on what your team learned and on the class discussion, record your own list of useful **strategies** for graphing polynomial functions. Use as many of the new vocabulary words as you can and write down the ones you are not sure of yet. You will add to and refine this list over the next several lessons.

METHODS AND MEANINGS

Polynomials, Degree, Coefficients

MATH NOTES

A **polynomial** in one variable is an expression that can be written as the sum or difference of terms of the form:

$$(\text{any number}) \cdot x^{(\text{whole number})}$$

Polynomials with one variable (often x) are usually arranged with powers of x in order, starting with the highest, left to right. Polynomials can include only the operations of addition, subtraction, or multiplication.

The highest power of the variable in a polynomial of one variable is called the **degree** of the polynomial. The numbers that multiply each term are called **coefficients**. See the examples below.

Example 1: $f(x) = 7x^5 + 2.5x^3 - \frac{1}{2}x + 7$ is a polynomial function of degree 5 with coefficients $7, 0, 2.5, 0, -\frac{1}{2}$, and 7. Note that the last term, 7, is called the **constant** term but represents the variable expression $7x^0$, since $x^0 = 1$.

Example 2: $y = 2(x+2)(x+5)$ is a polynomial in factored form with degree 2 because it can be written in standard form as $y = 2x^2 + 14x + 20$. It has coefficients 2, 14, and 20.

The following are not polynomial functions: $y = 2^x - 3$, $f(x) = \frac{1}{x^2 - 2x} + x$, and $y = \sqrt{x-2}$.

9-8.   For each equation below, make tables that include x-values from –2 to 2 and draw each graph.

a. $y = (x-1)^2(x+1)$

b. $y = (x-1)^2(x+1)^2$

c. $y = x^3 - 4x$

d.   What are the parent functions for these equations?

9-9.   **Polynomials** are expressions that can be written as a sum of terms of the form:

$$(\text{any number}) \cdot x^{(\text{whole number})}$$

Which of the following equations are polynomial equations? For those that are not polynomials, explain why not. Check the lesson 9.1.1 Math Notes box for further details about polynomials.

a. $f(x) = 8x^5 + x^2 + 6.5x^4 + 6$ b. $y = \frac{3}{5}x^6 + 19x^2$

c. $y = 2^x + 8$ d. $f(x) = 9 + \sqrt{x} - 3$

e. $P(x) = 7(x-3)(x+5)^2$ f. $y = x^2 + \frac{1}{x^2+5}$

g.   Write an equation for a new polynomial function and then write an equation for a new function that is not a polynomial.

9-10.   Describe the possible numbers of intersections for each of the following pairs of graphs. Sketch a graph for each possibility. For example, a circle could intersect a line twice, once, or not at all. Your solution to each part should include all of the possibilities and a sketched example of each one.

a.   Two different lines.   b.   A line and a parabola.

c.   Two different parabolas.   d.   A parabola and a circle.

9-11.   Solve the following system: $y = x^2 - 5$
                                                        $y = x + 1$

9-12.   A table can be used as a useful tool for finding some inverse functions. When the function has only one x in it, the function can be described with a sequence of operations, each applied to the previous result. Consider the following table for $f(x) = 2\sqrt{x-1} + 3$.

	1st	2nd	3rd	4th
What f does to x:	subtracts 1	$\sqrt{\ }$	multiplies by 2	adds 3

Since the inverse must undo these operations, in the opposite order, the table for $f^{-1}(x)$ would look like the one below.

	1st	2nd	3rd	4th
What does f^{-1} to x:	subtracts 3	divides by 2	$(\ )^2$	adds 1

a.   Copy and complete the following table for $g^{-1}(x)$ if $g(x) = \frac{1}{3}(x+1)^2 - 2$

	1st	2nd	3rd	4th
What g does to x:	adds 1	$(\ )^2$	divides by 3	subtracts 2
What g^{-1} does to x:				

b.   Write the equations for $f^{-1}(x)$ and $g^{-1}(x)$.

9-13.   Describe the difference between the graphs of $y = x^3 - x$ and $y = x^3 - x + 5$.

9-14.   Solve the equations below.

   a. $\frac{3x}{x+2} + \frac{7}{x-2} = 3$

   b. $\frac{x-7}{x-5} = \frac{6}{x}$

9-15.   An arithmetic sequence starts out −23, −19, −15 ...

   a.   What is the rule?

   b.   How many times must the generator be applied so that the result is greater than 10,000?

9-16.   Artemis was putting up the sign at the County Fair Theater for the movie "ELVIS RETURNS FROM MARS." He got all of the letters he would need and put them in a box. He reached into the box and pulled out a letter at random.

   a.   What is the probability that he got the first letter he needed when he reached into the box?

   b.   Once he put the first letter up, what is the probability that he got the second letter he needed when he reached into the box?

9-17.   Without a calculator, find two solutions $0° \le \theta < 360°$ that make each of the following equations true.

   a. $\cos \theta = \frac{1}{2}$ b. $\tan \theta = -1$ c. $\sin \theta = \frac{\sqrt{3}}{2}$ d. $\cos \theta = -\frac{\sqrt{3}}{2}$

9-18.   Which of the following equations are polynomial functions? For each one that is not, **justify** why not.

   a. $y = 3x^2 + 2x^2 + x$

   b. $y = (x-1)^2(x-2)^2$

   c. $y = x^2 + 2^x$

   d. $y = 3x - 1$

   e. $y = (x-2)^2 - 1$

   f. $y^2 = (x-2)^2 - 1$

   g. $y = \frac{1}{x^2} + \frac{1}{x} + \frac{1}{2}$

   h. $y = \frac{1}{2}x + \frac{1}{3}$

   i. $y = x$

   j. $y = -7$

9-19.   Samantha thinks that the equation $(x-4)^2 + (y-3)^2 = 25$ is equivalent to the equation $(x-4)+(y-3)=5$. Is she correct? Are the two equations equivalent? Explain how you know. If they are not equivalent, explain Samantha's mistake.

9-20.   Find the **roots** (the solutions when $y=0$) of each of the following polynomial functions.

   a. $y = x^2 - 6x + 8$ b. $f(x) = x^2 - 6x + 9$

   c. $y = x^3 - 4x$

9-21.   Sketch a graph of $y = x^2 - 7$.

   a.   How many roots does this graph have?

   b.   What are the roots of the function?

9-22.   Solve $x^2 + 2x - 5 = 0$.

   a.   How many x-intercepts does $y = x^2 + 2x - 5$ have?

   b.   Approximately where does the graph of $y = x^2 + 2x - 5$ cross the x-axis?

9-23.   This is a checkpoint for finding the equation for the inverse of a function.

Consider the function $f(x) = 2\sqrt{3(x-1)} + 5$.

   a.   Find the equation for the inverse of $f(x)$.

   b.   Sketch the graph of both the original and the inverse.

   c.   Check your results by referring to the Checkpoint 17 materials located at the back of your book.

   If you needed help to write the equation of the inverse of this function, then you need more practice with inverses. Review the Checkpoint 17 materials and try the practice problems. Also, consider getting help outside of class time. From this point on, you will be expected to write equations for inverses of functions such as this one quickly and easily.

9-24. Graph the inequality $x^2 + y^2 \le 25$, and then describe its graph in words.

9-25. Find x if $2^{p(x)} = 4$ and $p(x) = x^2 - 4x - 3$.

9-26. Start with the graph of $y = 3^x$, then write new equations that will shift the graph as described below.

   a.   Down 4 units.   b.   Right 7 units.

9-27. THE COUNTY FAIR FERRIS WHEEL

Consider this picture of a Ferris wheel. The wheel has a 60-foot diameter and is drawn on a set of axes with the Ferris wheel's hub (center) at the origin. Use a table like the one below and draw a graph that relates the angle (in standard position) of the spoke leading to your seat to the approximate height of the top of your seat above or below the height of the central hub. The table below starts at $-90°$, your starting position before you ride around the wheel.

x (angle)	$-90°$	$-45°$	$0°$	$45°$	$90°$	$135°$	$180°$	....	$270°$
y (height)	$-30'$								

   a.   The wheel goes around (counter-clockwise) several times during a ride. How could you reflect this fact in your graph? Update your graph.

   b.   What is the maximum distance above or below the center that the top of your seat attains during the ride?

   c.   Find an equation to fit the County Fair Ferris wheel ride.

9.1.2 How can I predict the graph?

More Graphs of Polynomials

Today you will use what you learned in the "Polynomial Function Investigation" to respond to some questions. Thinking about how to answer these questions should help you clarify and expand on some of your ideas as well as help you learn how to use the vocabulary involved with polynomials.

9-28. Use your finger to trace an approximate graph of polynomial functions in the air, as directed by your teacher. Or you may sketch each of the polynomial functions below quickly on paper. Just sketch the graph without the x- and y- axes.

a. $P(x) = (x+10)(x+7)(x-12)$

b. $Q(x) = (x+6)(x+3)(x-5)(x-8)$

c. $R(x) = -(x+4)(x+2)(x-6)(x-10)$

d. $W(x) = (x+7)^2(x-7)^2$

e. $S(x) = (x+6)(x+3)(x-5)(x-8)(x-12)$

9-29. Look back at the work you did in Lesson 9.1.1 (problem 9-2, "Polynomial Function Investigation"). Then answer the following questions.

a. What is the maximum number of roots a polynomial of degree 3 can have? Sketch an example.

b. What do you think is the maximum number of roots a polynomial of degree n can have?

c. Can a polynomial of degree n have fewer than n roots? Under what conditions?

9-30. For each polynomial function shown below, state the minimum degree its equation could have.

i.   ii.   iii.   iv.

a. Which of the graphs above show that as the x-values get very large the y-values continue to get larger and larger?

b. How would you describe the other graphs for very large x-values?

c. When the y-values of a graph get very large as the x-values get large, the graph has **positive orientation**. When the y-values of a graph get very small as the x-values get large, the graph has **negative orientation**. How is each of the above graphs oriented?

9-31.   For each graph in problem 9-30, you decided what the minimum degree of its equation could be. Under what circumstances could graphs that look the same as these have polynomial equations of a *higher* degree?

Consider the graphs of $y = (x-1)^2$ and $y = (x-1)^4$.

a.   How are these graphs similar? How are they different?

b.   Could the equation for graph (*ii*) from the previous problem have degree 4?

c.   Could it have degree 5? Explain.

d.   How is the graph of $y = x^3$ similar to or different from the graph of $y = x^5$?

e.   How do the shapes of graphs of $y = (x-2)^3$ and $y = (x+1)^5$ differ from the shapes of graphs of equations that have three or five factors that are all different?

9-32.   In $P_1(x) = (x-2)(x+5)^2$ (the first example from the "Polynomial Function Investigation"), $(x+5)^2$ is a factor. This produces what is called a **double root** of the function.

a.   What effect does this have on the graph?

b.   Check your equations for a **triple root**. What effect does a triple root have on the graph?

9-33.   We can use a number line to represent the *x*-values for which a polynomial graph is above or below the *x*-axis. The bold parts of each number line below show where the output values of a polynomial function are positive (that is, where the graph is above the *x*-axis). The open circles show locations of the *x*-intercepts or roots of the function. Where there is no shading, the value of the function is negative. Sketch a possible graph to fit each number line, and then write a possible equation. (Each number line represents the *x*-axis for a different polynomial.)

a.

b.

c.

d.

9-34.   What can you say about the graphs of polynomial functions with an even degree compared to the graphs of polynomial functions with an odd degree? Use graphs from the "Polynomial Functions Investigation" (and maybe some others), to **justify** your response.

9-35. Choose three of the polynomials you graphed in the "Polynomial Functions Investigation" (problem 9-2) and create number lines for their graphs similar to the ones in problem 9-33.

9-36. Create a new number-line description (like the ones in problem 9-33) and then trade with a partner. (Each team member should create a different number line.) After you have traded, find a possible graph and equation for a polynomial function to fit the description you have received. Then **justify** your results to your team and check your team members' results.

9-37. Without using a calculator, sketch rough graphs of the following functions.

a. $P(x) = -x(x+1)(x-3)$

b. $P(x) = (x-1)^2(x+2)(x-4)$

c. $P(x) = (x+2)^3(x-4)$

METHODS AND MEANINGS

Roots and Zeros

The **roots** of a polynomial function, $p(x)$, are the **solutions** of the equation $p(x) = 0$. Another name for the roots of a function is **zeros of the function** because at each root, the value of the function is zero. The real roots (or zeros) of a function have the same value as the x-values of the x-intercepts of its graph because the x-intercepts are the points where the y-value of the function is zero.

Sometimes roots can be found by factoring. In the "Parabola Lab" (problems 4-13 and 4-14), you discovered how to make a parabola "sit" on the x-axis (the polynomial has one root), and you looked at ways of making parabolas intersect the x-axis in two specific places (two roots).

Review & Preview

9-38. Where does the graph $y = (x+3)^2 - 5$ cross the x-axis?

9-39. If you were to graph the function $f(x) = (x-74)^2(x+29)$, where would the graph intersect the x-axis?

9-40.   For each pair of intercepts given below, write an equation for a quadratic function in standard form.

     a. $(-3,0)$ and $(2,0)$ b. $(-3,0)$ and $(\frac{1}{2},0)$

9-41.   What is the degree of each polynomial function below?

     a. $P(x)=0.08x^2+28x$ b. $y=8x^2-\frac{1}{7}x^5+9$

     c. $f(x)=5(x+3)(x-2)(x+7)$ d. $y=(x-3)^2(x+1)(x^3+1)$

9-42.   Are parabolas polynomial functions? Are lines polynomial functions? Are cubics? Exponentials? Circles? In all cases, explain why or why not.

9-43.   A sequence of pentagonal numbers is started at right.

     a.   Find the next three pentagonal numbers.

     b.   What kind of sequence do the pentagonal numbers form?

     c.   What is the equation for the nth pentagonal number?

1   5   9

9-44.   A circle with its center on the line $y=3x$ in the 1st quadrant is tangent to the y-axis.

     a.   If the radius is 2, what is the equation of the circle?

     b.   If the radius is 3, what is the equation of the circle?

9-45.   Sketch the graph of each function below on the same set of axes.

     a. $y=2^x$ b. $y=2^x+5$ c. $y=2^x-5$

9-46.   For each equation, find two solutions $0° \le \theta < 360°$, which make the equation true. You should not need a calculator.

     a. $\sin\theta=\frac{1}{2}$ b. $\tan\theta=\sqrt{3}$

     c. $\cos\theta=\frac{\sqrt{3}}{2}$ d. $\sin\theta=-\frac{\sqrt{2}}{2}$

9.1.3 How can I find the equation?

Stretch Coefficients for Polynomial Functions

In Lesson 9.1.2 you found possible equations for the graphs of polynomial functions based on their x-intercepts. Many of the sketches you used did not even include the scale on the y-axis. In this lesson, you will focus on figuring out equations that represent *all* of the points on the graphs.

9-47.   Find reasonable equations for each of the following polynomial functions. Without using a graphing calculator, how can you check the accuracy of your equations? How can you check to see whether the y-values (or stretch factor) are accurate? Show how you checked the accuracy in each case. Were your equations accurate?

a.

b.

c.

9-48.   What is the difference between the graphs of the functions $y = x^2(x-3)(x+1)$ and $y = 3x^2(x-3)(x+1)$?

9-49.   ARE THE INTERCEPTS ENOUGH?

Melvin wrote the equation $y = (x+3)(x+1)(x-2)^2$ to represent the graph at right. How well does this equation represent the graph?

a.   Explain how you can decide how well the equation represents the graph. What can you do to the equation to make it a better fit for the graph? What equation would fit better?

b.   Before you figured it out, you could have written the polynomial for this graph as $P(x) = a(x+3)(x+1)(x-2)^2$. What if you did not have a graphing calculator, but you were told that the graph goes through the point (1, 16)? How could you use that information to determine the exact equation? Once you have decided on a method with your team, try it. How can you test the accuracy of your equation?

9-50. THE COUNTY FAIR COASTER RIDE

Now that you have more expertise with polynomial equations and their graphs, the Mathamericaland Carnival Company has hired your team to find the *exact* equation to represent its roller-coaster track.

The numbers along the *x*-axis are in hundreds of feet. At 250 feet, the track will be 20 feet below the surface. This gives the point $(2.5, -0.2)$.

a. What degree polynomial represents the portion of the roller coaster represented by the graph at right?

b. What are the roots?

c. Find an exact equation for the polynomial that will generate the curve of the track.

d. What is the deepest point of the roller coaster's tunnel?

9-51. Write an exact equation for each graph below.

a.

b.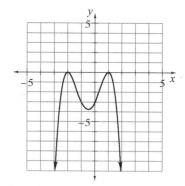

9-52. Write a polynomial equation for a function with a graph that bounces off the *x*-axis at $(-1,0)$, crosses it at $(4,0)$, and goes through the point $(-2,-18)$.

9-53. Armando came up with the equation $y = 3(x+1)^4(x-4)$ for problem 9-52. Does his equation fit all of the given criteria? Why or why not? Is it the same as the equation you came up with?

9-54.   What if problem 9-52 also had said that the graph went through the point $(1, -36)$? Is there still more than one possible equation? Explain.

9-55.   What information about the graph of a polynomial function is necessary to determine exactly one correct equation? Discuss this with your team.

LOOKING DEEPER

Notation for Polynomials

A general equation to represent all polynomials: The general equation of a second-degree (quadratic) polynomial is often written in the form $f(x) = ax^2 + bx + c$, and the general equation of a third-degree (cubic) polynomial is often written in the form $f(x) = ax^3 + bx^2 + cx + d$.

For a polynomial with an undetermined degree n, it is unknown how many letters will be needed for the coefficients, so instead of using a, b, c, d, e, etc., mathematicians use only the letter a, and they put on subscripts, as shown below.

$$f(x) = (a_n)x^n + (a_{n-1})x^{(n-1)} + \ldots + (a_1)x^1 + a_0$$

This general polynomial has degree n and coefficients a_n, a_{n-1}, ..., a_1, a_0.

For example, for $7x^4 - 5x^3 + 3x^2 + 7x + 8$, the degree is 4. In this specific case, a_n is a_4 and $a_4 = 7$, a_{n-1} is $a_3 = -5$, a_{n-2} is $a_2 = 3$, $a_1 = 7$, and $a_0 = 8$.

Review & Preview

9-56.   What is the stretch factor (the value of a) for the equation of the graph in part (c) of problem 9-47? Write the exact equation of the function.

9-57.   For each of the following polynomial expressions, find the degree, list the coefficients, and then label them a_0 through a_n. Refer to the example in the Lesson 9.1.3 Math Notes box above about polynomial notation.

a. $6x^4 - 3x^3 + 5x^2 + x + 8$ b. $-5x^3 + 10x^2 + 8$

c. $-x^2 + x$ d. $x(x-3)(x-5)$

e. x f. 10

9-58.   Write a polynomial equation for a graph that has three x-intercepts: $(-4, 0), (1, 0)$, and $(3, 0)$, and passes through the point $(-1, 60)$.

9-59.   The x-intercepts of a quadratic polynomial are given below. Find a possible quadratic equation in standard form.

a. $x = \frac{3}{4}, x = -2$

b. $x = -\sqrt{5}, x = \sqrt{5}$

9-60.   Consider the functions $y = \frac{1}{2}$ and $y = \frac{16}{x^2 - 4}$. Find the coordinates where the graphs of the functions intersect.

9-61.   Find the center and radius of each circle below.

a. $(y - 7)^2 = 25 - (x - 3)^2$

b. $x^2 + y^2 + 10y = -9$

c. $x^2 + y^2 + 18x - 8y + 47 = 0$

d. $y^2 + (x - 3)^2 = 1$

9-62.   Without using a calculator, write the solution to each equation.

a. $2^x = 17$

b. $\log_3(x + 1) = 5$

c. $\log_3(3^x) = 4$

d. $4^{\log_4(x)} = 7$

9-63.   Consider the function $y = x^2 + 5x + 7$.

a.   Complete the square to find the vertex.

b.   Find the y-intercept.

c.   Use the vertex, the y-intercept, and the symmetry of parabolas to find a third point and sketch the graph.

9-64.   Write a possible equation for the graph at right.

9.2.1 What are imaginary numbers?

Introducing Imaginary Numbers

In the past, you have not been able to solve some quadratic equations like $x^2 + 4 = 0$ and $x^2 + 1 = 0$, because there are no real numbers you can square to get a negative answer. To solve this issue, mathematicians created a new, expanded number system based on one new number. But this was not the first time mathematicians had invented new numbers! To read about other such inventions, refer to the Math Notes box that follows problem 9-65.

In this lesson, you will learn about imaginary numbers and how you can use them to solve equations you were previously unable to solve.

9-65.   Consider the equation $x^2 = 2$.

    a.   How do you "undo" squaring a number?

    b.   When you solve $x^2 = 2$, how many solutions should you get?

    c.   How many x-intercepts does the graph of $y = x^2 - 2$ have?

    d.   Solve the equation $x^2 = 2$. Write your solutions both as radicals and as decimal approximations.

LOOKING DEEPER

MATH NOTES

Historical Note: Irrational Numbers

In Ancient Greece, people believed that all numbers could be written as fractions of whole numbers (what are now called **rational numbers**). Many individuals realized later that some numbers could not be written as fractions (such as $\sqrt{2}$), and these individuals challenged the accepted beliefs. Some of the people who challenged the beliefs were exiled or outright killed over these challenges.

The Greeks knew that for a one-unit square, the length of the diagonal, squared, yielded 2. When it was shown that no rational number could do that, the existence of what are called *irrational numbers* was accepted and symbols like $\sqrt{2}$ were invented to represent them.

The problem $x^2 = 3$ also has no rational solutions; fractions can never work exactly. The rational (i.e., decimal) solutions that calculators and computers provide are only approximations; the exact answer can only be represented in radical form, namely, $\pm\sqrt{3}$.

9-66.   Mathematicians throughout history have resisted the idea that some equations may not be solvable. Still, it makes sense that $x^2 + 1 = 0$ cannot be solved because the graph of $y = x^2 + 1$ has no x-intercepts. What happens when you try to solve $x^2 + 1 = 0$?

(L)OOKING DEEPER

Historical Note: Imaginary Numbers

In some ways, each person's math education parallels the history of mathematical discovery. When you were much younger, if you were asked, *"How many times does 3 go into 8?"* or *"What is 8 divided by 3?"* you might have said, *"3 doesn't go into 8."* Then you learned about numbers other than whole numbers, and the question had an answer. Of course, in some situations you are only interested in whole numbers, and then the first answer is still the right one. Later, if you were asked, *"What number squared makes 5?"* you might have said, *"No number squared makes 5."* Then you learned about numbers other than rational numbers, and you could answer that question.

Similarly, until about 500 years ago, the answer to the question, *"What number squared makes –1?"* was, *"No number squared makes –1."* Then something remarkable happened. An Italian mathematician named Bombelli used a formula for finding the roots of third-degree polynomials. Within the formula was a square root, and when he applied the formula to a particular equation, the number under the square root came out negative. Instead of giving up, he had a brilliant idea. He had already figured out that the equation had a solution, so he decided to see what would happen if he pretended that there *was* a number he could square to make a negative. Remarkably, he was able to continue the calculation, and eventually the "imaginary" number disappeared from the solution. More importantly, the resulting answer worked; it solved his original equation. This led to the acceptance of these so-called **imaginary numbers**. The name stuck, and mathematicians became convinced that all quadratic equations do have solutions. Of course, in some situations you will only be interested in real numbers (that is, numbers not having an imaginary part), and then the original answer, that there is no solution, is still the correct one.

9-67.   In the 1500s, an Italian mathematician named Rafael Bombelli invented the imaginary number $\sqrt{-1}$, which is now called i. $\sqrt{-1} = i$ implies that $i^2 = -1$. After this invention, it became possible to find solutions for $x^2 + 1 = 0$; they are i and $-i$. What would be the value of $\sqrt{-16} = \sqrt{16(-1)} = \sqrt{16i^2} = ?$ Use the definition of i to rewrite each of the following expressions.

a. $\sqrt{-4}$ b. $(2i)(3i)$ c. $(2i)^2(-5i)$ d. $\sqrt{-25}$

9-68. Graph the function $y = x^2 - 4x + 5$.

    a. Does the graph cross the x-axis? Should the equation $x^2 - 4x + 5 = 0$ have real solutions?

    b. Use the Quadratic Formula to solve $x^2 - 4x + 5 = 0$. Use your new understanding of imaginary numbers to simplify your results as much as possible.

    c. A real number plus (or minus) a multiple of i (like each of the solutions to $x^2 - 4x + 5 = 0$) is called a **complex number**. Check one of your solutions from part (b) by substituting it into the equation for x and simplifying the result.

9-69. When a graph crosses the x-axis, the x-intercepts are often referred to as the **real roots** of the equation that results when $y = 0$. You have seen that solutions to equations can be real or complex, so it follows that roots can also be real or complex. Compare and contrast what happens with the graphs and equations for the three cases in parts (a) through (c) below.

    a. Sketch the graph of $y = (x + 3)^2 - 4$. What are the roots?

    b. Sketch the graph of $y = (x + 3)^2$. What are the roots?

    c. Sketch the graph of $y = (x + 3)^2 + 4$. Can you find the roots by looking at the graph? Why or why not? Find the roots by solving $(x + 3)^2 + 4 = 0$.

    d. Make **general** statements about the relationship between graphs of parabolas and the kinds of roots their equations have.

9-70. Consider the equations $y = x^2$ and $y = 2x - 5$.

    a. On one set of axes, sketch the graphs and label the intersection.

    b. Use algebra to solve the system of equations.

    c. Discuss your results with your team. What could these solutions mean?

9-71. Do the graphs of $y = \frac{1}{x}$ and $y = -x + 1$ intersect? What kind of algebraic solutions will this system have? Verify your answer by solving the system.

METHODS AND MEANINGS

Imaginary and Complex Numbers

MATH NOTES

The **imaginary number** that solves the equation $x^2 = -1$ is i, so $i^2 = -1$, and the two solutions of the equation are i and $-i$.

In general, i follows the rules of real number arithmetic. The sum of two imaginary numbers is imaginary (unless it is 0). Multiplying the imaginary number i by every possible real number would yield the set of all the imaginary numbers.

The set of numbers that solve equations of the form $x^2 =$ (a negative real number) is called the set of **imaginary numbers**. Imaginary numbers are not positive, negative, or zero. The collection (set) of positive and negative numbers (integers, rational numbers (fractions), and irrational numbers), are referred to as the **real numbers**.

The sum of a real number (other than zero) and an imaginary number, such as $2 + i$, is generally neither real nor imaginary. Numbers such as these, which can be written in the form $a + bi$, where a and b are real numbers, are called **complex numbers**. Each complex number has a real component, a, and an imaginary component, bi. The real numbers are considered to be complex numbers with $b = 0$, and the imaginary numbers are complex numbers with $a = 0$.

9-72.   Write each of the following expressions in the form $a + bi$.

   a. $-18 - \sqrt{-25}$ b. $\frac{2 \pm \sqrt{-16}}{2}$

   c. $5 + \sqrt{-6}$

9-73.   Explain why $i^3 = -i$. What does i^4 equal?

9-74.   If $f(x) = x^2 + 7x - 9$, calculate the values in parts (a) through (c) below.

   a. $f(-3)$ b. $f(i)$ c. $f(-3 + i)$

9-75.   Is $5 + 2i$ a solution to $x^2 - 10x = -29$? How can you be sure?

9-76.   Solve $16^{(x+2)} = 8^x$.

9-77.   Is $(x - 5)^2$ equivalent to $(5 - x)^2$? Explain why or why not.

9-78.   Calculate the value of each expression below.

   a. $\sqrt{-49}$ b. $\sqrt{-2}$ c. $(4i)^2$ d. $(3i)^3$

9-79.   Find the inverse functions below.

   a.   If $f(x) = 2x - 3$, then what does $f^{-1}(x)$ equal?

   b.   If $h(x) = (x - 3)^2 + 2$, then what does $h^{-1}(x)$ equal?

9-80.   Solve each equation.

   a. $5.2(3.75)^x = 100$ b. $4 + 3x^4 = 81$

9.2.2 What are complex roots?

Complex Roots

In this lesson, you will solve equations as well as **reverse your thinking** to **investigate** the relationship between the complex solutions to a quadratic equation and the equation they came from.

9-81.   Find the roots of each of the following quadratic functions by solving for x when $y = 0$. Does the graph of either of these functions intersect the x-axis?

   a. $y = (x + 5)^2 + 9$

   b. $y = x^2 - 4x + 9$

9-82.   What do you notice about the complex solutions in problem 9-81? Describe any patterns you see. Discuss these with your team and write down everything you can think of.

9-83.   In parts (a) through (d) below, look for patterns as you calculate the sum and the product for each pair of complex numbers. Use what you find to answer parts (e) through (g).

   a. $2 + i,\ 2 - i$

   b. $3 - 5i,\ 3 + 5i$

   c. $-4 + i,\ -4 - i$

   d. $1 + i\sqrt{3}, 1 - i\sqrt{3}$

   e.   What complex number can you multiply $3 + 2i$ by to get a real number?

   f.   What happens when you multiply $(-4 + 5i)(-4 + 3i)$?

   g.   What complex number can you multiply $a + bi$ by to get a real number?

9-84. WHAT EQUATION HAS THESE SOLUTIONS?

Each of the four pairs of complex numbers in problem 9-83 could be the roots of a quadratic function.

Your task: With your team, create a quadratic equation for each pair of complex numbers in parts (a) through (d) of problem 9-83 such that those numbers are the roots. Discuss the methods you use for writing the equations and write summary statements describing your methods.

Discussion Points

How can we **reverse** the process of solving and work backwards?

How can we use what we know about factors and zeros?

How are the solutions related to the standard form of the equation?

Further Guidance

9-85. Problem 9-83 made Mariposa curious about sums and products. She decided to solve the equation $x^2 - 6x + 25 = 0$ and look at the sums and products of its solutions. What patterns can you help her find that might give her ideas about the equation once she knows the solutions?

9-86. Austin had another idea. He knew that if 3 and –5 were solutions of a quadratic equation then $(x - 3)$ and $(x + 5)$ would be factors that could be multiplied to get a quadratic polynomial. How could his idea be used with the pairs of complex solutions in problem 9-83? Choose one pair and show how to use your idea.

9-87. Melvin had still another idea. *"Why not just let $x = -4 \pm i$ and work backwards?"* He asked. Would his idea work?

—————— *Further Guidance* ——————
section ends here.

9-88. For each pair of numbers below, find a quadratic equation that has these numbers as solutions.

a. $\frac{3}{4}$ and –5

b. $3i$ and $-3i$

c. $5 + 2i$ and $5 - 2i$

d. $-3 + \sqrt{2}$ and $-3 - \sqrt{2}$

METHODS AND MEANINGS

The Discriminant and Complex Conjugates

For any quadratic equation $ax^2 + bx + c = 0$, you can determine whether the roots are real or complex by examining the part of the quadratic formula that is under the square-root sign. The value of $b^2 - 4ac$ is known as the **discriminant**. The roots are real when $b^2 - 4ac \geq 0$ and complex when $b^2 - 4ac < 0$.

For example, in the equation $2x^2 - 3x + 5 = 0$,
$b^2 - 4ac = (-3)^2 - 4(2)(5) = -31 < 0$, so the equation has two complex roots and the parabola $y = 2x^2 - 3x + 5$ does not intersect the x-axis.

Complex roots of quadratic equations with real coefficients will have the form $a - bi$ and $a + bi$, which are called **complex conjugates**. The sum and product of two complex conjugates are always real numbers.

For example, the conjugate for the complex number $-5 + 3i$, is $-5 - 3i$.
$(-5 + 3i) + (-5 - 3i) = -10$ and $(-5 + 3i)(-5 - 3i) = 25 - 9i^2 = 34$.

Note: With the introduction of complex numbers, the use of the terms *roots* and *zeros* of polynomials expands to include complex numbers that are solutions of the equations when $p(x) = 0$.

9-89. For each of the following sets of numbers, find the equation of a function that has these numbers as roots.

a. $-3 + i$ and $-3 - i$

b. $5 + \sqrt{3}$ and $5 - \sqrt{3}$

c. $-2, \sqrt{7}$, and $-\sqrt{7}$

d. $4, -3 + i$, and $-3 - i$

9-90.   Raul claims that he has a shortcut for deciding what kind of roots a function has. Jolene thinks that a shortcut is not possible. She says you just have to solve the quadratic equation to find out. They are working on $y = x^2 - 5x - 14$.

Jolene says, *"See, I just start out by trying to factor. This one can be factored $(x - 7)(x + 2) = 0$, so the equation will have two real solutions and the function will have two real roots."*

"But what if it can't be factored?" Raul asked. *"What about $x^2 + 2x + 2 = 0$?"*

"That's easy! I just use the Quadratic Formula," says Jolene. *"And I get... let's see... negative two plus or minus the square root of... two squared... that's 4... minus... eight..."*

"Wait!" Raul interrupted. *"Right there, see, you don't have to finish. 2^2 minus $4 \cdot 2$, that gives you -4. That's all you need to know. You'll be taking the square root of a negative number so you will get a complex result."*

"Oh, I see," said Jolene. *"I only have to do part of the solution, the part you have to take the square root of."*

Use Raul's method to tell whether each of the following functions has real or complex roots without completely solving the equation. Note: Raul's method is summarized in the Math Notes box for this lesson.

a. $y = 2x^2 + 5x + 4$ b. $y = 2x^2 + 5x - 3$

9-91.   Decide which of the following equations have real roots, and which have complex roots without completely solving them.

a. $y = x^2 - 6$ b. $y = x^2 + 6$

c. $y = x^2 - 2x + 10$ d. $y = x^2 - 2x - 10$

e. $y = (x - 3)^2 - 4$ f. $y = (x - 3)^2 + 4$

9-92.   Consider this geometric sequence: $i^0, i^1, i^2, i^3, i^4, i^5, ..., i^{15}$.

a.   You know that $i^0 = 1$, $i^1 = i$, and $i^2 = -1$. Calculate the result for each term up to i^{15}, and describe the pattern.

b.   Use the pattern you found in part (a) to calculate i^{16}, i^{25}, i^{39}, and i^{100}.

c.   What is i^{4n}, where n is a positive whole number?

d.   Based on your answer to part (c), simplify i^{4n+1}, i^{4n+2}, and i^{4n+3}.

e.   Calculate i^{396}, i^{397}, i^{398}, and i^{399}.

9-93.　Use the pattern from the previous problem to help you to evaluate the following expressions.

　　a.　i^{592}　　　　b.　i^{797}　　　　c.　$i^{10,648,202}$

9-94.　Describe how you would evaluate i^n where n could be any integer.

9-95.　Consider the graph below.

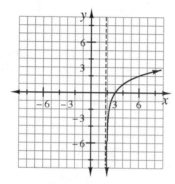

　　a.　What is the parent for this function?

　　b.　What is the equation of the vertical asymptote?

　　c.　Write a possible equation for this graph.

9-96.　In one of the games at the county fair, people pay to shoot a paint pistol at the target shown at right. The center has a radius of one inch. Each concentric circle has a radius one inch larger than the preceding circle. Assuming the paint pellet hits the target randomly, what is the probability that it hits:

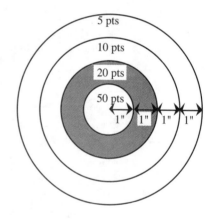

　　a.　The 50-point ring?

　　b.　The 20-point ring?

9-97.　Given $C = \begin{bmatrix} 3 & -2 \\ -5 & 1 \end{bmatrix}$, $D = \begin{bmatrix} 0 & 3 \\ 4 & -3 \end{bmatrix}$ find:

　　a.　CD　　　　　　　　　　b.　$C + D$

　　c.　C^2　　　　　　　　　　d.　X if $2X + C = D$

9.2.3 Where are the complex numbers?

More Complex Numbers and Equations

If the number line is filled with real numbers, how can imaginary and complex numbers be represented geometrically? In this lesson, you will learn a way to graph complex numbers and interpret the graphical meaning of complex solutions.

9-98.   Avi and Tran were trying to figure out how they could represent complex numbers geometrically. Avi decided to make a number line horizontal like the x-axis to represent the real part as well as a vertical line like the y-axis to represent the imaginary part.

    a.   Draw a set of axes and label them as Avi described.

    b.   How could Avi and Tran graph a point to represent the complex number $3 + 4i$? Be prepared to share your **strategies** with the class.

    c.   Use the method you developed in part (b) to plot points to represent the six numbers below.

        i. $2 + 5i$ *ii.* $6 - i$ *iii.* $-5 - 3i$

        iv. 4 *v.* $7i$ *vi.* $-4 + 2i$

9-99.   On a new set of **complex axes** (like those drawn by Avi and Tran in problem 9-98), locate points representing all of the following complex numbers

    a. $3 + 4i$, $3 - 4i$, $-3 + 4i$, and $-3 - 4i$.

    b.   The four complex numbers represented by $\pm 4 \pm 3i$.

    c. 5, -5, $5i$, and $-5i$.

    d.   What do you notice about your graph? How far from $(0, 0)$ is each point?

9-100.   On the real number line, the distance from 0 to a point on the line is defined as the absolute value of the number. Similarly, in the **complex plane** (the plane defined by a set of complex axes), the **absolute value** of a complex number is its distance from zero or the origin $(0, 0)$. In the previous problem, the absolute value of all of those complex numbers was 5. For each of the following questions, a sketch in the complex plane will help in visualizing the result.

   a.   What is the absolute value of $-8 + 6i$?

   b.   What is the absolute value of $7 - 2i$?

   c.   What is $|4 + i|$?

   d.   What is the absolute value of $a + bi$?

9-101.   Based on the following graphs, how many *real* roots does each polynomial function have?

   a.

   b.

   Graphs (a) and (b) above have been vertically shifted to create graphs (c) and (d) shown below. How many *real* roots does each of these new polynomial functions have?

   c.

   d.

   The polynomials in parts (c) and (d) do not have fewer roots. Polynomial (c) still has *two* roots, but now the roots are complex. Polynomial (d) has *three* roots: two are complex, and only one is real.

9-102.   Recall that a polynomial function with degree n crosses the x-axis at most n times. For instance, $y = (x+1)^2$ intersects the x-axis once, while $y = x^2 + 1$ does not intersect it at all. The function $y = x^2 - 1$ intersects it twice. These graphs are shown below.

$y = (x+1)^2$

$y = x^2 + 1$

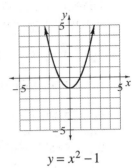

$y = x^2 - 1$

a.   A third-degree equation might intersect the x-axis one, two, or three times. Make sketches of all these possibilities.

b.   Can a third-degree equation have zero real roots? Explain why or why not.

9-103.   Now consider the graph of $y = x^3 - 3x^2 + 3x - 2$.

a.   How many real solutions could $x^3 - 3x^2 + 3x - 2 = 0$ have?

b.   Check to verify that $x^3 - 3x^2 + 3x - 2 = (x-2)(x^2 - x + 1)$.

c.   Find all of the solutions of $x^3 - 3x^2 + 3x - 2 = 0$.

d.   How many x-intercepts does $y = x^3 - 3x^2 + 3x - 2$ have? How many real roots and how many non-real roots (complex)?

9-104.   Sketch the graph of $f(x) = x^2 + 4$ and solve the equation $x^2 + 4 = 0$ to find its roots.

a.   Describe the parabola. Be sure to include the vertex and the equation of its axis of symmetry.

b.   With a partner, obtain a copy of the Lesson 9.2.3 Resource Page from your teacher, and follow the directions below to make a 3-D model that will show the location of the complex roots in a complex plane that is perpendicular to the real plane in which you drew the graph of the parabola.

i.   Fold the paper on the line marked *bi* and *–bi*. This is a "mountain" fold, so the printing is on the outside.

Problem continues on next page. →

9-104.   *Problem continues from previous page.*

  ii. Cut the paper exactly along the dotted line. Do not cut beyond the dotted portion.

  iii. Now make "valley" folds on the two lines parallel to the first fold.

  iv. Hold the two ends of the paper and push them toward the center so the center pops up, and then fold the top and bottom of the paper back on the line marked "center."

You should have a three-dimensional coordinate system with the *xy*-plane facing you and the *i*-axis coming out toward you. The equation $f(x) = x^2 + 4$ should be in the lower right corner. Now locate the roots of the function on your 3-D model.

MATH NOTES

METHODS AND MEANINGS

Graphing Complex Numbers

To represent imaginary numbers, an imaginary axis and a plane are needed. Real numbers are on the horizontal axis and imaginary numbers are on the vertical axis, as shown in the examples below. Complex numbers are graphed using the same method that coordinate points are: the number $2 + 3i$ is located at $(2, 3)$, and the number i or $0 + 1i$ is located at $(0, 1)$. The number -2 or $-2 + 0i$ is located at $(-2, 0)$. This representation is called the **complex plane**.

In the complex plane, $a + bi$ is located at the point (a, b). Its distance from the origin is its **absolute value.** To find the absolute value, calculate the distance from $(0, 0)$ to (a, b):

$$|a + bi| = \sqrt{a^2 + b^2}$$

Examples:

$$|-2 + 3i| = \sqrt{(-2)^2 + 3^2} = \sqrt{13}$$

$$|-1 - i| = \sqrt{(-1)^2 + (-1)^2} = \sqrt{2}$$

$$|5i| = 5$$

9-105.   In parts (a) through (d) below, for each polynomial function $f(x)$, the graph of $f(x)$ is shown. Based on this information, tell how many linear and quadratic factors the factored form of its equation should have and how many real and complex (non-real) solutions $f(x) = 0$ might have. (Assume a polynomial function of the lowest possible degree for each one.)

Example: $f(x)$ at right will have three linear factors, therefore three real roots and no complex roots.

a.

b.

c.

d.

9-106.   Make a sketch of a graph $p(x)$ so that $p(x) = 0$ would have the indicated number and type of solutions.

a.   5 real solutions

b.   3 real and 2 complex

c.   4 complex

d.   4 complex and 2 real

e.   For parts (a) through (d), what is the lowest degree each function could have?

9-107.   Consider the function $y = x^3 - 9x$.

    a.   What are the roots of the function? (Factoring will help!)

    b.   Sketch a graph of the function.

9-108.   Make rough sketches of the graphs of each of the following polynomial functions. Be sure to label the x- and y- intercepts.

    a. $y = x(2x + 5)(2x - 7)$ b. $y = (15 - 2x)^2(x + 3)$

9-109.   The management of the Carnival Cinema was worried about breaking even on their movie "Elvis Returns from Mars." To break even, they had to take in $5000 on the matinee. They were selling adult tickets for $8.50 and children's tickets for $5.00. They knew they had sold a total of 685 tickets. How many of those tickets would have to have been adult tickets for them to meet their goal?

9-110.   You are given the equation $5x^2 + bx + 20 = 0$. For what values of b does this equation have real solutions?

9-111.   Show that each of the following equations is true.

    a. $(i - 3)^2 = 8 - 6i$ b. $(2i - 1)(3i + 1) = -7 - i$

    c. $(3 - 2i)(2i + 3) = 13$

9-112.   Kahlid is going to make a table to graph $y = \sqrt{x^2}$, but Aaron says that it would be a waste of time to make a table because the graph is the same as $y = x$.

    a.   Use Kahlid's equation to make the table and draw the graph.

    b.   As you can see, Aaron was wrong, but you did get a graph that you have seen before. What other equation has the same graph? Explain why this is reasonable.

9-113.   Multiply each of the following expressions.

    a. $(x - 3)^2$ b. $2(x + 3)^2$ c. $(a - b)(a^2 + ab + b^2)$

9.3.1 How can I divide polynomials?

Polynomial Division

When you graphed polynomial functions in the first section of this chapter, you learned that the factored form of a polynomial is very useful for finding the roots of the function or the *x*-intercepts of the graph. But what happens when you do not have the factored form and you need to find all of the roots?

9-114. Andre needs to find the exact roots of the function $f(x) = x^3 + 2x^2 - 7x - 2$. When he uses his graphing calculator, he can see that one of the *x*-intercepts is 2, but there are two other intercepts that he cannot see exactly. What does he need to be able to do to find the other roots?

Andre remembers that he learned how to multiply binomials and other polynomials using generic rectangles. He figures that since division is the inverse (or undo) operation for multiplication, he should be able to **reverse** the multiplication process to divide. As he thinks about that idea, he comes across the following news article.

Polydoku Craze Sweeping Nation!

(CPM) – Math enthusiasts around the nation have entered a new puzzle craze involving the multiplication of polynomials. The goal of the game, which enthusiasts have named Polydoku, is to fill in squares so that the multiplication of two polynomials will be completed.

	1	2	3	4	5
A	×	$2x^3$	$-x^2$	$+3x$	-1
B	$3x$	$6x^4$	$-3x^3$	$9x^2$	$-3x$
C	-2	$-4x^3$	$2x^2$	$-6x$	2

$$6x^4 \quad -7x^3 \quad +11x^2 \quad -9x \quad +2$$

The game shown at right, for example, represents the multiplication of $(3x - 2)(2x^3 - x^2 + 3x - 1) = 6x^4 - 7x^3 + 11x^2 - 9x + 2$.

Most of the squares are blank at the start of the game. While the beginner level provides the factors (in the gray squares), some of the factors are missing in the more advanced levels.

9-115. Andre decided to join the craze and try some Polydoku puzzles, but he is not sure how to fill in some of the squares. Help him by answering parts (a) and (b) below about the Polydoku puzzle in the news article he read (found in problem 9-114), then complete part (c).

   a.   Explain how the term $2x^2$ in cell C3 of the news article was generated.

   b.   What values were combined to get $-7x^3$ in the news article answer?

   c.   Copy and complete the Polydoku puzzle at right.

	1	2	3	4	5
A	×	$4x^3$	$+6x^2$	$-2x$	-5
B	$2x$				
C	-3				

9-116.   POLYDOKU TEAM CHALLENGE

Work with your team to complete the puzzle at right. Find the factors and the product for the puzzle. If you get stuck, you can consult parts (a) through (c) below for ideas.

	1	2	3	4	5
A	×			$-2x$	
B	x	$2x^4$			
C	-4		$12x^2$		

$12x$

   a.   How is cell B2 related to the answer?

   b.   How did you find the third term in the answer?

   c.   What cells did you use to get the value in cell B5?

9-117.   Jessica is about to start the intermediate-level Polydoku puzzle shown at right. Show Jessica how to complete the puzzle. Make sure you can **justify** your solution.

Use your results to complete the statements below.

	1	2	3	4
A	×			
B	$2x$			
C	$+5$			

$6x^3$ $+7x^2$ $-16x$ $+10$

$$\frac{6x^3 + 7x^2 - 16x + 10}{2x + 5} = \underline{\hspace{2cm}} \quad \text{and} \quad (2x+5) \cdot \underline{\hspace{2cm}} = \underline{\hspace{2cm}}$$

9-118.   Unfortunately, Jessica made a mistake when she copied the problem. The constant term of the original polynomial was supposed to have the value + 18 (not + 10). She does not want to start all over again to solve the puzzle.

   a.   Jessica realizes that she now has 8 remaining from the original expression. What is the significance of this 8?

   b.   Jessica writes her work as shown below:

$$\frac{6x^3 + 7x^2 - 16x + 18}{2x + 5} = \frac{(6x^3 + 7x^2 - 16x + 10) + 8}{2x + 5} = 3x^2 - 4x + 2 \text{ , remainder 8.}$$

   Gina thinks that there is a way to write the answer without using the word "remainder." Discuss this with your team and find another way to write the result. Be prepared to share your results and your reasoning with the class.

   c.   Use Jessica and Gina's method to divide $(6x^3 + 11x^2 - 12x - 1) \div (3x + 1)$.

9-119.   Create your own Polydoku puzzles that can be used to solve each of the polynomial-division problems below. Express any remainders as fractions and use your results to write a multiplication and a division statement such as those in problem 9-117.

   a. $\dfrac{6x^4 - 5x^3 + 10x^2 - 18x + 5}{3x - 1}$

   b. $(x^4 - 6x^3 + 18x - 4) \div (x - 2)$

   c. $x - 3 \overline{\smash{\big)}\, x^3 + x^2 - 14x + 3}$

   d. $\dfrac{x^5 - 1}{x - 1}$

9-120.   Now work with your team to help Andre solve his original problem (problem 9-114). Find all of the roots (exact zeros) of the polynomial.

Polynomial Division

The examples below show two methods for dividing $x^4 - 6x^3 + 18x - 1$ by $x - 2$. In both cases, the remainder is written as a fraction.

Using long division:

$$
\begin{array}{r}
x^3 - 4x^2 - 8x + 2 \\
x-2\overline{)x^4 - 6x^3 + 0x^2 + 18x - 1} \\
\underline{x^4 - 2x^3} \\
-4x^3 + 0x^2 \\
\underline{-4x^3 + 8x^2} \\
-8x^2 + 18x \\
\underline{-8x^2 + 16x} \\
2x - 1 \\
\underline{2x - 4} \\
3
\end{array}
$$

Answer: $x^3 - 4x^2 - 8x + 2 + \frac{3}{x-2}$

Using generic rectangles:

Remainder

	x^3	$-4x^2$	$-8x$	$+2$	
x	x^4	$-4x^3$	$-8x^2$	$+2x$	3
-2	$-2x^3$	$+8x^2$	$+16x$	-4	

$x^4 - 6x^3 \quad +0x^2 \quad +18x \quad -1$

Answer: $x^3 - 4x^2 - 8x + 2 + \frac{3}{x-2}$

Therefore, $(x^4 - 6x^3 + 18x - 1) \div (x - 2) = x^3 - 4x^2 - 8x + 2 + \frac{3}{x-2}$ and

$(x - 2)(x^3 - 4x^2 - 8x + 2 + \frac{3}{x+2}) = x^4 - 6x^3 + 18x - 1$

9-121. Carlos is always playing games with his graphing calculator, but now his calculator has contracted a virus. The TRACE, ZOOM, and WINDOW functions on his calculator are not working. He needs to solve $x^3 + 5x^2 - 16x - 14 = 0$, so he graphs $y = x^3 + 5x^2 - 16x - 14$ and sees the graph at right in the standard window.

a. From the graph, what appears to be an integer solution to the equation?

b. Check your answer from part (a) in the equation.

c. Since $x = -7$ is a solution to the equation, what is the factor associated with this solution?

d. Use polynomial division to find the other factor.

e. Use your new factor to complete this equation:

$$x^3 + 5x^2 - 16x - 14 = (x + 7)(other\ factor) = 0$$

f. The "other factor" leads to two other solutions to the equation. Find these two new solutions and give all three solutions to the original equation.

9-122. Now Carlos needs to solve $2x^3 + 3x^2 - 8x + 3 = 0$, but his calculator will still only create a standard graph. He sees that the graph of $y = 2x^3 + 3x^2 - 8x + 3$ crosses the x-axis at $x = 1$. Find all three solutions to the equation.

9-123. Without actually multiplying, decide which of the following polynomials could be the product of $(x - 2)(x + 3)(x - 5)$. **Justify** your choice.

a. $x^3 - 4x^2 - 11x - 5$ b. $2x^3 - 4x^2 - 11x + 30$

c. $x^3 - 4x^2 - 11x + 30$ d. $2x^3 - 4x^2 - 11x - 5$

9-124.   Which of the following binomials could be a factor of $x^3 - 9x^2 + 19x + 5$? Explain your reasoning.

    a. $x - 2$ b. $x - 5$ c. $x + 3$ d. $x + 2$

9-125.   Now divide $x^3 - 9x^2 + 19x + 5$ by the factor that you chose in the preceding problem. If it is a factor, use it and the resulting factor to find all the zeros of the polynomial. If it is not a factor, reconsider your answer to the preceding problem and try a different factor.

9-126.   Consider the equation $5x^2 - 7x - 6 = 0$ as you answer the questions in parts (a) through (d) below.

    a.   What are the factors of $5x^2 - 7x - 6$?

    b.   What are the solutions to the equation?

    c.   Explain the relationship between the factors of the polynomial expression and the solutions to the equation.

    d.   How are the solutions to the equation related to the lead coefficient and constant term in the original polynomial?

9-127.   This is a checkpoint for solving systems of three equations and three unknowns.

Use elimination or matrix multiplication to solve the system of equations at right.

$$x + y - z = 12$$
$$3x + 2y + z = 6$$
$$2x + 5y - z = 10$$

Check your solution by referring to the Checkpoint 18 materials located at the back of your book.

If you needed help to solve this system correctly, then you need more practice solving 3×3 systems. Review the Checkpoint 18 materials and try the practice problems. Also, consider getting help outside of class time. From this point on, you will be expected to solve systems such as these accurately.

9-128.   Given the equation: $3x + y - z = 6$.

    a.   Draw a graph.

    b.   Is $(1, 2, -1)$ on the graph? **Justify** your answer.

9-129. Frank says that $\frac{a}{x+b} = \frac{a}{x} + \frac{a}{b}$, while Fred does not think that the two expressions are equivalent. Who is correct? **Justify** your answer.

9-130. The area of $\triangle ABC$ is 24 square inches. If $\overline{AB} \perp \overline{BC}$ and $BC = 8$ inches, find AC.

9.3.2 How can I solve it?

Factors and Integral Roots

You already know several methods for solving quadratic equations, such as factoring, completing the square, and using the Quadratic Formula. Mathematicians have developed formulas for solving third- and fourth-degree polynomial equations, but these formulas are far more complicated and messy than the Quadratic Formula is, and they are rarely used. Furthermore, for polynomials of degree greater than four, there is no single formula to use. For many polynomials, you can develop more useful methods than a formula based on what you already know.

9-131. SEARCHING FOR ROOTS OF POLYNOMIALS

By combining what you know about graphing, factoring, and polynomial division, and then applying what you know about solving quadratic equations, you will be able to find the roots of the higher-degree polynomial functions in this lesson.

Your task: Find all of the zeros of the polynomial below and then write the polynomial in factored form with factors of degree 2 or 1.

$$P(x) = x^4 - x^3 - 5x^2 + 3x + 6$$

Discussion Points

What are some possible linear factors?

How can the graph help us decide which factors to try?

How can we use the known factors to figure out other factors?

What do we need to do to write the polynomial in factored form and find the zeros?

Further Guidance

9-132. Using only integers for a, and just by looking at the polynomial expression, list all of the possible linear factors $(x \pm a)$ for the polynomial $P(x) = x^4 - x^3 - 5x^2 + 3x + 6$.

a. Could $x - 5$ be included on your list of possible linear factors? Explain.

b. Not all of the *possibilities* will actually be factors. Use your graphing calculator to decide which members of your list are the best possibilities.

c. Now that you have shortened the list of possibilities, which factors on the shortened list really are factors of $P(x)$? **Justify** your answer.

d. If you haven't already divided, divide the polynomial by one of the factors from part (c) and write the polynomial as a product of a linear and a cubic factor.

e. Now divide the cubic factor from part (d) by the other linear factor that worked, and write the original polynomial as a product of two linear factors and one quadratic factor.

f. From the factored form, you can find all of the solutions to $x^4 - x^3 - 5x^2 + 3x + 6 = 0$ and the exact x-intercepts for the graph of $P(x)$. What are they?

————— *Further Guidance section ends here.* —————

9-133. LEARNING LOG

As a team, look back over the work you did to find the linear factors of $P(x)$ and make a list of steps you can use to find all of the zeros of a given polynomial. Then record your ideas in your Learning Log. Use diagrams, arrows, and other math tools to help demonstrate your ideas. Label the list "Factors and Roots of Polynomial Functions."

9-134. Your teacher will assign your team one of the following polynomial functions. Use the list of steps your team developed to factor the polynomial and find all of its roots. Then prepare a poster in which you illustrate and **justify** each of your steps. Be sure to include the graph on your poster and clearly explain the relationship between the solutions of the equation and the x-intercepts.

a. $Q_1(x) = x^3 + 3x^2 + 1x - 5$

b. $Q_2(x) = 6x^4 + 7x^3 - 36x^2 - 7x + 6$

c. $Q_3(x) = x^4 + 2x^3 + 10x^2 + 18x + 9$

d. $Q_4(x) = x^4 - 8x^3 + 18x^2 - 16x + 5$

e. $Q_5(x) = x^5 - 4x^3 - x^2 + 4$

f. $Q_6(x) = x^3 + x^2 - 7x - 7$

9-135.   LEARNING LOG

Make additions and adjustments to your Learning Log entry from
problem 9-133 to reflect what you leaned from the posters.

9-136.   Use the procedures you developed to factor each of the following polynomial
expressions. Each final answer should be a linear factor times a quadratic factor. Look
for patterns in the factors.

a. $x^3 - 1$ b. $x^3 + 8$ c. $x^3 - 27$ d. $x^3 + 125$

9-137.   If you **generalize** the patterns for the factors in problem 9-136, you will discover a
shortcut for factoring cubic polynomials that are described as the sum or difference of
two cubes. Write the factors for each polynomial expression below.

a. $x^3 + a^3$ b. $x^3 - b^3$

c.   Write a description of how to get the factors without having to divide.

9-138.   Are there similar patterns for $x^4 + a^4$ and $x^4 - b^4$? Explain.

9-139.   BUILDING POLYNOMIALS

For each of the following descriptions of polynomial functions with integral
coefficients, answer each question below.

i.   What are the possible numbers of real zeros?

ii. How many complex zeros are possible?

iii. For each number of possible real zeros, give an example of a polynomial in
factored form.

a.   A third-degree polynomial function.

b.   A fourth-degree polynomial function.

c.   A fifth-degree polynomial function.

METHODS AND MEANINGS

The Factor and Integral Zero Theorems

Factor Theorem: If a is a zero of a polynomial function, then $(x - a)$ is a factor of the polynomial, and if $(x - a)$ is a factor of the polynomial, then a is a zero.

Example: We know that -3, $\frac{1}{2}$, and $1 \pm i\sqrt{7}$ are zeros of the polynomial $p(x) = 2x^4 + x^3 + 22x^2 + 80x - 24$. (You can test each value by substituting it into the equation to verify that the resulting value of the function is 0.) According to the Factor Theorem, $(x + 3)$, $(x - \frac{1}{2})$, $(x - (1 + i\sqrt{7}))$, and $(x - (1 - i\sqrt{7}))$ are factors of the polynomial. Notice that the theorem does not state that they are the *only* factors of the polynomial. In order to show that these are factors, we must show that they can each be part of a product that results in $p(x)$. We start by multiplying the factors together. To make the operations simpler, we multiply the complex factors first, as shown below.

$$(x + 3)(x - \tfrac{1}{2})(x - (1 + i\sqrt{7}))(x - (1 - i\sqrt{7}))$$
$$= (x + 3)(x - \tfrac{1}{2})(x^2 - 2x + 8)$$

We then notice that if we multiply this expression by 2, we can eliminate the fraction in $(x - \frac{1}{2})$ without changing the roots. For convenience, we multiply $2(x - \frac{1}{2})$ first and then multiply the rest of the factors together.

$$2(x + 3)(x - \tfrac{1}{2})(x^2 - 2x + 8)$$
$$= (x + 3)(2x - 1)(x^2 - 2x + 8)$$
$$= 2x^4 + x^3 + 22x^2 + 80x - 24 = p(x)$$

Integral Zero Theorem: For any polynomial with integral coefficients, if an integer is a zero of the polynomial, it must be a factor of the constant term.

Example: Suppose the integers $a, b, c,$ and d are zeros of a polynomial. Then, according to the Factor Theorem, $(x - a)(x - b)(x - c)(x - d)$ are factors of the polynomial.

When you multiply these factors together, the constant term will be $abcd$, so $a, b, c,$ and d are factors of the constant term.

9-140.   Carlo was trying to factor the polynomial
$p(x) = x^4 - 4x^3 - 4x^2 + 24x - 9$ and find all of its
roots. He had already found one factor by making a
guess and trying it, so he had
$p(x) = (x-3)(x^3 - x^2 - 7x + 3)$. He was trying to
factor $x^3 - x^2 - 7x + 3$, and he had tried $(x+3)$,
$(x+1)$, and $(x-1)$, but none worked. Then Teo came
by and said, *"You should look at the graph."*

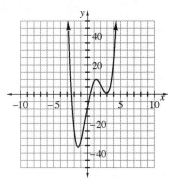

a.   How does the graph help?

b.   Complete the problem.

9-141.   Spud has a problem. He knows that the solutions for a quadratic equation are
$x = 3 + 4i$ and $x = 3 - 4i$, but in order to get credit for the problem he was supposed to
have written down the equation. Unfortunately, he lost the paper with the original
equation on it. His friends are full of advice.

a.   Alexia says, *"Look, just remember when we made polynomials. If you wanted
7 and 4 to be the answers, you just used $(x-7)(x-4)$. So you just do x minus
the first one times x minus the other."* Use $(x-(3+4i))(x-(3-4i))$ to find the
quadratic expression.

b.   Hugo says, *"No, no, no. You can do it that way, but that's too complicated.
I think you just start with $x = 3 + 4i$ and work backward. So $x - 3 = 4i$, then,
hmmm. Yeah, that'll work."* Try Hugo's method.

c.   Which way do you think Spud should use? Explain your choice.

9-142.   So far you have been able to extend the rules for real numbers to add, subtract, and
multiply complex numbers, but what about dividing? Can you use what you know
about real numbers to divide one complex number by another? In other words, if a
problem looks like this:

$$\frac{3 + 2i}{-4 + 7i}$$

What needs to be done to get an answer in the form of a single complex number,
$a + bi$?

Natalio had an idea. He said, *"I'll bet we can use the conjugate!"*

"How?" asked Ricki.

Problem continues on next page.→

9-142.   *Problem continued from previous page.*

   "Well, it's a fraction. Can't we multiply the numerator and denominator by the same number?" Natalio replied.

   a.   Natalio was not very clear in his explanation. Show Ricki what he meant they should do.

   b.   Using Natalio's ideas you probably still came up with a fraction in part (a), but the denominator should be a whole number. To write a complex number such as $\frac{c+di}{m}$ in the form $a + bi$, just use the distributive property to rewrite the result as $\frac{c}{m} + \frac{d}{m}i$. Rewrite your result for part (a) in this form.

9-143.   Use the method developed in problem 9-142 to do the following division problems.

   a. $\frac{2-5i}{1-2i}$

   b. $(-3+i) \div (2+3i)$

9-144.   Find the inverse of $g(x) = (x + 1)^2 - 3$ with the domain $x \geq -1$. Sketch both graphs and tell the domain and range of the inverse function.

9-145.   Sketch the graph of each polynomial function below and find all of the zeros.

   a. $y = x^3 + 1$

   b. $y = x^3 - 8$

9-146.   Solve the system of equations at right for (x, y, z).

$$x = y + z$$
$$2x + 3y + z = 17$$
$$z + 2y = 7$$

9-147.   Sketch the graph of each equation below.

   a. $y = 3 \sin\left(x + \frac{\pi}{2}\right)$

   b. $y = -2 \sin(4x)$

9-148.   Spud has done it again. He's lost another polynomial function. This one was a cubic, written in standard form. He knows that there were two complex zeros, $-2 \pm 5i$ and one real zero, -1. What could his original function have been?

9-149.   Given the equation $x^3 - 6x^2 + 7x + 2 = 0$.

    a.   Verify that $x = 2$ is a solution.

    b.   What is one factor of $x^3 - 6x^2 + 7x + 2$?

    c.   Use (b) to find another factor.

    d.   What are all the solutions of $x^3 - 6x^2 + 7x + 2 = 0$?

9-150.   Rewrite each of the following division problems as a single complex number.

    a. $\frac{5+3i}{5-3i}$ b. $\frac{7+3i}{1-i}$

9-151.   Where do the graphs below intersect? You should be able to do these without a graphing calculator.

    a. $2x + y = 10$ b. $2x + y = 10$
           $x + y = 25$ $x^2 + y^2 = 25$

9-152.   Sketch both the circle $x^2 + y^2 = 25$ and the parabola $y = x^2 - 13$.

    a.   How many points of intersection are there?

    b.   Find the coordinates of these points algebraically.

9-153.   Solve each equation. Be sure to check your answers.

    a. $\sqrt{x} + 2 = x$ b. $\sqrt{x} + 2 = \sqrt{x+6}$

9-154.   Find the distance between each pair of points.

    a. $(2, 3)$ and $(4, 7)$ b. $(2, 3)$ and (x, y)

9-155.   For each equation, find two solutions $0 \le x < 2\pi$, which make the equation true. No calculator necessary.

    a. $\cos x = -\frac{1}{2}$ b. $\tan x = \frac{\sqrt{3}}{3}$ c. $\sin x = 0$ d. $\cos x = \frac{\sqrt{2}}{2}$

9-156.   Rewrite each of the following division problems as a single complex number in simplest form.

   a. $\dfrac{2-6i}{4+2i}$

   b. $\dfrac{5}{1+2i}$

9-157.   A long lost relative died and left you $15,000! Your parents say that you need to save the money for college, so you put it an account that pays 8% interest compounded annually. How many years will it take until your account is worth $25,000?

9-158.   Solve each equation.

   a. $\log_3(2x-1) = -2$

   b. $5^{\log_5(x)} = 3$

   c. $\log_2(x) - \log_2(3) = 4$

   d. $\log_3(5) = x$

9-159.   Verify that the graphs of the equations $x^2 + y^3 = 17$ and $x^4 - 4y^2 - 8xy = 17$ intersect at $(3, 2)$.

9-160.   The graphs of $y = \log_2(x-1)$ and $y = x^3 - 4x$ intersect at two points: $(2, 0)$ and approximately $(1.1187, -3.075)$. Use that information to solve $\log_2(x-1) = x^3 - 4x$.

9-161.   Each dartboard below is a target at the county fair dart-throwing game. What is the probability of hitting the darkened region of each target? Assume you always hit the board but the location on the board is random.

a.   b.   60°
c.   d.

e.   f.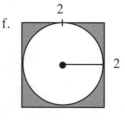

9-162.   Use your knowledge of the unit circle to explain why the graphs of $y = \sin\theta$ and $y = \cos(\theta - \frac{\pi}{2})$ are the same.

9-163.   For homework, Londa was asked to simplify the expression $\sqrt{-7} \cdot \sqrt{-7} =$. She got the answer 7, but when she checked, she learned that the correct answer was -7.

a.   Show Londa the steps she could take to get -7.

b.   What steps do you think Londa took to get 7 as a result?

c.   What does she need to consider in order to avoid making this mistake in the future?

d.   Londa's example means that it is not always true that $\sqrt{a} \cdot \sqrt{b} = \sqrt{ab}$ for real numbers a and b. What restriction needs to be placed on the numbers a and b?

9-164.   Change each angle from degrees to radians.

a.   60°   b.   75°   c.   210°   d.   225°

9.3.3 How can I use it?

An Application of Polynomials

In this lesson, you will have the opportunity to use the equation and graph of a polynomial function to solve a problem involving a game at the county fair.

9-165.   COUNTY FAIR GAME TANK

The Mathamericaland Carnival Company wants to create a new game. It will consist of a tank filled with ping-pong balls of different colors. People will pay for the opportunity to crawl around in the tank blindfolded for 60 seconds, while they collect ping-pong balls. Most of the ping-pong balls will be white, but there will be a few of different colors. The players will win $100 for each red, $200 for each blue, and $500 for each green ping-pong ball they carry out of the tank.

The tank will be rectangular, open at the top, and will be made by cutting squares out of each corner of an 8.5-meter by 11-meter sheet of translucent miracle material that can be bent into shape. The owner of the company thinks that she will make the greatest profit if the tank has maximum volume. She has hired your team to figure out the exact dimensions of the tank that creates the maximum value.

Your task: Your team will write a report of your findings to the Carnival Company that includes each of the following elements.

- Any data or conjectures your team made based on experimental paper tanks.

- A diagram of the tank with the dimensions clearly labeled with appropriate variables.

- A graph of the volume function that you found with notes on a reasonable domain and range.

- An equation that matches your graph.

- Your conclusions and observations.

Further Guidance

9-166.   Use a full sheet of 8.5" x 11" paper, which is the same shape as the material for the tank. Each member of your team should choose a different sized square to cut out of the corners. Measure the side of the square you cut out and write along the edge of the large piece of paper. Use either inches or centimeters. Your paper should look like the figure at right.

Fold the paper up into an open box (fold on the dotted lines). Then tape the cut parts together so that the box holds its shape. Measure the dimensions of the tank. Record the dimensions directly on the model tank.

9-167.   Make a table like the one below for your team's results. Consider "extreme" tanks, the ones with the largest possible cutout and the smallest possible cutout. For example, imagine cutting a square out of each corner zero inches on a side.

Height of Tank	Width of Tank	Length of Tank	Volume of Tank

a.   Examine the data in the table with your team and make some conjectures about how to find the maximum volume.

b.   Label the height as x. Using x for the height, find expressions for the length and width.

c.   Write an equation to represent the volume of the tank.

d.   Sketch the graph of your function by using the roots and determining the orientation.

e.   What domain and range make sense for your function?

f.   Approximate the maximum volume of the tank and the dimensions of the tank that will generate this volume.

9-168. Use your graph and your tank model to write your report. Include your answers to the following questions.

   a. Which points on the graph represent tanks that can actually be made? Explain.

   b. How are the dimensions of the tank related? In other words, what happens to the length and width as the height increases?

   c. Make a drawing of your tank. (You may want to use isometric dot paper.) Label your drawing with its dimensions and its volume.

Further Guidance section ends here.

METHODS AND **M**EANINGS

MATH NOTES

Factoring Sums and Differences

The difference of two squares can be factored: $a^2 - b^2 = (a+b)(a-b)$

The sum of two cubes can be factored: $a^3 + b^3 = (a+b)(a^2 - ab + b^2)$

The difference of two cubes can be factored: $a^3 - b^3 = (a-b)(a^2 + ab + b^2)$

9-169. A polynomial function has the equation $P(x) = x(x-3)^2(2x+1)$. What are the x-intercepts?

9-170. Sketch a graph of a fourth-degree polynomial that has no real roots.

9-171. Generally, when you are asked to factor, it is understood that you are only to use integers in your factors. If you are allowed to use irrational or complex number, *any* quadratic can be factored.

By setting the polynomial equal to zero and solving the quadratic equation, you can work backwards to "force factor" any quadratic. Use the solutions of the corresponding quadratic equation to write each of the following expressions as a product of two linear factors.

a. $x^2 - 10$ b. $x^2 - 3x - 7$ c. $x^2 + 4$ d. $x^2 - 2x + 2$

9-172. Sketch the graphs and find the area of the intersection of the inequalities below.
$$y > |x + 3|$$
$$y \le 5$$

9-173. Determine whether $x = -2$ is a solution to the equation $x^4 - 4x = 8x^2 - 40$. Show why or why not.

9-174. Use your solving skills to complete parts (a) and (b) below.

a. Solve $\frac{x+3}{x-1} - \frac{x}{x+1} = \frac{8}{x^2-1}$ for x.

b. In part (a), the result of solving the equation is $x = 1$, but what happens when you substitute 1 for x? What does this mean in relation to the solutions for this equation?

9-175. The roots of two quadratic polynomials are given below. Write possible quadratic functions in standard form.

a. $x = -i, x = i$ b. $x = 1 + \sqrt{2}, x = 1 - \sqrt{2}$

9-176. Graph two cycles of each function.

a. $y = -2\cos(x + \frac{\pi}{2})$ b. $y = \sin(x - \frac{\pi}{2})$

Chapter 9 Closure What have I learned?

Reflection and Synthesis

The activities below offer you a chance to reflect on what you have learned in this chapter. As you work, look for concepts that you feel very comfortable with, ideas that you would like to learn more about, and topics you need more help with. Look for connections between ideas as well as connections with material you learned previously.

①   TEAM BRAINSTORM

With your team, brainstorm a list for each of the following categories. Be as detailed as you can. How long can you make your list? Challenge yourselves. Be prepared to share your team's ideas with the class.

Topics: What have you studied in this chapter? What ideas and words were important in what you learned? Remember to be as detailed as you can.

Connections: How are the topics, ideas, and words that you learned in previous courses connected to the new ideas in this chapter? Again, make your list as long as you can.

② MAKING CONNECTIONS

Below is a list of the vocabulary used in this chapter. Make sure that you are familiar with all of these words and know what they mean. Refer to the glossary or index for any words that you do not yet understand.

coefficient	complex	conjugate
degree	discriminant	factor
imaginary	integral roots	polynomial
quotient	real	remainder
root	solution	x-intercept
zero		

Make a concept map showing all of the connections you can find among the key words and ideas listed above. To show a connection between two words, draw a line between them and explain the connection, as shown in the example below. A word can be connected to any other word as long as you can **justify** the connection. For each key word or idea, provide a sketch of an example.

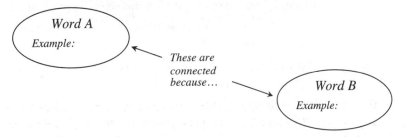

Your teacher may provide you with vocabulary cards to help you get started. If you use the cards to plan your concept map, be sure either to re-draw your concept map on your paper or to glue the vocabulary cards to a poster with all of the connections explained for others to see and understand.

While you are making your map, your team may think of related words or ideas that are not listed above. Be sure to include these ideas on your concept map.

③ GROWTH OVER TIME

This section gives you an opportunity to show growth in your understanding of key mathematical ideas over time as you complete this course.

Part 1: Answer the following question on a separate sheet of paper. Be sure to include everything you have learned since the last time you did this problem, and do not leave out anything you included in your earlier attempts.
How many different kinds of graphs can you create that have

i.   No x-intercepts? **ii.**   One x-intercept?

iii.   Two x-intercepts? *iv.*   Three or more x-intercepts?

For each type of graph, show a sketch, label the key points, and give its equation. Make sure that each graph you give as an example represents a different family and describe the family in words or with a general equation. Show how to calculate the x-intercepts of each of your sample graphs.

Part 2: Compare your three responses to this "Growth Over Time" problem. Write an evaluation of your growth based on your responses. Consider each of the following questions as you write your answer.

- What new concepts did you include the second time you did the problem? In what ways was your response better than your first attempt?

- How was your final version different from the first two? What new ideas did you include?

- Did you omit anything in the final version that you used in one of the earlier versions? Why did you omit it?

- Rate your three attempts by making three bars like the ones below and shading each bar to represent how much you knew on each attempt.

First Attempt:	
Second Attempt:	
Final Attempt:	

- Is there anything you want to add to your current version? If so, add it and keep this version for future reference.

④ SUMMARIZING MY UNDERSTANDING

This section gives you an opportunity to show what you know about certain math topics or ideas.

With your team, make a list of the **big ideas** of this chapter. Discuss the important ideas of the chapter and try to agree on a short list of no more than five big ideas. Be prepared to share your list in a whole class discussion. When the class has reached agreement on a list, continue with parts (a) and (b) below.

a.   Write your own description of each big idea.

b.   For each big idea, provide one or two representative example problems. Solve each problem completely, using multiple representations, if applicable.

⑤   WHAT HAVE I LEARNED?

This section will help you evaluate which types of problems you feel comfortable with and which you need more help with. This section will appear at the end of every chapter to help you check your understanding. Even if your teacher does not assign this section, it is a good idea to try these problems and find out for yourself what you know and what you need to work on.

Solve each problem as completely as you can. The table at the end of this closure section has answers to these problems. It also tells you where you can find additional help and practice on similar problems.

CL 9-177. Decide if each of the following equations is a polynomial. If it is, state the degree. If it is not, explain how you know.

     a. $f(x) = 3x^3 - 2x + 5$ b. $y = 0.25x^7 - 5x$

     c. $y = 3^x - x^2$ d. $f(x) = x^2 - \sqrt{x} + 2$

     e. $Q(x) = 3(x - 4)^2(x + 2)$ f. $y = x^2 - 3x + 5 - \frac{2}{x-2}$

CL 9-178. Where do the graphs of each of the following functions cross the x-axis?

     a. $f(x) = (x - 2)^2 - 3$ b. $f(x) = (x - 19)^2(x + 14)$

CL 9-179. Write a polynomial equation for a graph that has three x-intercepts at $(-3, 0)$, $(2, 0)$, and $(5, 0)$, and passes through the point $(1, 56)$.

CL 9-180. Decide if each of the following functions has real or complex roots.

     a. $y = 3x^2 + 5x + 4$ b. $y = 3x^2 + 5x - 4$

CL 9-181. Make a sketch of a graph $q(x)$ such that $q(x) = 0$ would have the number and type of solutions indicated below.

     a.   7 real solutions   b.   5 real and 2 complex solutions

     c.   4 complex solutions   d.   2 complex and 4 real solutions

CL 9-182. Sketch graphs of each of the following polynomial functions. Be sure to label the x- and the y-intercepts of each graph.

    a. $y = x(2x + 3)(2x - 5)$

    b. $y = (11 - 2x)^2(x - 2)$

CL 9-183. Simplify each expression

    a. $(3 + 4i) + (7 - 2i)$

    b. $(3 + 5i)^2$

    c. $(7 + i)(7 - i)$

    d. $(3i)(2i)^2$

    e. i^3

    f. i^{32}

CL 9-184. Divide: $(2x^3 + x^2 - 19x + 36) \div (x + 4)$

CL 9-185. The graph of $f(x) = x^3 + 3x^2 + x - 5$ is shown at right. Use it to determine all real and complex roots.

CL 9-186. The roots of a quadratic polynomial are given below. Find a possible quadratic equation in standard form.

    a. $x = 2i, x = -2i$

    b. $x = 2 + \sqrt{3}, x = 2 - \sqrt{3}$

CL 9-187. Use the system at right to answer each of the following questions.

$$y = 2x$$
$$y = x^2 + 5$$

    a.   Without graphing, what is the solution to the system?

    b.   What does the solution to the system tell you about the graphs?

CL 9-188. Check your answers using the table at the end of this section. Which problems do you feel confident about? Which problems were hard? Have you worked on problems like these in math classes you have taken before? Use the table to make a list of topics you need help on and a list of topics you need to practice more.

HOW AM I THINKING?

This course focuses on five different **Ways of Thinking**: **justifying**, **generalizing**, **choosing a strategy**, **investigating**, and **reversing thinking**. These are some of the ways in which you think while trying to make sense of a concept or attempting to solve a problem (even outside of math class). During this chapter, you have probably used each Way of Thinking multiple times without even realizing it!

Review each of the five Ways of Thinking described in the closure sections of Chapters 1 through 5. Then choose three of these Ways of Thinking that you remember using while working on this chapter. Show and explain where and how you used each one. Describe why thinking in this way helped you solve a particular problem or understand something new. Be sure to include examples to demonstrate your thinking.

Answers and Support for Closure Activity #5
What Have I Learned?

Problem	Solutions	Need Help?	More Practice
CL 9-177.	a. yes; degree 3 b. yes; degree 7 c. no; it contains a power of x d. no; it contains a power of $\frac{1}{2}$ e. yes; degree 3 f. no; it contains a negative power of x	Math Notes boxes in Lessons 9.1.1 and 9.1.3	Problems 9-9, 9-18, 9-30, 9-41, and 9-57
CL 9-178.	a. $x = \pm\sqrt{3} + 2$ b. $x = 19$ and $x = -14$	Math Notes box in Lesson 9.1.2	Problems 9-20, 9-21, 9-22, 9-38, 9-39, 9-107, 9-126, 9-134, and 9-169
CL 9-179.	$y = 3.5(x + 3)(x - 2)(x - 5)$	Lesson 9.1.3	Problems 9-40, 9-47, 9-49, 9-50, 9-51, 9-52, 9-58, and 9-59
CL 9-180.	a. complex roots b. real roots	Lessons 9.2.1 and 9.2.2 Math Notes boxes in Lessons 9.2.2 and 9.3.2	Problems 9-68, 9-69, 9-81, 9-91, 9-103, and 9-139

Problem	Solutions	Need Help?	More Practice
CL 9-181.	a. b. c. d.	Math Notes box in Lesson 9.2.3	Problems 9-69, 9-101, 9-102, 9-103, 9-104, 9-105, 9-106, and 9-170
CL 9-182.	a. b.	Lessons 9.1.1 and 9.1.2	Problems 9-3, 9-4, 9-8, 9-37, and 9-108
CL 9-183.	a. $10 + 2i$ b. $-16 + 30i$ c. 50 d. $-12i$ e. $-i$ f. 1	Lesson 9.2.1 Math Notes box in Lesson 9.2.1	Problems 9-67, 9-72, 9-73, 9-78, 9-83, and 9-111
CL 9-184.	$2x^2 - 7x + 9$	Math Notes box in Lesson 9.3.1	Problems 9-117, 9-118, 9-119, and 9-125
CL 9-185.	$x = 1, -2 \pm i$	Lesson 9.3.2	Problems 9-120, 9-121, 9-122, 9-125, 9-134, and 9-145
CL 9-186.	a. $y = x^2 + 4$ b. $y = x^2 - 4x + 1$	Lessons 9.1.2 and 9.1.3 Math Notes boxes in Lessons 9.1.2 and 9.3.2	Problems 9-40, 9-47, 9-51, 9-52, 9-58, 9-59, 9-88, 9-89, and 9-175
CL 9-187.	a. $(1 \pm 2i, 2 \pm 4i)$ b. graphs do not intersect	Lesson 9.2.1	Problems 9-11, 9-60, 9-70, 9-71, and 9-151

CHAPTER 10   Probability and Counting

In this chapter, you will develop your understanding of probability, which is often important when making decisions in business or politics. Your knowledge of probability will most likely impact future decisions you will make.

As you work through this chapter, you will learn **strategies** for counting the number of possible outcomes of a situation. You will also discover that the order of events and whether they can occur repeatedly makes a difference in the total possibilities.

Knowing how to calculate the number of **permutations** or **combinations** in a given situation can make some problems much easier. In this chapter, you will work on a wide range of problems, from carnival games and games of chance, to making decisions on social issues.

In this chapter, you will learn:

Guiding Questions

Think about these questions throughout this chapter:

How many outcomes are there?

Are they equally likely?

Does order matter?

What tools can I use?

What are the connections?

> ➤ The fundamental principle for counting the number of outcomes by multiplying.

> ➤ How to count possibilities in situations that require a particular order and in situations where order is not important.

> ➤ How to use counting principles to calculate probabilities.

> ➤ New connections between algebra, geometry, and probability.

Chapter Outline

Section 10.1   In the first section, you will use tree and area diagrams, probability, independent events, and expected value to solve problems and resolve questions of fairness.

Section 10.2   Here, you will use the Fundamental Principle of Counting, permutations, and combinations, both to count outcomes for complex situations and to compute probabilities.

10.1.1 Is this game fair?

. . . .

Probability and Expected Value

In this lesson you will review ideas of probability as you use strategic lists, tree diagrams, and area models. You will find that certain tools may work better for particular problems. In one problem a tree diagram or list might be most efficient, while in another problem an area model may be the best choice.

You will also be asked to decide whether a game is **fair** and to think about **expected values**. A game is **fair** if over many plays, a person would expect to neither win nor lose points or money by playing the game. **Expected value** is what you expect to win per play, on average, based on playing the game many times. Discuss the following focus questions as you work:

What are the possible outcomes?

Are the outcomes equally likely?

Will a tree diagram, list, or area model help?

10-1.   ROCK, PAPER, SCISSORS

Your team will play a variation of "Rock, Paper, Scissors" (sometimes called "Rochambeau") and record points. You will need to work in a team of four. Have one person act as recorder while the other three play the game.

a.   List the names of the people in your team alphabetically. The first person on the list is Player A, the next is Player B, the third is Player C, and the fourth is the recorder. Write down who has each role.

b.   Your team will play "Rock, Paper, Scissors." The recorder should record the winner for each round. Assign points as follows:

- Player A gets a point each time all three players match.

- Player B gets a point each time two of the three players match.

- Player C gets a point each time none of the players match.

First, discuss with your team which player you think will receive the most points by the end of the game. Now, play "Rock, Paper, Scissors" at least 20 times.

c.   Does this game seem fair? How could you calculate the theoretical probabilities of each outcome (Player A, Player B, or Player C winning)? Discuss this with your team and be prepared to share your ideas with the class.

Problem continues on next page.→

10-1. *Problem continued from previous page.*

d. Jenna is Player A in her team and she has decided to make a tree diagram to help her calculate the probability that she will win. The diagram she started is shown at right. Work with your team to complete this diagram. How many of the branches represent Jenna winning? Which ones? Calculate the probability that Jenna will win.

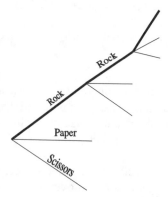

e. Calculate the probabilities that Player B will win and that Player C will win. Is this a fair game?

10-2.   BASKETBALL: Shooting One-and-One Free Throws

Rimshot McGee has a 70% free throw average. The opposing team is ahead by one point. Rimshot is at the foul line in a one-and-one situation with just seconds left in the game. (A one-and-one situation means that the player shoots a free throw. If he makes the shot, he is allowed to shoot another. If he misses the shot, he gets no second shot. Each shot made is worth one point.)

a. First, take a guess. What do you think is the most likely outcome for Rimshot: zero points, one point, or two points?

b. Draw a tree diagram to represent this situation.

c. Jeremy is working on the problem with Jenna and he remembers that area models are sometimes useful for solving problems related to probability. They set up the area model at right. Discuss this model with your team. Which part of the model represents Rimshot getting one point? How can you use the model to help calculate the probability that Rimshot will get exactly one point?

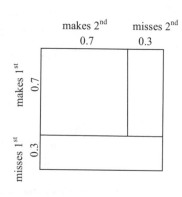

Problem continues on next page. →

10-2. *Problem continued from previous page.*

    d. Use either your tree diagram or the area model to help you calculate the probabilities that Rimshot will get either 0 or 2 points. What is the most likely of the three outcomes?

    e. Many people, when faced with this same problem, guess that one point is the most likely outcome. Their confusion comes from their intuitive understanding of **expected value**, which is the average number of points you would expect over many repetitions of the situation. In this case, if Rimshot McGee were in 100 one-and-one free throw situations, what would we expect to be his average number of points? Discuss this with your team and be ready to share your ideas with the class.

10-3. With your team, take a minute to examine the area model for problem 10-2.

    a. What are the dimensions of the rectangle? Explain why these dimensions make sense.

    b. What is the total area of the model? Express the area as a product of the dimensions and as a sum of the parts.

    c. What probability is represented by the entire area of the model?

10-4. DOUBLE SPIN

"Double Spin" is a new game at the fair. The player gets to spin a spinner twice, but wins only if the same amount comes up both times. The $100 sector is $\frac{1}{8}$ of the circle. Make an area model or tree diagram to show the probabilities of every outcome of two spins and then answer the following questions.

    a. What is the probability of winning $100 ?

    b. What is the probability of winning anything at all?

    c. How did your team choose whether to use an area model or a tree diagram? Now that you have calculated the probabilities, do you think you made the right choice? Why or why not?

    d. What is the **expected value** for a winner of this game? That is, what is the average amount of money the carnival should expect to pay to players each turn over a long period of time?

    e. If it costs $3.00 for you to play this game, should you expect to break even in the long run?

10-5.   Marty and Gerri had just lost playing "Double Spin" when they ran into another game they had never heard of called "Pick a Tile," in which the player has to reach into a bag and choose one square tile and one circular tile. The bag contains three yellow, one blue and two red squares as well as one yellow and two red circles. In order to win the game (and a large stuffed animal), a player must choose one blue square and one red circle.

Since it costs $2 to play the game, Marty and Gerri decided to calculate the probability of winning before deciding whether to play.

Gerri suggested making a list of all the possible color combinations, squares first then circles:

RY	*BY*	*YY*
RR	*BR*	*YR*

"So," says Gerri, "*the answer is* $\frac{1}{6}$."

"*That doesn't seem quite right,*" says Marty. "*There are more yellow squares in there than blue ones. I don't think the chance of getting a yellow square and a red circle should be the same as getting a blue square and a red circle. Maybe we need to account for all three yellow squares with* Y_1, Y_2, Y_3 ."

a.   Make a tree diagram or a systematic list of all the possibilities, using subscripts to account for the colors for which there is more than one square or circle.

b.   Find the probability of a player choosing the blue-red combination.

c.   Should Gerri and Marty play this game? Would you? Why or why not?

10-6.   How could the area model at right help Marty and Gerri calculate all of the probabilities?

a.   Complete the area model and use it to calculate the probability of each possible color combination of a square and a circular tile.

b.   Talk with your team about how this model is related to the systematic list or tree diagram that you made in problem 10-5. Find as many connections as you can and be prepared to share your ideas with the class.

$P(R) =$ $P(Y) =$

$P(Y) =$

$P(R) =$

$P(B) =$

10-7.   BASKETBALL: Shooting One-and-One Free Throws Revisited

Dunkin' Delilah Jones has a 60% free throw average.

a.   What would be the most likely result when she shoots a one-and-one?

b.   Is it more likely that Delilah would make no points or that she would score some points? Explain.

c.   On average, how many points would you expect Dunkin' Delilah to make in a one and one free throw situation? That is, what is the expected value?

d.   Try at least three other possible free throw percentages and make a note of the most likely outcome.

e.   Is there some free-throw percentage that would make two points and zero points equally likely outcomes? If so, find this percentage.

f.   If you did not already do so, draw an area model or tree diagram for part (e) using x as the percentage and write an equation to represent the problem. Write the solution to the equation in simplest radical form.

10-8.   Suppose that you were going to flip three coins: a penny, a nickel, and a dime.

a.   Make a systematic list that shows all the possible outcomes. This list of all the possible outcomes is known as the **sample space** for this experiment. Does it matter which coin is flipped first?

b.   How many outcomes are there?

c.   Find the probability of flipping each of the following. Be sure to show your thinking clearly:

    i.   Three heads   ii.   At least two heads
    iii.   One head and two tails   iv.   At least one tail
    v.   Exactly two tails   vi.   At least one head and one tail

d.   Which is more likely, flipping at least 2 heads or at least 2 tails? Explain.

e.   If you have not done so already, represent this sample space with an area model or a tree diagram. Is there one model that makes more sense than the other in this situation? Explain.

10-9.   For what kinds of probability problems might area models be most useful? What about tree diagrams? Are there any types of problems in which either model would be impossible to use? Explain.

METHODS AND MEANINGS

Probability Models

When all the possible outcomes of an event are **equally likely** (in other words have the same probability), the probability of a sequence of such events can be found by making a simple **systematic list**. However, when some outcomes are more likely than others, a more sophisticated model is required.

Spinner #1

$P(I) = \frac{1}{2}$

$P(U) = \frac{1}{6}$

$P(A) = \frac{1}{3}$

Spinner #2

$P(T) = \frac{1}{4}$

$P(F) = \frac{3}{4}$

One such model is an **area model**. In this type of model, the situation is represented by a square with dimensions 1X1 so that the areas of the parts are the probabilities of the different events that can occur. For example, suppose you spin the two spinners shown above. The probabilities of the outcomes are represented as the lengths along the sides of the area model at right. Notice that the "U" column takes up $\frac{1}{6}$ of the width of the table since $P(U) = \frac{1}{6}$. Similarly, the "T" row takes up $\frac{1}{4}$ of the height of the table, since $P(T) = \frac{1}{4}$. Then the probability that the spinners come out "U" and "T" is equal to the area of the $P(U) \times P(T)$ rectangle in the table: $\frac{1}{6} \cdot \frac{1}{4} = \frac{1}{24}$.

Spinner #1

	I($\frac{1}{2}$)	A($\frac{1}{3}$)	U($\frac{1}{6}$)
T ($\frac{1}{4}$)	IT	AT	UT
F ($\frac{3}{4}$)	IF	AF	UF

Spinner #2

The situation can also be represented with a **tree diagram**. In this model, the branching points indicate the events, and the branches stemming from each event indicate the possible outcomes for the event. For example, in the tree diagram at right the first branching point represents spinning the first spinner.

The first spinner can come out "I" "A" or "U", so each of those options has a branch. The number next to each letter is the probability that the letter occurs.

The numbers at the far right of the table represent the probabilities for each sequence of events. For example, $P(U \text{ and } T)$ can be found at the end of the bold branch of the tree. This probability, $\frac{1}{24}$, can be found by multiplying the fractions that appear on the bold branches.

10-10.   Eddie told Alfred, *"I'll bet if I flip three coins I can get exactly two heads."* Alfred replied, *"I'll bet I can get exactly two heads if I flip four coins!"* Eddie scoffed, *"Well, so what? That's easier."* Alfred argued, *"No, it's not. It's harder."* Who is correct? Show all of your work and be prepared to defend your conclusion.

10-11.   Use an area model or a tree diagram to represent the sample space for rolling two standard six-sided dice.

  a. In the standard casino dice game the roller wins on the first roll if he rolls a sum of 7 or 11. What is the probability of winning on the first roll?

  b. The player loses on the first roll if he rolls a sum of 2, 3, or 12. What is the probability of losing on the first roll?

  c. If the player rolls any other sum, he continues to roll the dice until that sum comes up again or until he rolls a 7, whatever happens sooner. What is the probability that the game continues after the first roll?

10-12.   What is the probability that $x^2 + 7x + k$ is factorable if $0 \leq k \leq 20$ and k is an integer?

10-13.   Rondal High School had a student enrollment of 1245 in 2005, 1328 in 2006, and 1413 in 2007. School officials predicted that the 2008 enrollment would be 1505. The capacity of the school is 1800 students.

  a. Graph this data. Determine the line of best fit and write a possible equation for that line.

  b. What do the slope and y-intercept of the line represent?

  c. Based on this information, when do you predict that the school will reach its capacity?

  d. According to your graph and data, estimate the enrollment of Rondal High in the year 2000.

  e. When do you think that Rondal High was built? Explain your thinking.

10-14.   Find all values of a for which the equation $ax^2 + 5x + 6 = 0$ has a solution that is a real number. Express a in terms of one or more inequalities.

10-15.   Solve each equation for $0 \leq \theta \leq 360$. You may need your calculator, but remember that your calculator only gives *one* answer. Most of these problems have more than one answer. Think about all four quadrants.

  a. $\sin \theta = 0.5$ b. $\cos \theta = -0.5$ c. $4 \tan \theta - 4 = 0$ d. $3 \sin^2 \theta = 1$

10-16.   Verify algebraically that $g(x) = \frac{5x-2}{3}$ is the inverse function of $f(x) = \frac{3x+2}{5}$.

10-17.   As you may remember, earthquake magnitudes are measured by the amount of energy that is released. Since the amount of energy released from a large earthquake can be millions of times greater than the energy released by a small quake, a scale was created (the **Richter scale**) to give magnitudes in numbers that are easy to use. An earthquake measuring 3.4 on the Richter scale, for example, releases $10^{3.4}$ kilojoules of energy.

a.   How many times more energy is released by an earthquake that measures 6.5 on the Richter scale than an earthquake that measures 5.5?

b.   How many times more energy is released by an earthquake that measures 5.1 than an earthquake that measures 4.3? Give your answer both as a power of 10 and as a decimal.

c.   What would the magnitude be of an earthquake that released half as much energy as an earthquake measuring 6.2 on the Richter scale?

10-18.   A Nevada roulette wheel has 38 slots numbered 00, 0, 1, 2, 3, ... , 36. Eighteen of the numbers 1, 2, ..., 36 are red and 18 are black; 0 and 00 are green.

a.   What is the probability of landing on red?

b.   What is the probability of not landing on red?

c.   The bettor put his money on red twice in a row. Use an area or a tree diagram to show how to find the probability that he won both bets.

10-19.   One way to win in a game with two dice is to roll a sum of six before getting a sum of seven. (Anything else that happens – sums of 2, 3, 4, 5, 8, 9, 10, 11, or 12 – are ignored.)

a.   How many ways are there to get a sum of six?

b.   How many ways are there to get seven?

c.   How many possible outcomes are important in this problem?

d.   What is the probability of getting a six before a seven?

10-20.   Harold sorted his jellybeans into two jars. He likes purple ones best and the black ones next best, so these are both in one jar. His next favorites are yellow, orange, and white, and these are in another jar. He threw all the rest in the garbage. Harold allows himself to eat only one jellybean from each jar per day. He wears a blindfold when he selects his jellybeans so he cannot choose his favorites first. What is the probability that Harold gets one black jellybean and one orange jellybean, if the first jar has 60% black and 40% purple jellybeans and the second jar has 30% yellow, 50% orange, and 20% white jellybeans?

10-21.   Solve this system for y and z: $\frac{z+y}{2} + \frac{z-y}{4} = 3$

$$\frac{4z-y}{2} + \frac{5z+2y}{11} = 3$$

10-22.   Solve each equation.

    a. $\log_2(x) + \log_2(x-2) = 3$ b. $\log(2x) - \log(x^2) = -2$

10-23.   Convert the following angle measurements from degrees to radians.

    a.   30°   b.   15°   c.   −75°   d.   630°

10-24.   Find the exact equation of this graph.

10-25.   Find the value of x.

    a.

    b.

10-26.   A conveyor belt carries grain to the top of a barn, where it drops the grain so that it forms a pile on the ground. The pile is in the shape of a cone. Recall that $V = \frac{1}{3}\pi r^2 h$ is the formula for the volume of a cone.

    a.   Find the volume of the grain when the height of the pile is ten feet and the radius of the base is four feet.

    b.   The cone-shaped piles during each stage of grain dropping are all similar. If the radius of the base is four feet when the height is ten feet, what is the radius of the base when the height is 15 feet?

    c.   Consider the angle the side of the cone-shaped pile makes with the ground. Is this angle changing? **Justify** your answer. If not, what is the measure of the angle?

10.1.2 What are the chances if…?

Conditional Probabilities

In some problems (such as problems 10-2 and 10-7 involving basketball), you need to find the probability of an event when you know that some other event that could affect it has already happened. In other words, you need to find the **conditional probability**. In cases where the other event does not affect the one you are interested in, the two events are called **independent events**. Discuss the following questions as you work with your team:

> How can we represent the different probabilities with a tree diagram?
> Or with an area model?
>
> What representation is most helpful for understanding the problem?
>
> Which representation is most useful for solving the problem?

10-27.   On the midway at the county fair, there are many popular games to play. One of them is "Flip to Spin or Roll." You start by flipping a coin. If heads comes up, you get to spin the big wheel, which has ten equal sectors: three red, three blue, and four yellow. If the coin shows tails, you get to roll a cube with three red sides, two yellow sides, and one blue side. If your spin lands on blue, or if the blue side of the cube comes up, you win a stuffed animal.

   a.   Draw *both* an area diagram and a tree diagram to represent the sample space for this game.

   b.   Which diagram was easier to make? From which diagram is most useful for showing what result is most likely?

   c.   What is the probability of winning a stuffed animal, P(blue)?

   d.   About how many times would you expect to have to play this game in order to win a stuffed animal?

   e.   If it cost a dollar to play the game and the stuffed animal could have been purchased at the Bob's Bargain Basement for $3.50, was it worth the money? Explain.

   f.   Suppose that you know that Tyler won a stuffed animal. Talk with your team and use your area model to help you figure out what the probability that he started off with heads is? Be prepared to share your ideas with the class.

   g.   In part (f), you calculated the conditional probability of having started with heads given that you knew you rolled or spun blue. Which diagram shows this relationship most clearly? Explain.

Algebra 2 Connections

10-28.   Imagine rolling two standard six-sided dice. Use an area model to represent all possible combinations of numbers.

a.   What is the probability of rolling a sum of eight?

b.   Maribelle has a sum of eight. What is the probability that she rolled a three and a five?

10-29.   BUILD-A-FARM

In the children's game, "Build-a-Farm," each player first spins a spinner. Half of the time the spinner comes up red. Half of the time the spinner comes up blue. If the spinner is red, you reach into the red box. If the spinner is blue, you reach into the blue box. The red box has 10 chicken counters, 10 pig counters, and 10 cow counters, while the blue box has 5 chicken counters, 4 pig counters, and 1 cow counter.

a.   Sketch an area diagram for the situation where a child spins and then draws. Note that the parts corresponding to the two boxes of animal markers will be quite different.

b.   Shade the parts of the diagram corresponding to getting a pig counter. What is $P(\text{pig})$?

c.   Find P(cow counter), the probability of getting a cow counter.

d.   Now, supposing you got a cow counter, what is the probability that your spin was red?

e.   Find the conditional probability that if you got a cow counter, your spin was blue.

10-30.   If Letitia studies for her math test tonight, she has an 80% chance of getting an A. If she does not study, she only has a 10% chance. Whether she can study or not depends on whether she has to work at her parents' store. Earlier in the day, her father said he was feeling sick and there is a 50% chance he will not be able to work tonight.

a.   Draw a diagram for the situation.

b.   Find the probability that Letitia gets an A.

c.   What are the chances that Letitia studied, given that she got an A?

10-31. La Troy has been studying very hard for his English test. He thinks that given any question, he has a 99% chance of getting it right.

a. What is the probability that he gets the first three questions right?

b. If the test has fifty questions, what is the probability that he gets them all correct?

c. Suppose La Troy wanted a 90% chance he would get every question on the test correct. What would his chances of getting each question correct have to be?

d. If you did not do so already, write an equation to represent part (c) and solve it.

10-32. When he was in first grade, Harvey played games with spinners. One game he especially liked had two spinners and several markers that you moved around a board. You were only allowed to move if your color came up on *both* spinners. Harvey always chose purple because that was his favorite color.

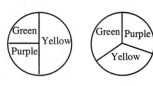

a. What was the probability that Harvey could move his marker?

b. What was the probability for the better choice of color?

c. How often did no one get to move?

d. There are at least two ways to figure out part (c). Discuss your solution method with your team and show a second way to solve part (c).

10-33. Sometimes it is easier to figure out the probability that something will *not* happen than the probability that it *will*. Show two ways to solve the problem below and decide which way you prefer and explain why.

Crystal is spinning the spinner at right and claims she has a good chance of having the spinner land on red at least once in three tries. What is the probability that the spinner will land on red at least once in three tries?

10-34.   Eddie is arguing with Tana about the probability of flipping three coins. They decided to flip a penny, nickel, and a dime. If they flipped three coins, would a tree diagram or an area model be better for determining the sample space? **Justify** your answer.

a.   How many outcomes are in the sample space?

b.   What is the probability of getting each of the following outcomes? Show all of your reasoning.

i.   Three tails?   ii.   At least two tails?

iii.   Exactly two tails?   iv.   At least one head?

c.   How would the probabilities change if Tana found out that Eddie was using weighted coins, coins that were not fair, so that the probability of getting heads for each coin was $\frac{4}{5}$ instead of $\frac{1}{2}$? Would this change the size of the sample space? Recalculate the probabilities in part (b) based on the new information.

10-35.   A spinner has just two colors, red and blue. The probability the spinner will land on blue is x.

a.   What is the probability it will land on red?

b.   Sketch an area diagram for spinning twice.

c.   When it is spun twice, what is the probability it will land on the same color both times?

d.   Given that it lands on the same color twice, what is the probability that it landed on blue both times?

10-36.   On another spinner, blue occurs a fraction x of the time, while the red and green portions have equal area. There are no other colors.

a.   Represent the probability that the spinner will land on green.

b.   Sketch an area diagram for spinning twice.

c.   Shade the region on your area diagram corresponding to getting the same color twice.

d.   What is the probability that both spins give the same color?

e.   If you know that you got the same color twice, what is the conditional probability that the color was blue?

10-37. **LEARNING LOG**

Looking back at the problems in the last two lessons, examine the use of systematic lists, tree diagrams, and area models. For what types of problems or subproblems is a systematic list most helpful? Tree diagrams? Area models? Reflect on these strategies. Explain how they can be used to represent the sample space in a problem and how they can help find probabilities. Title this entry "Representing Sample Spaces using Systematic Lists, Tree Diagrams, and Area Models" and label it with today's date.

METHODS AND MEANINGS

Sample Spaces, Events, Probability, Expected Values, Fair Games

A **sample space** is the set of all possible outcomes of an experiment, and an **event** is a group of outcomes within the sample space.

If an experiment has n equally likely outcomes, the **probability** of an event, E, with $m \leq n$ equally likely outcomes is:

$$P(E) = \frac{m}{n} \text{ and } 0 \leq P(E) \leq 1$$

To calculate the **expected value** of a set of mutually exclusive events (events that cannot happen at the same time), multiply the probability of each event by the value (or pay-off) for that event, and add the results together. For example, suppose a game-show contestant rolls one die to determine her grand prize. If she rolls a 6, she wins $10,000, but if she rolls anything else she wins $1000. The expected value for her prize is:

$$\tfrac{1}{6}(\$10,000) + \tfrac{5}{6}(\$1000) = \$2500$$

In a **fair game**, the cost to play equals the expected value. If you play a game against several people, then the game is fair if the individual expected values are equal.

10-38. Guess what? Another spinner. This time the spinner lands on red half of the time and on green one third of the time. The rest of the time it lands on blue.

    a. Draw an area diagram for spinning twice and shade the region that corresponds to getting the same color on both spins, for each of the three colors.

    b. Suppose you know that the spinner landed on the same color twice. What is the probability that that color was green?

Algebra 2 Connections

10-39.   What is the probability that $x^2 + kx + 12$ will factor if $0 \le k \le 8$ and k is an integer? Make an organized list (sample space) to help you determine the probability.

10-40.   You decide to park your car in a parking garage that charges $3.00 for the first hour and $1.00 for each hour (or any part of an hour) after that.

    a.   How much will it cost to park your car for 90 minutes?

    b.   How much will it cost to park your car for 118 minutes? 119 minutes?

    c.   How much will it cost to park your car for 120 minutes? 121 minutes?

    d.   Graph the cost in relation to the length of time your car is parked.

    e.   Is this function continuous?

10-41.   Victoria is playing with her balance scale and balances 3 blue blocks and 2 red blocks on one side with 5 blue blocks and a red block on the other. Later, her brother balances 2 red blocks and a blue block with a 40-gram weight. How much does each block weigh?

10-42.   Factor and reduce to simplify: $\frac{3x+6}{x^2+7x+10}$. **Justify** each step.

10-43.   Simplify and add $\frac{x-4}{x+2} + \frac{4x+12}{x^2+5x+6}$. **Justify** each step.

10-44.   After paying $20,000 for a car you read that this model has decreased in value 15% per year over the last several years. If this trend continues, in how many years will your car be worth only half of what you paid for it?

10-45.   Change the angle measurements below from radians to degrees or from degrees to radians.

    a. $144°$ b. $300°$ c. $\frac{5\pi}{9}$

    d. $\frac{17\pi}{12}$ e. $\frac{19\pi}{2}$ f. $220°$

10-46.   Antonio and Giancarlo are playing a board game that uses three
           spinners, which are shown in the diagrams at right. The first is
           two-thirds red and one-third green. The second is all red and split
           into four equal parts with the numbers 0, 2, 4, and 6 in each quarter.
           The third is all green and split into three unequal sections, marked
           with a 6, a 4, and a 2. On each turn the player has to spin two of the
           spinners to determine how far he gets to move his marker. The color
           that comes up on the first spinner determines which of the other two
           spinners the player has to spin to get the number of spaces to move.

Spinner #1

Spinner #2
Red

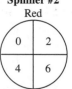

     a.   Make an area model or tree diagram to represent the possible
           outcomes.

     b.   What is the probability that Giancarlo will get to move his
           marker 4 or 6 spaces?

Spinner #3
Green

     c.   What is the probability he will have to stay put?

     d.   What is the probability that he will get to move?

     e.   Antonio was moving his marker 2 spaces. What is the
           probability that he had spun green on the first spinner?

10-47.   Rearrange each equation into a more useful form for graphing. State the locator point
           and draw the graph.

     a. $y = 2x^2 + 8x + 5$ b. $x^2 + y^2 - 2x - 6y = 0$

10-48.   Solve the system of equations at right.

$$8x - 3y - 2z = -8$$
$$-2x + 8y + 7z = 26$$
$$4x + y - 5z = 23$$

10-49.   Divide: $(x^3 - 2x^2 + 25x - 50) \div (x - 2)$.

10-50.   Use your answer from the previous problem to solve $x^3 - 2x^2 + 25x - 50 = 0$.

10-51.   Write the reciprocal of each of the following in simplest form.

     a. $\sqrt{2} + \sqrt{2}i$ b. $1 - \sqrt{3}$

10-52.   If $\cos\theta = \frac{8}{17}$, find $\sin\theta$.

10-53.   Simplify each expression.

a. $\dfrac{1}{x+2} + \dfrac{3}{x^2-4}$

b. $\dfrac{3}{2x+4} - \dfrac{x}{x^2+4x+4}$

c. $\dfrac{x^2+5x+6}{x^2-9} \cdot \dfrac{x-3}{x^2+2x}$

d. $\dfrac{4}{x-2} \div \dfrac{8}{2-x}$

10-54.   Solve each equation.

a. $\dfrac{15}{x-2} = \dfrac{16}{x}$

b. $\dfrac{1}{x} + \dfrac{1}{2x} = 9$

10-55.   Graph $y \geq |x+2| - 3$ and $y \leq 2$ on the same set of axes.

10.2.1 What if the sample space is very large?

. . . .

The Fundamental Principle of Counting

Phone numbers in the U.S. are composed of a three-digit area code followed by seven digits. License plates in some states are made up of three letters followed by a three-digit number. Postal ZIP codes are made up of five digits, and another four digits are often added. To win the lottery in one state you need to select the right five numbers from all the possible choices of five numbers out of 56. Consider these questions:

- How likely is it that you could win the lottery?
- Are there enough phone numbers for the exploding increase in cell phones?
- Jay wants to know the probability of randomly getting JAY on his license plates so he can avoid paying the extra amount for a special plate.

The sample spaces for these questions are huge. Imagine trying to draw a tree diagram! Tree diagrams with three or four branches, branching two or three times, are messy enough. You need a way to count possibilities without having to draw a complete diagram. In this and the next two lessons, you and your team will develop some strategies that will allow you to account for all possibilities without having to make a complete list or draw a complete tree diagram. As you work on the problems in this lesson, discuss the following questions with your team:

What decisions are we making when we make a systematic list?

How many decisions do we need to make?

How many ways are there to make each decision?

How can we use the patterns in a tree diagram to find the total number of branches?

10-56. Nick came across the following problem: If a 4-digit number is randomly selected from all of the 4-digit numbers that use the digits 1, 2, 3, 4, 5, 6, and 7, with repeated digits allowed, what is the probability that the selected number is 2763? Nick knew that he had to figure out how many such numbers were possible, in order to know the size of his sample space.

a. Nick started to make a systematic list of the possibilities, but after the first few he gave up. What is the difficulty here in trying to create a list?

b. Next he started a tree diagram. What problem did he encounter with the tree?

c. He decided he needed a shortcut strategy for organizing this problem; otherwise he was going to be up all night. He started by asking himself, *"How many decisions (about the digits) do I need to make?"* With your team discuss his first question and then consider his next, *"How many choices do I have for each decision (each digit)?"*

d. Audrey was working alone at home on the same problem at the same time. She was thinking of a tree diagram, when she asked herself, *"How many branch-points will this tree have?"* and *"How many branches at each point?"* Were these the same questions Nick was pondering?

e. At the same moment they text messaged each other that they were stuck. When they talked, they realized they were on the same track. The problem asks for *four-digit numbers*, so there are *four* decisions. Simultaneously they said, "We need a **decision chart**."

_____   _____   _____   _____
1st digit   2nd digit   3rd digit   4th digit

How many choices are there for each decision? How many four digit numbers are there?

f. What is the probability that the randomly selected number will be 2763?

10-57. How many four-digit numbers could you make with the digits 1, 2, 3, 4, 5, 6, and 7 if you could not use any digit more than once in the four-digit number? Show a decision chart. Explain the similarities and differences between this situation and the one described in problem 10-56.

10-58. Use a decision chart to answer each question below.

a. A game contains nine discs, each with one of the numbers 1, 2, 3, 4, 5, 6, 7, 8, or 9 on it. How many different three-digit numbers can be formed by choosing any three discs, without replacing the discs?

Problem continues on next page. →

10-58.   *Problem continued from previous page.*

    b.   A new lotto game called "Quick Spin" has three wheels, each with the numbers 1, 2, 3, 4, 5, 6, 7, 8, and 9 equally spaced around the rim. Each wheel is spun once, and the number the arrow points to is recorded. How many three-digit numbers are possible?

    c.   Explain the similarities and differences between part (a) and part (b).

10-59.   Marcos is selecting classes for next year. He plans to take English, physics, government, pre-calculus, Spanish, and journalism. His school has a six-period day, so he will have one of these classes each period. How many different schedules are possible?

    a.   What is the probability that Marcos will get first-period pre-calculus?

    b.   What is the probability that Marcos will get both first-period pre-calculus *and* second-period physics?

10-60.   On your calculator, find a button labeled *n*! or !. On many graphing calculators, it is a function in the math menu and probability submenu. This is the **factorial** function button.

    a.   Find the value of 8 factorial (written 8!), then 7!, then 6!, 5!, ... , 1!

    b.   Which result is the same as the number of Marcos's possible schedules?

    c.   What do you think 6! means? Why does it give the correct solution to the possible number of ways to arrange Marcos's schedule?

    d.   Explain why 4! gives the correct solution to the possible number of ways to arrange the letters **M A T H**.

10-61.   Remembering what *n*! means can help you do some messy calculations quickly, as well as help you do problems that might be too large for your calculator's memory.

For instance, if you wanted to calculate $\frac{9!}{6!}$, you could use the *n*! button on your calculator and find that $9! = 362,880$ and $6! = 720$, so $\frac{9!}{6!} = \frac{362880}{720} = 504$.

You could also use a simplification technique. Since $9! = 9 \cdot 8 \cdot 7 \cdot 6 \cdot 5 \cdot 4 \cdot 3 \cdot 2 \cdot 1!$ and $6! = 6 \cdot 5 \cdot 4 \cdot 3 \cdot 2 \cdot 1$, you can rewrite $\frac{9!}{6!} = \frac{9 \cdot 8 \cdot 7 \cdot 6 \cdot 5 \cdot 4 \cdot 3 \cdot 2 \cdot 1}{6 \cdot 5 \cdot 4 \cdot 3 \cdot 2 \cdot 1} = 9 \cdot 8 \cdot 7 = 504$.

Use this simplification technique to simplify each of the following problems before computing the result.

    a. $\frac{10!}{8!}$ b. $\frac{20!}{18!2!}$ c. $\frac{7!}{4!3!}$ d. $\frac{75!}{72!}$

ETHODS AND MEANINGS

Conditional Probability, Independent Events

The probabilities you computed in problem 10-29 (Build-a-Farm) parts (d) and (e) are **conditional probabilities**. In part (d) you calculated the probability that you spun red given that you got a cow counter. $P(R|C)$ is shorthand notation for $P(\text{Red}|\text{Cow})$, or "probability of a red spin, given that you got a cow."

One way to compute this conditional probability is to write $P(\text{Red}|\text{Cow}) = P(\text{Red Cow})/P(\text{Cow})$:

$$P(R|C) = \frac{P(R \text{ and } C)}{P(C)} = \frac{\frac{1}{6}}{\frac{13}{60}} = \frac{10}{60} \div \frac{13}{60} = \frac{10}{13}$$

In general, the probability of an event B, given that event A has already occurred is written:

$$P(B|A) = \frac{P(B \text{ and } A)}{P(A)}$$

Two events, A and B are **independent** when the probability of one does not depend on whether the other has occurred. In other words, the probability of B is the same as the probability of B, given A, or $P(B) = P(B|A)$.

10-62.　A Scrabble® player has four tiles with the letters A, N, P, and S.

　　a.　How many arrangements of these letters are possible?

　　b.　Draw a tree diagram that shows how to get the arrangements and explain how a decision chart represents the tree.

　　c.　What is the probability of a two-year-old randomly making a word using the four letters?

10-63.　How many different batting orders can be made from the nine starting players on a baseball team? Write the answer using factorials and as a number.

Algebra 2 Connections

10-64.   How many distinct rearrangements of the letters in the word FRACTIONS are there?

10-65.   Five students are running for Junior class president. They must give speeches before the election committee. They draw straws to see who will go first, second, etc. In how many different orders could they give their speeches?

10-66.   If $f(n) = n!$, evaluate each of the following ratios.

a. $\dfrac{f(5)}{f(3)}$ b. $\dfrac{f(6)}{f(4)}$ c. $\dfrac{f(9)}{f(7)f(2)}$

10-67.   Eight friends go to the movies. They want to sit together in a row with a student on each aisle. (Assume the row is 8 seats wide including 2 aisle seats.)

a.   How many ways can they sit in the row?

b.   If Kristen wants to sit in an aisle seat, how many ways can they all sit in the row?

c.   If Annabeth wants to sit on an aisle seat with Ian next to her, how many ways can the eight students sit?

10-68.   In the casino game of Roulette, some players think that when the ball lands on red several times in a row that it will be more likely to land on black on the next spin. You can calculate to the conditional probability to demonstrate that this is not the case. In other words, the outcome of one spin of an honest roulette wheel does not have any effect on the outcome of the next one.

a.   Make an area diagram for two spins of the wheel. Remember that there are 18 red numbers, 18 black numbers, and two greens.

b.   What is the probability that the ball will land on red twice in a row?

c.   Based on your diagram what is the total probability that the ball will land on red on the second spin? (P(RR, BR, GR))

d.   Calculate the conditional probability that the first spin was red given that the second spin is red.

e.   How do your answers to parts (d) compare to the simple probability of the ball landing on red for any single spin? The fact that they are all the same means you have demonstrated that the probability of the ball landing on red is independent of where it landed before.

10-69. How many solutions are there to the system of equations at right? **Justify** your response.

$$y = x^2 - 2x + 2$$
$$y = 2x - 2$$

10-70. Graph $y = \sqrt{(4 - x^2)}$. Imagine revolving this graph around the x-axis, faster and faster, so that it appears to form a sphere. Sketch the sphere and then find its volume. Note: The volume of a sphere is given by $V = \frac{4}{3}\pi r^3$.

10.2.2 How can I count arrangements?

Permutations

There are many kinds of counting problems. In this chapter you will learn to recognize problems that involve arrangements and others that do not. In some cases outcomes will be repeated, but in others they will not. A list of **permutations** includes different arrangements of distinct objects chosen from a set of objects. In other words, permutations are arrangements of elements without using any element more than once, or without repetition. As you work on the problems in this lesson discuss the following questions with your team:

> When we make a decision chart, how many choices do we have after we make the first choice? The second? The third? …

> Can we use the same choice we already made again?

> Can this situation be represented as a list of permutations?

> What patterns can we find in these problems?

10-71. Jasper finally managed to hold on to some money long enough to open a savings account at the credit union. When he went in to open the account, the accounts manager told him that he needed to select a four-digit pin (personal identification number). She also said that he could not repeat a digit, but that he could use any of the digits 0, 1, 2, …, 9 for any place in his four-digit pin.

a. How many pins are possible?

b. Notice that the decision chart for this problem looks like the beginning of 10!, but it does not go all the way down to 1. Factorials can be used to represent this problem, but you must compensate for the factors that you do not use, so you can write $\frac{10!}{6!}$. Discuss with your team how this method gives the same result as your decision chart.

10-72.   Twenty-five art students submitted sculptures to be judged at the county fair. Awards will be given for the six best sculptures. You have been asked to be the judge. You must choose and arrange in order the best six sculptures.

a.   If you did this randomly, in how many ways could you choose the six best?

b.   Show how to simplify the expression: $\frac{25!}{19!}$.

c.   Where did the 19 come from in the original expression? How could you know the 19 from the numbers in the original problem? Why did 19! in the denominator become an important step in coming up with an answer to the problem? Discuss this with your team.

10-73.   With your team, discuss how you could use factorials to represent each of the following situations. Then find the solutions. Four of the five problems involve permutations, and one does not. As you work, discuss with your team which problems fit the definition for permutations and why or why not.

a.   Fifty-two contestants are vying for the Miss Teen pageant crown. In how many different ways can the judges pick the next Miss Teen and the runners-up one, two, and three?

b.   The volleyball team is sponsoring a mixed-doubles sand court volleyball tournament and sixteen pairs have signed up for the chance to win one of the seven trophies and cash prizes. In how many different ways can the teams be chosen and arranged for the top seven slots?

c.   Carmen is getting a new locker at school, and the first thing she must do is decide on a new locker combination. The three-number locker combination can be picked from the numbers 0 through 35. How many different locker combinations could she make up if none of the numbers can be repeated?

d.   How many three-digit locker combinations could Carmen make up if zero could only be the second or third number and none of the numbers can be repeated?

e.   How many locker combinations can Carmen have if she can use any of the numbers 0 through 35 and she can repeat numbers? Is this still a list of permutations?

10-74.   Problems about batting orders and questions about how many numbers you could make without repeating any digits are called **permutations**. The following lists give some more examples for determining what is or is not a permutation.

Permutations:

i.   All the arrangements a child can make on a line on the refrigerator door with three magnetic letters A, B, and C.

ii.   All the 4-digit numbers you could make using seven square tiles numbered 2, 3, 4, 5, 6, 7, and 8.

iii.   From a group of 8 candidates, one will become president, one vice-president, and one secretary of the school senate.

Not-permutations:

iv.   All of the possible three letter license plates using A, B, and C.

v.   The possible 4-digit numbers you could write if you could choose any digit from the numbers 2, 3, 4, 5, 6, 7, 8.

vi.   From a group of 8 candidates, three will be selected to be on the spirit committee.

a.   Below is a list of all of the license plate letter triples that can be made with the letters A, B, and C.

AAA	BBB	CCC	AAB	ABA
BAA	AAC	ACA	CAA	ABB
BAB	BBA	ACC	CAC	CCA
ABC	ACB	CAB	BAC	CBA
BCA	BCC	CBC	CCB	CBB
BCB	BBC			

How is this list different from the list of arrangements of three cards with the letters A, B, and C printed on them? Explain and make the list of cards to demonstrate your ideas.

b.   Imagine two lists of three selected from 8 candidates (for descriptions *iii* and *vi* above). How do they differ? Which list would be longer?

c.   What are the important characteristics that a counting problem has to have in order to classify it as a permutations problem?

d.   Discuss with your team a *general* method for solving the examples above in the "Permutation" column and write a description for your general method that would work for any problem that could be identified as a permutations problem.

10-75.   For the homecoming football game the cheerleaders printed each letter of the name of your school's mascot on a large card. Each card has one letter on it, and each cheerleader is supposed to hold up one card. At the end of the first quarter, they realize that someone has mixed up the cards.

a.   How many ways are there to arrange the cards?

b.   If they had not noticed the mix up, what would be the probability that the cards would have correctly spelled out the mascot?

METHODS AND MEANINGS

Fundamental Principle of Counting and n!

The **fundamental principle of counting** provides a shortcut for counting the branches of a symmetric tree diagram (finding the size the sample space) by multiplying.

For independent events, if an event A can occur in m different ways and an event B can occur in n different ways, then event A followed by event B can happen in $m \cdot n$ different ways. For a sequence of independent events, a **decision chart** is a useful tool.

For example: Ivan always has a sandwich for lunch. He may choose from three kinds of bread (white, wheat, or rye), four lunch meats (salami, ham, bologna, or pastrami), and two greens (lettuce or sprouts). Thus, he has three decisions to make: which bread, which lunchmeat, and which green. The decision chart for this situation is shown below.

$$\underbrace{3}_{\text{1st decision}} \cdot \underbrace{4}_{\text{2nd decision}} \cdot \underbrace{2}_{\text{3rd decision}} = 24 \text{ choices}$$

Factorial is shorthand for the product of a list of consecutive, descending whole numbers from the largest down to 1:
$$n! = n(n-1)(n-2)\ldots(3)(2)(1)$$

For example, 4 factorial or $4! = 4 \cdot 3 \cdot 2 \cdot 1 = 24$ and $6! = 6 \cdot 5 \cdot 4 \cdot 3 \cdot 2 \cdot 1 = 720$.

Review & Preview

10-76.   Mr. Dobson is planning to give a quiz to his class tomorrow. Unfortunately for his students, Mr. Dobson is notorious for writing quizzes that seem to have no relevance to the subject. With this in mind, his students know that their efforts will be purely guesswork. If the quiz contains ten questions that the students will have to match with ten given answers, what is the probability that Rodney Random will get all ten questions matched correctly?

10-77.   Which is bigger: $(5-2)!$ or $(5-3)!$? Justify your answer.

10-78.   Write an equivalent expression for each of the following situations that does not include the factorial (!) symbol.

    a.   The first five factors of $(n-3)!$

    b.   The first five factors of $(n+2)!$

    c. $\dfrac{n!}{(n-3)!}$

    d. $\dfrac{(n+2)!}{(n-2)!}$

10-79.   What do you think 0! is equal to?

   a.   Try it on your calculator to see what you get.

   b.   What does $_8P_8$ mean? What *should* $_8P_8$ be equal to? Write $_8P_8$ using the
         factorial formula. Why is it necessary for 0! to equal 1?

   c.   Do you remember how to show that $2^0 = 1$? You can use a sequence of powers
         of 2 ($\frac{2^4}{2} = 2^3$, $\frac{2^3}{2} = 2^2$, $\frac{2^2}{2} = 2^1$, so $\frac{2^1}{2} = 2^0$), but we also know that $\frac{2^1}{2} = 1$.
         Therefore $2^0 = 1$.

         You can construct a similar pattern for 0!, starting with $\frac{5!}{5} = 4!$ and then $\frac{4!}{4} = 3!$
         Continue the pattern and make an argument to justify that 0! = 1.

10-80.   A state is chosen at random from the 50
          states. Find the probability that the state
          meets each of the following criteria:

          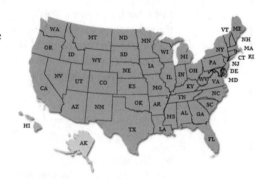

   a.   It is on the east coast.

   b.   It has at least one representative in
          the House of Representatives.

   c.   It has three U.S. senators.

   d.   It does not border an ocean or the
          Gulf of Mexico.

10-81.   Compute the quotient $\frac{(4-7i)}{(8-9i)}$.

10-82.   In the year 2006, the Postal Service required 39 cents
          postage on a first-class letter weighing less than, but
          not equal to 1 ounce. An additional 23 cents was
          added for each ounce, or part of an ounce above that.
          Graph the relationship between price and weight for
          first-class mail in 2006.

10-83.   Graph at least two cycles of the following functions.

   a. $f(x) = 3\sin 2(x - \frac{\pi}{4}) + 1$ b. $g(x) = \frac{1}{2}\cos\frac{1}{4}(x + \pi)$

10.2.3 How many groups are possible?

Combinations

In the previous lesson you learned a method for counting arrangements, or permutations. In this lesson you will consider questions such as how many five-card poker hands are possible, how many spirit committees can be selected from the Junior class, or your chances of winning the lottery.

In a five-card poker hand, the **arrangement** of the cards does *not* matter. Since all the spirit committee members have equal status, the **order** in which they are selected does *not* matter. If you have a winning lottery ticket, you will not care about the order in which the numbers are drawn. In these situations, you need to count the **combinations**. As you work with your team on the problems in this lesson, use the following questions to help focus your discussion:

Does the particular arrangement matter?

What are the relationships among these situations?

10-84. Five members of the Spirit Club have volunteered for the club governing board. These members are Al, Barbara, Carl, Dale, and Ernie. The club members will select three of the five as board members for the next year. One way to do this would be to elect a governing committee of three in which all members would have the same title. A second way would be to select a president, vice-president, and secretary.

a. How many different lineups of officers are possible? This means a president, vice-president, and a secretary are chosen. Al as president, Barbara as vice-president, and Carl as secretary is considered a different possibility from Al as president, Barbara as secretary, and Carl as vice-president.

b. How many different governing committees are possible? In this case, it is a good idea to make a list of all the possibilities, which are called **combinations**.

c. Felicia decides that she wants to volunteer as well.

   i. How many different possibilities for officers are possible now?

   ii. How many different governing committees are possible now? Again, make the list of all of the possibilities, or combinations.

Problem continues on next page. →

10-84.   *Problem continues from previous page.*

    d.   Since there are more volunteers, the spirit club has decided to appoint another committee member.

        i.   If they add a treasurer to the list of officers, how many different ways are there to select the four officers are possible?

        ii.   If they choose a governing committee of four, how many possibilities are there?

10-85.   Compare the results you got for each set of numbers in problem 10-84 when the roles were determined (permutations) and when there were no specific roles (combinations).

    a.   Work with your team to develop a conjecture about the mathematical relationship between permutations and combinations chosen from the same sized groups. Be prepared to share your thinking with the class.

    b.   Test your conjecture by calculating the number of permutations and combinations of 2 items chosen from 6. Does it work?

    c.   How can you generalize your conjecture so that it can be applied to permutations and combinations of r items chosen from n? Write a formula relating permutations (written $_nP_r$) and combinations (written $_nC_r$).

10-86.   Now you will use your graphing calculator to test the formula you wrote in problem 10-85. Try 4 items chosen from 20. Does your formula work?

    a.   How many possibilities would you have to test to be sure that your formula is correct?

    b.   With your team, find a way to justify the logic of your formula. How can you convince someone that it has to be correct for all numbers?

10-87.   In one state lottery there are 56 numbers to choose from. How many ways are there to choose 6 of the 56 numbers? How many combinations of 6 numbers can be chosen from the list of 56? Does the order in which the numbers are chosen matter?

    a.   Find the number of possible combinations for the lottery.

    b.   What is the probability of selecting the six winning numbers?

10-88.   In the game of poker called "Five-Card Draw," each player is dealt five cards from a standard deck of 52 cards. While players tend to arrange the cards in their hands, the order in which they get them does not matter. How many five-card poker hands are possible? Use the methods you developed in today's investigation.

METHODS AND MEANINGS

Permutations

Eight people are running a race. In how many different ways can they come in first, second, and third?

This is a problem of counting **permutations,** or arrangements, and the result can be represented $_8P_3$, which means the number of ways to **choose *and* arrange** three different (not repeated) things from a set of eight. There are several ways to write $_8P_3$:

$$_8P_3 = 8 \cdot 7 \cdot 6 = \frac{8 \cdot 7 \cdot 6 \cdot 5 \cdot 4 \cdot 3 \cdot 2 \cdot 1}{5 \cdot 4 \cdot 3 \cdot 2 \cdot 1} = \frac{8!}{5!} = \frac{8!}{(8-3)!} = 336$$

In general, $_nP_r = \frac{n!}{(n-r)!} = n(n-1)(n-2)...(n-r+1)$ for n items chosen r at a time.

10-89.   There are twelve people signed up to play darts during lunch. How many ways can a three-person dart team be chosen?

10-90.   Find the value of each permutation below.

   a. $_5P_3 = ?$ b. $_7P_4 = ?$ c. $_8P_2 = ?$ d. $_{10}P_3 = ?$

10-91.   The first four factors of 7! are $7, 6, 5,$ and 4 or $7, (7-1), (7-2),$ and $(7-3)$.

   a.   Show the first four factors of 12! in the same way the factors of 7! are shown above.

   b.   What are the first six factors of $n!$?

   c.   What is $_nP_6$?

10-92. On a six-person bowling team, only four players bowl in any game. How many different four-person teams can be made if the order in which they bowl does not matter?

10-93. How many different bowling lineups of four players can be made in the previous problem if order does matter?

10-94. Here is another way to think about the question: *"What is 0! ?"*

    a.   How many ways are there to choose all five items from a group of five items? What happens when you substitute into the factorial formula to compute $_5C_5$? Since you know (logically) what the result has to be, use this to explain what 0! must be equal to.

    b.   On the other hand, how many ways are there to choose *nothing* from a group of five items? And what happens when you try to use the factorial formula to compute $_5C_0$?

10-95. In the card game called "Twenty-One," two cards are dealt from a randomly shuffled deck (a regular deck of 52 cards). The player's goal is to get the sum of his or her cards to be as close to 21 as possible, without going over 21. To establish the sample space for this problem, you need to think of choosing two from a set of 52.

    a.   How many ways are there to do this?

    b.   The tens, jacks, queens, and kings all have a value of 10 points. There are four of each in a standard deck. How many ways are there to choose two cards with a value of 10 out of the 16 that are in the deck? What is the probability of being dealt two ten-valued cards?

    c.   If you did not already do so, write your solution to part (b) in the form $\frac{_aC_b}{_dC_e}$.

    d.   What is the probability of being dealt two face cards? (Face cards are Kings, Queens and Jacks, the cards that have faces.)

    e.   If you did not already do so, write your solution to part (d) in the form $\frac{_aC_b}{_dC_e}$.

10-96.   Given seven points in a plane, no three of which are collinear:

    a.   How many different lines are determined by these points?

    b.   How many distinct triangles can be formed?

    c.   How many distinct quadrilaterals can be formed?

    d.   Explain why the answers to parts (b) and (c) are the same.

10-97.   If $n > 3$, write a shorter equivalent expression for $n \cdot (n-1) \cdot (n-2) \cdot (n-3)$.

10-98.   Find the value of each of the following combinations.

    a. $_{10}C_8$ b. $_{12}C_7$ c. $_7C_1$

10-99.   Simplify each expression below. Think about how you could use rules of exponents, the distributive property, and the multiplicative property of one to find shortcuts.

    a. $3^{-2} \cdot 3^4$ b. $3^{-4} \cdot 3^4$

    c. $(3^{-1} + 3^{-3}) \cdot 3^4$ d. $\dfrac{3^{-2} - 3^{-1}}{3^{-3} + 3^{-4}}$

10.2.4 What kind of counting problem is this?

Categorizing Counting Problems

One of the biggest challenges in solving problems that involve counting techniques is deciding which method of counting to use. Selecting a counting method depends on whether different arrangements of elements will be considered to be different outcomes and on whether elements can be repeated or not in an outcome. As you work with your team on the Ice Cream Shop problem, starting a list of possibilities will be a useful strategy. The list may be too long to complete, but starting it should help.

10-100.   THE ICE-CREAM SHOP

Friday was the seventh day of the heat wave with temperatures over 95°, and DJ's Gourmet Ice-Cream Shop had only five flavors left: chocolate fudge, French vanilla, maple nut, lemon custard, and blueberry delight. Some customers ordered their ice cream in cones and some in a dish, but everyone ordered three scoops, the maximum DJ was allowing to ensure that the inventory would last.

On Saturday the temperature hit 100°. DJ still had five flavors, but he decided to allow no more than one scoop of a particular flavor per customer in order to keep a balanced variety on hand. On Friday, the customers had more choices because they could order a cone (which most people eat from the top down) or a dish (where scoops can be eaten in any order) and they could have different flavors or more than one scoop of their favorite.

DJ's advertises **Over 100 Choices!** When his customers complained that he did not have 100 flavors, he responded, "But I still offer over 100 *choices*!" Was that true on both days?

Your task: There are four counting problems here, two for Friday and two for Saturday. Describe each situation and show how to calculate the number of choices customers have once they decide on a cone or a dish.

Discussion Points

What are some possible outcomes for this situation? Can we start a list?

Does the arrangement or order of the scoops matter?

Can the choices be repeated?

Does our description of the outcomes for this situation fit any of the counting formulas we know?

Further Guidance

10-101. It is useful to organize the information in a large 2×2 chart with columns for Friday and Saturday and rows for dishes and cones. With your team set up a 2×2 chart or obtain the Lesson 10.2.4 Resource Page from your teacher and use it to organize the different possibilities. Describe each problem in relation to whether it involves arrangements or repeats elements, and make a prediction about which situation has the greatest number of choices and which has the least.

10-102. Use what you have learned about the Fundamental Principal of Counting, permutations, and combinations to solve three of the four problems.

10-103. The fourth problem is more cumbersome because the order of the scoops does not matter and all of the scoops could be different, two could be the same and one different, or all could be the same. This problem has a number of subproblems, and for at least one of them you may need to make a list. Work with your team to identify and solve each subproblem.

*Further Guidance
section ends here.*

10-104. Charlie and his nephew Jake, who is a bottomless hunger pit, went to the state fair. Charlie had promised he would buy Jake three snacks, one when they arrived, one mid-afternoon, and one when they were about to leave. As they were arriving, Jake was trying to negotiate to get them all at once. At the food stand the menu included seven items:

Corn Dogs	Popcorn
Root Beer	Orange Soda
Sno Cones	Cotton Candy
Candied Apples	

Jake has a dilemma. He likes everything on the menu so much that he would not mind having any three items or even any two or three of the same thing. Uncle Charlie thinks variety is good so he wants Jake to choose three different things.

Your task: With your team, categorize the alternatives for Jake and Charlie in terms of arrangements and repetition. Then describe and justify the solution method you would use to count the number of possibilities for each situation. Finally, figure out how many possible ways there are for Jake to choose his snacks for each situation.

10-105.   When Jake and Charlie disagree, Jake has a two-thirds chance of getting his way. Draw an area model or tree diagram and calculate the probability that Charlie prevails and Jake has to order three different items and have his snacks spread out.

10-106.   LEARNING LOG

Explain the difference between combinations, permutations, and other counting problems that involve the Fundamental Principle of Counting. Make your explanation so clear and thorough that a student who is just transferring into your class can understand counting techniques. Include information about whether arrangements are important and whether elements can be repeated and give examples that illustrate the different possibilities. Title this entry, "Counting Problems and Strategies" and label it with today's date.

METHODS AND **M**EANINGS

Combinations

In selecting committees, it matters who is selected but not the **order** of selection or any **arrangement** of the groups. Selections of committees, or of lists of groups without regard to the order within the group, are called **combinations**. Note that **combinations** do not include repeated elements.

For example: Eight people are eligible to receive $500 scholarships, but only three will be selected. How many different ways are there to select a group of three?

This is a problem of counting **combinations**. $_8C_3$ represents the number of ways to choose three from a set of eight. This is sometimes read as "eight **choose** three."

To compute the number of combinations, first calculate the number of permutations and then divide by the number of ways to arrange each permutation.

$$_8C_3 = \frac{_8P_3}{3!} = \frac{8!}{5!3!} = 56$$

In general:

$$\text{Number of ways to choose} = \frac{\text{\# of ways to choose and arrange}}{\text{\# of ways to arrange}}$$

$$_nC_r = \frac{_nP_r}{r!} = \frac{n!}{(n-r)!r!}$$

10-107.   On Friday, Randy Random went to DJ's to get a cone.

   a.   If he made a random selection, what is the probability that he got *all* three scoops the same?

   b.   What is the probability that he got all three different?

10-108.   Connie and Nora went into Ready Scoop to get ice cream cones, but Nora can't make up her mind.   The have 23 flavors and she wants 3 scoops.

   a.   If Nora is very particular about the order of the scoops, how many choices does she have if all of the scoops are different?

   b.   Nora changes her mind. She wants a dish, not a cone, but she still wants three different flavors, how many ways can she order?

   c.   Connie says, *"I still want a cone with dark chocolate on the bottom and then any other two scoops."* How many cones are possible with dark chocolate on the bottom?

   d.   Vlad came in as they were leaving and saw Connie's cone. He said, *"Oh, that's what I want, a cone with chocolate on the bottom and then two other flavors."* The clerk, said, *"Okay, but we have four kinds of chocolate."* Vlad replied, *"Any kind of chocolate will do."* How many different cones could fill Vlad's order?

10-109.   John has to graph a set of parabolas of the form $y = x^2 - 4x + 2^n$ where n is an integer and $0 \le n \le 6$. What is the probability that one of these parabolas, chosen at random, will have:

   a.   One x-intercept?

   b.   Two x-intercepts?

   c.   No x-intercepts?

10-110.   If $\tan\theta = \frac{1}{2}$ and $\pi \le \theta \le \frac{3\pi}{2}$, what is the value of $\sin\theta$?

10-111.   Jenny and Gina were trying to solve $\sqrt{x+5} + \sqrt{x} = 5$. They knew they would have to square the equation to get rid of the radicals, but when they tried it, they got $x + 5 + 2\sqrt{x(x+5)} + x = 25$, which did not look much easier to deal with. Gina had an idea.

"*Let's start by putting the radicals on opposite sides of the equation and then squaring.*" she said. Her work is shown at right.

$$\sqrt{x+5} + \sqrt{x} = 5$$
$$\sqrt{x+5} = 5 - \sqrt{x}$$
$$x + 5 = 25 - 10\sqrt{x} + x$$

"*But there's still a radical!*" she exclaimed, disappointed.

"*That's okay,*" said Jenny, "*there's only one now, so we can get the term with the radical by itself and then square everything again.*"

a.   Follow Jenny's advice and solve this equation.

b.   Use Jenny and Gina's method to solve $\sqrt{2x-2} - \sqrt{x} = 1$.

10-112.   If you deposit $1000 into an account that pays 6% interest compounded monthly, how long do you have to wait until the account is worth $4000?

10-113.   Graph each of the following trig functions:

a. $y = 2\sin(x)$ and $y = \cos(x)$ on the same set of axes.

b.   Use your answer to part (a) to graph $y = 2\sin(x) + \cos(x)$.

10-114.   You are given a bag that you are told contains eight marbles. You draw out a marble, record its color, and put it back.

a.   If you repeat this eight times and you do not record any red marbles, can you conclude that there are not any red marbles in the bag? Explain.

b.   If you repeat this 100 times and you do not record any red marbles, can you conclude that there are not any red marbles in the bag? Explain.

c.   How many times do you have to draw marbles (putting them back each time) to be absolutely certain that there are no red marbles in the bag?

10-115.   Divide $(x^3 + 8)$ by $(x+2)$. Then use your answer to factor $x^3 + 8$.

10-116.   If $a = 2 + 3i$ and $b = 1 - i$, compute each of the following operations:

    a. $a + b$ b. $a - b$ c. ab d. $\frac{a}{b}$

10.2.5 What kind of problem is this?

Choosing Counting Methods

The problems in this lesson will require you to use of a variety of counting strategies. You will need to work with your team to interpret each problem in relation to whether arrangements matter and repetition is allowable and whether the situation can be seen as one set of outcomes or must be treated as several alternative sets of outcomes. Discuss these issues as you encounter each problem. The following questions can help focus your discussions.

What does an outcome look like? What are its elements?

Will a different arrangement of the same elements count as a different outcome?

Is it okay to repeat elements within one outcome?

Are there several alternative types of outcomes here?

10-117.   Joaquin is getting a new locker at school and the first thing he must do is decide on a new combination. The three number locker combination can be selected from the numbers 0 through 21.

    a.   How many different locker combinations can Joaquin choose if none of the numbers can be repeated?

    b.   With your understanding of permutations, combinations, and factorials, discuss with your team whether the name "combination lock" is appropriate.

    c.   How many mathematical combinations are possible?

    d.   How many choices would there be if you could repeat a number, but not use the same number twice in a row?

10-118.   The new worker at Pauli's Pizza Parlor made up a
           whole rack of three topping individual pizzas but forgot
           to label the boxes. He made one pizza for each possible
           choice of three different toppings of the ten that were
           available.

    a.   How many pizzas are on the rack?

    b.   How many have Canadian bacon, pineapple, and
          one other topping?

    c.   What is the probability of getting a pizza that has mushrooms on it?

10-119.   For each of the following problems you may need to consider several subproblems.

    a.   How many numbers less than 500 can you make using the digits 0, 2, 4, 6, 8?

    b.   How many numbers less than 500 are there if the digits 0, 2, 4, 6, 8 cannot be
          repeated?

10-120.   ANAGRAMS

    a.   How many distinct ways can the letters in the word MASH be arranged?

    b.   How many distinct ways can the letters in the word SASH be arranged?

    c.   How many distinct ways can the letters in the word SASS be arranged?

    d.   What makes each of the problems above different? How are they related?

10-121.   If a coin is flipped 10 times, in how many different sequences can heads or tails
           come up?

    a.   How many ways can 10 heads come up?

    b.   In how many ways can 5 of the 10 coins show heads?

    c.   In how many ways can 0, 1, 2 or 3 heads show, with the rest tails?

    d.   Calculate the probability that each of the events in parts (a), (b), and (c) occurs.

    e.   What is the probability that at least 4 heads come up?

10-122.   Four brown dogs and two white dogs are in a large dog house. Someone tells you that exactly two dogs are asleep.

a.   What is the probability that the two dogs are brown?

b.   What is the probability that the two dogs are both white?

c.   What is the probability that one dog is white and the other is brown?

d.   If someone also told you the two sleeping dogs were the same color, what is the probability they are brown?

10-123.   LEARNING LOG

Reread your Learning Log entry from Lesson 10.2.4, which contains an explanation of the difference between combinations, permutations, and other counting problems that involve the Fundamental Principle of Counting. Revise your explanation to include any new information you learned from this lesson and add any examples that could remind you of what to look for in a new problem. Add today's date to this entry.

10-124.   A pizza parlor has 12 toppings other than cheese. How many different pizzas can they create with five *or fewer* toppings? List all subproblems and calculate the solution.

10-125.   Andrea has just purchased a five-digit combination lock. It allows her to set up her own combination. She can use the numbers 0 through 9 for her combination, and she must use five digits.

a.   How many five-digit combinations can she make so that no digit is repeated?

b.   How many five-digit combinations are possible if she *can* repeat the digits, but cannot use the same digit twice in a row?

10-126.   Beethoven wrote nine symphonies and Mozart wrote 27 piano concertos.

   a.   If the local radio station KALG wants to play two pieces, a Beethoven symphony and then a Mozart concerto, in how many ways can this be done?

   b.   The station manager has decided that on each successive night (seven days a week), a Beethoven symphony will be played, followed by a Mozart concerto, followed by a Schubert string quartet (there are 15 of those). How long could this policy be continued before exactly the same program would have to be repeated?

10-127.   Solve each absolute value inequality.

   a. $|2x+1|<5$

   b. $2|3x-2|\geq 10$

10-128.   The roots of a polynomial are given below. Find two linear factors and the corresponding quadratic factor.

   a. $x=-2+\sqrt{3}, x=-2-\sqrt{3}$

   b. $x=-2+i, x=-2-i$

10-129.   Graph the inequalities $y\geq|x-2|$ and $y\leq 4-|x|$ then find the area of the enclosed region.

10-130.   Joanne was making repairs to her deck and needed to buy some supplies. She purchased two posts, three boards, and four piers for $52. Needing more materials, she went back to the lumberyard and bought one post and five boards for $13. Realizing she did not need the piers she made a third trip where she bought three more boards, returned the four piers and ended up with a refund of $34. What was the cost of each item?

10-131.   Use the equation $f(x)=(x+3)^3-1$ to complete each of the following tasks.

   a.   Find the inverse equation.

   b.   Graph the inverse equation.

   c.   Is the inverse a function? Explain.

10.2.6 What are my chances of winning?

. . . .

Some Challenging Probability Problems

In this lesson, you will have the opportunity to apply what you have learned about probability and counting principles to solve some interesting (and very challenging) problems. As you work with your team on one of the following problems, you will probably get stuck at some point along the way. Below are discussion questions that can help to get started again.

What subproblems do we need to solve?

What simpler problem would help us to understand this problem?

How would we start a tree or a list?

Does order matter? Are the outcomes combinations, permutations, or something else?

Are these separate groups of outcomes? Are the probabilities independent?
Should we add or do we need to multiply?

Would it be easier to consider what is *not* an outcome?

10-132.   THE CANDY DISH

A bowl contains three candies: two red and one green. Work with a partner and decide who is player A and who is player B. Then take turns choosing a candy from the bowl without looking. Player A takes one and keeps it, then player B takes one. If the colors match, player A gets a point; if they differ, player B gets a point. Is this a fair game? First try the game experimentally. Then show your analysis of the probabilities.

Now put four candies in the bowl, three of one color and one of another. Will this game be fair? Again, check experimentally then give your analysis using probabilities.

Are there other ways to put different numbers of two colors of candy in the bowl that would lead to a fair game while keeping the rest of the rules the same as in the previous two problems? Try a number of different possibilities (up to at least a total of 20 candies). Analyze each one using probability, make some hypotheses, and report any patterns you see in the results, conclusions, or generalizations that you can **justify** mathematically.

Your task: Prepare a report or poster to be evaluated based on:
- The number and variety of cases you investigate and analyze.
- Your organization of the data, your analyses, and your general conclusions.
- The extent to which you can mathematically generalize your observations and justify your generalizations.

10-133.   CASINO DICE GAME

To play this game, you roll two
dice. If your total on the first
roll is 7 or 11 points, you win.
If your total is 2, 3, or 12 points,
you lose. If you get any other
number (4, 5, 6, 8, 9, or 10), that
number becomes your point.
You then continue to roll until
your point comes up again or
until a 7 comes up. If your point
comes up first, you win. If
7 comes up first, you lose. You
ignore any outcomes that are not
your point or 7.

In pairs, play the game ten times.
Record how many wins and
losses your team has. Combine
your information with other
teams working on the problem.
Are the results fairly even or were there many more wins or losses?

The game you have been playing is the basic dice game played in casinos worldwide.
What is the probability of winning?

Your task: To calculate the probability of winning, you will need to identify and solve
several subproblems. Prepare a report that shows each of the subproblems clearly, as
well as how you solved each one. Your report should also show the exact probability
of winning as a fraction as well as a decimal approximation.

10-134.   **An extra challenge:** Most casinos allow bettors to bet against the dice roller. In this
case, the bettor wins whenever the roller would lose *except when the roller gets a 12 on
the first roll.* When 12 comes up, the bettor does not win or lose and he or she just
waits for the next roll. What is the probability of winning a bet against the roller?
Which is the better bet, for or against? By how much?

Further Guidance

10-135.   Start with a list of the ways to get each sum 2, 3, ..., 12. For the remaining parts of the dice game, it will help to keep answers in fraction form.

   a.   Find the probability of winning on the first roll.

   b.   Find the probability of losing on the first roll.

   c.   Find the probability of the game ending on the first roll.

10-136.   Now consider the other ways to win by rolling the point before rolling a 7.

   a.   Find the probability of rolling a 4.

   b.   Find the probability of rolling a 4 before a 7. (Note that you are only interested in 4's and 7's for this problem.)

   c.   Find the probability of rolling a 4 and then rolling another 4 before a 7. In other words, what is the probability of getting the outcome in parts (a) and then the outcome in part (b)?

   d.   Find the probability of rolling a 5.

   e.   Find the probability of rolling a 5 before a 7. (You only care about 5's and 7's here.)

   f.   Find the probability of rolling a 5 and another 5 before a 7.

   g.   Find the probabilities for winning when your first roll is 6, 8, 9, or 10. Look for symmetry as you do this.

10-137.   Make a list of the all the ways to win.

   a.   What is the probability of winning?

   b.   If you won the game, what is the probability that you won by throwing 7 or 11 on the first throw?

   c.   What is the probability of losing this game?

   d.   Is it a fair game? Is it close to fair? Explain why casinos can allow betting on this game without expecting to lose money.

──────────   *Further Guidance*   ──────────
section ends here.

10-138.   TRIANGLES BY CHANCE

Obtain three dice from your teacher. You may also want some string, linguini, a compass, or some other building material. Roll the three dice and use the numbers on the dice to represent the lengths of sides of a triangle. Build (or draw) the triangle. Record the three numbers in a table according to the type of triangle formed (scalene, isosceles, equilateral, or no triangle). For example, if 3, 3, and 5 came up on the dice, you would record 3, 3, 5 under the heading **isosceles** since a triangle with sides of length 3, 3, and 5 is isosceles. Repeat this ten times, and then combine your information with the other teams working on this problem. Examine the data and discuss the results. Based on your discussion, make an estimate for the probability of each outcome. Then calculate the theoretical probabilities.

Your task: Complete a team report or poster that includes:

- Initial estimates of probabilities with your team **justification** for each one.

- The subproblems you solved, including how you counted the possible outcomes.

- The theoretical probability for each case.

Further Guidance

10-139.   First you will need to calculate the size of the sample space for rolling three dice.

a.   How many ways come up so that the result is an equilateral triangle?

b.   How many ways can the dice come up so that the result is an isosceles triangle?

c.   How many ways can the dice come up so that the result is a scalene triangle?

d.   How many outcomes lead to no triangle?

e.   Use your results from parts (a) through (d) to compute the probabilities for each outcome.

———— *Further Guidance* ————
section ends here.

10-140.　POKER

In the basic game of five-card-draw poker, five cards are dealt to each player from a standard deck of 52 cards. Players place bets based on their estimate of their chances of winning. They then draw any number of cards (up to five) to see if they can improve their hands, and they make another round of placing bets.

The winning poker hands (assuming no wild cards) are described below, in order from best to worst. Poker is a game that has been played for many centuries. Players had established the order of winning hands centuries before mathematicians developed the counting techniques, which verified that the order was actually mostly correct.

(Note: In the list below, J stands for Jack, Q stands for Queen, K stands for King, A stands for Ace, and X stands for any card.)

1. Royal flush: 10-J-Q-K-A, all the same suit.

2. Straight flush: 7-8-9-10-J, any five in a row, all the same suit (A can be used before 2 or after K).

3. Four of a kind: 2-2-2-2-X, four of a number or face card, and any other card.

4. Full house: 7-7-7-A-A-, three of one kind and two of another.

5. Flush: any five cards of the same suit, not all consecutive.

6. Straight: 3-4-5-6-7, any five in a row, a mixture of 2 or more suits.

7. Three of a kind: 8-8-8-J-A, three of a number or face card, the other two different.

8. Two pair: 9-9-5-5-2, pairs of two different numbers or face cards, with one other number or face card.

9. Two of a kind: A-A-7-8-J, any pair with three random others that do not match.

10. Bust: no matches, no runs of five in a row, different suits.

Your task: Calculate the number of five-card hands that can be selected from a deck of 52 cards, and then, for the first six of the above hands, calculate the number of ways the hand can be dealt, and the probability that a player will be dealt that hand. Prepare a team report or poster that describes your work on both the counting problems and the probabilities.

10-141.   The most difficult Poker hand to get is a royal flush. To calculate the probability of getting a royal flush, you first need to determine the size of the sample space. How many five-card hands are possible if there are 52 cards to choose from? Then decide how many ways there are to make a royal flush.

    a.   What is the probability of getting a royal flush?

    b.   How many straight flushes are there that are all spades? Making a list will help you decide. Then how many straight flushes are there altogether?

    c.   What is the probability of getting a straight flush that is not a royal flush?

10-142.   Flushes are five cards of one suit.

    a.   How many flushes are possible?

    b.   What is the probability of getting a flush?

10-143.   Straights are five cards in a row, such as 4-5-6-7-8 of any suit.

    a.   How many straights are possible that include 2 or more suits? In other words, how many straights are possible that are not also straight flushes or royal flushes?

    b.   What is the probability of getting a straight?

10-144.   How many ways are there to draw four cards that are the same number? Making a list will help. And how many ways are there to get the fifth card? What do you need to do to get the total number of five-card hands that contain four of a kind?

    a.   What is the probability of getting four of a kind?

    b.   Now consider a full house. First, think of listing the number of ways to get exactly three cards that are the same number. Once you know the three cards, how many ways are there to get the other two cards in your hand the same? What should you do with these two results to get the number of full houses possible?

    c.   What is the probability of getting a full house?

    d.   Recall your result for the number of ways to get three of a kind and figure out how many ways there are to get two cards that are different from the rest of the deck. Use this information to calculate the number of five-card hands with three matching numbers.

Problem continues on next page.→

10-144. *Problem continued from previous page.*

    e.   What is the probability of getting three of a kind?

    f.   Use a similar method for calculating the number of ways to get one pair and the probability of getting another pair.

    g.   Think about how you calculated the number of full houses and about how you calculated the number of hands with four of a kind. Then calculate the number of hands with two pairs.

    h.   What is the probability of drawing a hand that is a "bust?" How can you use the probabilities you have already calculated?

———————   *Further Guidance*   ———————
section ends here.

METHODS AND MEANINGS

Definition of 0!

The use of the combinations formula when $r = n$ (when the number to be chosen is the same as the total number in the group) leads to a dilemma, as illustrated in the following example.

Suppose the Spirit Club has a total of three faithful members. Only one three-member governance committee is possible. If we apply the formula for combinations, we get $_3C_3 = \frac{_3P_3}{3!} = \frac{3!}{(3-3)!\,3!} = \frac{3!}{0!\,3!} = 1$. Does this make sense?

To resolve this question and make the formulas useful for all cases, mathematicians decided on this definition: $0! = 1$.

10-145.   Jean Luc's favorite Asian restaurant has six dishes on its lunch menu. He wants to get their three-item combo for lunch and is reminded by the counter-person that he can order two or three servings of the same selection. How many different ways could he order lunch?

10-146.   Make a sketch of the graph of each of the following functions. Describe the graphs.

    a. $y = (x+1)^2(x-2)^2(x-5)^2$ b. $y = -(x+1)^2(x-2)^2(x-5)^2$

10-147.   You roll three different-colored dice and use the numbers on the dice to determine the lengths of the sides of a triangle. For example, 3-3-5 would be an isosceles triangle with base 5. What is the probability of building a right triangle?

10-148.   Given the function $h(x) = -2(x + 3)^2 + 2$:

   a.   What are the intercepts?   b.   What are the domain and range?

10-149.   Rewrite each equation in graphing form and identify the key points.

   a. $y = \frac{1}{4}x^2 + \frac{1}{2}x + \frac{5}{8}$ b. $y = \frac{1}{4}x^2 + 5x + 41$

10-150.   Rewrite each of the following in simplest complex or radical form.

   a. $\frac{\sqrt{2}+\sqrt{2}i}{\sqrt{2}-\sqrt{2}i}$ b.   The reciprocal of $\frac{1}{2} + \frac{\sqrt{5}}{2}$

10-151.   Find the distance between the two points.

   a. (x, y) and $(-3, y)$ b. (x, y) and $(-3, 2)$

10-152.   Imagine a circle with a radius of 4 units and a center at $(5, 6)$. This circle is rotated around the x-axis, always staying the same distance from the axis. It sweeps out a three-dimensional figure. What shape is formed? Make a sketch.

10-153.   Your teacher has decided that one person in your class will get an extra 50 points of credit. The lucky person has been narrowed down, so now it is between you and Newton. The teacher says, *"I'm thinking of a number between 0 and 10. Whoever can choose the number closest to it gets the 50 points."* Quickly, Newton yells out, *"Three!"* What number would you choose? **Justify** and explain your answer.

10-154.   Another pizza parlor is having a super special. They have a rack of small pizzas, each with three or four different toppings. The price is really low because they forgot to indicate on the boxes what toppings were on each pizza. They had eight toppings available, and they made one pizza for each of the possible combinations of three or four toppings.

   a.   How many pizzas are on the rack?

   b.   What is the probability of getting a pizza that has mushrooms on it?

10-155. Use the properties of logarithms to rewrite each expression as an equivalent one using only one logarithm.

    a. $\log_3(5) + \log_3(m)$ b. $\log_6(p) - \log_6(m)$

    c. $\log_2(r) + 3\log_6(z)$ d. $\log(90) + \log(4) - \log(36)$

10-156. Simplify each expression.

    a. $\dfrac{x+2}{x^2-2x-3} + \dfrac{x}{x^2-2x}$ b. $\dfrac{2}{x} - \dfrac{x}{x-2}$

    c. $\dfrac{x^2-x-6}{x^2-x-20} \cdot \dfrac{x^2+6x+8}{x^2-x-6}$ d. $\dfrac{x^3+8}{x} \div \dfrac{x+2}{x^2}$

10-157. Solve each equation.

    a. $\dfrac{x+1}{5} = \dfrac{5}{x-1}$ b. $\dfrac{1}{x} + \dfrac{1}{x+2} = 3$

10-158. Graph in three dimensions.

    a. $(2, -1, -3)$ b. $6x - 3y + 9z = 18$

10-159. Find the distance between each pair of points.

    a. $(17, 29)$ and $(-1, -1)$ b. (x, y) and $(-1, -1)$

10-160. In the diagram at right, the point (x, y) is the same distance from $(-3, 4)$ as it is from $(2, -1)$. There are many possibilities for (x, y). Algebraically, what do they have in common?

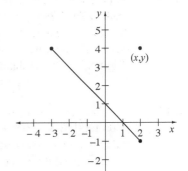

    a.   What is the distance from (x, y) to $(-3, 4)$?

    b.   What is the distance from (x, y) to $(2, -1)$?

    c.   Write the equation that states that the two expressions in (a) and (b) are equal and simplify.

    d.   What is the specific name of the geometric object represented by your equation from part (c)?

Chapter 10 Closure What have I learned?

Reflection and Synthesis

The activities below offer you a chance to reflect on what you have learned in this chapter. As you work, look for concepts that you feel very comfortable with, ideas that you would like to learn more about, and topics you need more help with. Look for connections between ideas as well as connections with material you learned previously.

① TEAM BRAINSTORM

With your team, brainstorm a list for each of the following categories. Be as detailed as you can. How long can you make your list? Challenge yourselves. Be prepared to share your team's ideas with the class.

Topics: What have you studied in this chapter? What ideas and words were important in what you learned? Remember to be as detailed as you can.

Connections: How are the topics, ideas, and words that you learned in previous courses connected to the new ideas in this chapter? Again, make your list as long as you can.

② **MAKING CONNECTIONS**

Below is a list of the vocabulary used in this chapter. Make sure that you are familiar with all of these words and know what they mean. Refer to the glossary or index for any words that you do not yet understand.

arrangement	choose	combination
conditional probability	decision chart	equally likely
event	expected value	experimental
factorial	fair game	independent
order	outcome	permutation
probability	repetition	subproblems
sample space	theoretical	

Make a concept map showing all of the connections you can find among the key words and ideas listed above. To show a connection between two words, draw a line between them and explain the connection, as shown in the example below. A word can be connected to any other word as long as there is a **justified** connection. For each key word or idea, provide a sketch of an example.

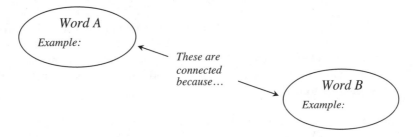

Your teacher may provide you with vocabulary cards to help you get started. If you use the cards to plan your concept map, be sure either to re-draw your concept map on your paper, or to glue the vocabulary cards to a poster with all of the connections explained for others to see and understand.

While you are making your map, your team may think of related words or ideas that are not listed above. Be sure to include these ideas on your concept map.

③   SUMMARIZING MY UNDERSTANDING

This section gives you an opportunity to show what you know about certain math topics or ideas.

With your team, make a list of the **big ideas** of this chapter. Discuss the important ideas of the chapter and try to agree on a short list of no more than five big ideas. Be prepared to share your list in a whole class discussion. When the class has reached agreement on a list, continue with parts (a) and (b) below.

a.   Write your own description of each big idea.

b.   For each big idea, provide one or two representative example problems. Solve each problem completely, using multiple representations, if applicable.

Your teacher may give you a "GO" page to work on (or you can download this from www.cpm.org). "GO" stands for "Graphic Organizer," a tool you can use to organize your thoughts and communicate your ideas clearly.

④   WHAT HAVE I LEARNED?

This section will help you evaluate which types of problems you feel comfortable with and which you need more help with. This section appears at the end of every chapter to help you check your understanding. Even if your teacher does not assign this section, it is a good idea to try these problems and find out for yourself what you know and what you need to work on.

Solve each problem as completely as you can. The table at the end of this closure section has answers to these problems. It also tells you where you can find additional help and practice on similar problems.

CL 10-161. Next June, Joanna is taking a vacation. She will make four stops while she is gone. They will be Pittsburgh, Washington D.C., Philadelphia, and New York City. Joanna is not sure in what order to visit these places. In how many ways can she organize her vacation?

CL 10-162. Four fair coins are flipped. What is the probability of getting three or more heads?

548   *Algebra 2 Connections*

CL 10-163. Part one of the final exam for Algebra 2 contains 10 questions and you get to choose any eight to answer.

  a.   How many different ways could you choose the eight problems?

  b.   If everyone must answer the first two questions, how many ways could you choose the remaining problems?

CL 10-164. How many permutations of all the letters in the word PYRAMID do not end with the letter D?

CL 10-165. A game at the County Fair has two spinners as shown at right. Each spinner is spun once.

  a.   What is the probability of both spinners landing on red?

  b.   What is the probability of both spinners landing on the same color?

  c.   What is the probability of both spinners landing on different colors?

  d.   If both spinners landed on the same color, what is the probability that is was blue?

CL 10-166. If you pay $2 to spin the spinners in the previous problem, you have a chance to win more money! The County Fair will pay you $7 if both spinners land on red, $5 if both spinners land on white, and $3 if both spinners land on blue. Is this game fair? What is the expected value?

CL 10-167. A bag contains eight blue marbles and four gold marbles. You choose three without replacement.

  a.   What is the probability of getting (in this order) blue, gold, and blue?

  b.   What is the probability of getting (in any order) two blues and a gold?

CL 10-168. Simplify each of the following expressions.

  a. $\dfrac{(n-1)!}{(n-3)!}$

  b. $\dfrac{n!}{(n-2)!}$

CL 10-169. If five cards are dealt from a shuffled deck of playing cards:

    a.   What is the probability of getting a five-card hand that is all red?

    b.   Express your solution to part (a) in the form $\frac{_aC_b}{_dC_e}$.

    c.   What is the probability of getting a five-card hand that is all clubs?

    d.   Express your solution to part (c) in the form $\frac{_aC_b}{_dC_e}$.

    e.   What is the probability of getting 5 cards from any one suit?

CL 10-170. Consider the following anagrams.

    a.   How many distinct ways can the letters in the word SAKE be arranged?

    b.   How many distinct ways can the letters in the word SEEK be arranged? Be careful!

    c.   How many distinct ways can the letters in the word SEES be arranged?

    d.   What makes these counts different?

CL 10-171. Check your answers using the table at the end of this section. Which problems do you feel confident about? Which problems were hard? Have you worked on problems like these in math classes you have taken before? Use the table to make a list of topics you need help with and a list of topics you need to practice more.

⑤   HOW AM I THINKING?

This course focuses on five different **Ways of Thinking**: justifying, generalizing, choosing a strategy, investigating, and reversing thinking. These are some of the ways in which you think while trying to make sense of a concept or attempting to solve a problem (even outside of math class). During this chapter, you have probably used each Way of Thinking multiple times without even realizing it!

Review each of the five Ways of Thinking described in the closure sections of Chapters 1 through 5. Then choose three of these Ways of Thinking that you remember using while working on this chapter. Show and explain where and how you used each one. Describe why thinking in this way helped you solve a particular problem or understand something new. Be sure to include examples to demonstrate your thinking.

Answers and Support for Closure Activity #4
What Have I Learned?

Problem	Solutions	Need Help?	More Practice
CL 10-161.	$_4P_4 = 4 \cdot 3 \cdot 2 \cdot 1 = 24$	Lesson 10.2.1 Math Notes boxes in Lessons 10.2.2 and 10.2.3	Problems 10-56, 10-57, 10-58, 10-59, 10-60, 10-62, 10-63, 10-64, 10-65, and 10-75
CL 10-162.	$\frac{5}{16}$	Lessons 10.1.1 and 10.1.2 Math Notes box in Lesson 10.1.1	Problems 10-1, 10-5, 10-8, 10-34, and 10-100, and 10-121
CL 10-163.	a. $_{10}C_8 = 45$ b. $_8C_6 = 28$	Lesson 10.2.3	Problems 10-87, 10-88, 10-89, 10-92, and 10-96
CL 10-164.	$7! - 6! = 4320$	Lessons 10.2.1 and 10.2.4	Problems 10-60, 10-119, 10-120, and 10-125
CL 10-165.	a. $\frac{1}{6}$ b. $\frac{1}{6} + \frac{1}{12} + \frac{1}{12} = \frac{1}{3}$ c. $1 - \frac{1}{3} = \frac{2}{3}$ d. $\frac{1}{12} \div \frac{1}{3} = \frac{1}{4}$	Lessons 10.1.1 and 10.1.2 Math Notes box in Lesson 10.2.1	Problems 10-2, 10-4, 10-27, 10-29, 10-30, 10-32, 10-33, 10-38, and 10-122
CL 10-166.	$7(\frac{1}{6}) + 5(\frac{1}{12}) + 3(\frac{1}{12}) \approx \$1.83 < \$2$ so no, but it is close.	Lesson 10.1.1	Problems 10-2, 10-4, and 10-5
CL 10-167.	a. $\frac{8}{12} \cdot \frac{4}{11} \cdot \frac{7}{10} = \frac{28}{165} \approx 0.17$ b. $\frac{_8C_2 \cdot _4C_1}{_{12}C_3} = \frac{28}{55} \approx 0.51$	Lessons 10.2.1 and 10.2.3 Math Notes box in Lesson 10.2.4	Problems 10-29, 10-59, 10-95, 10-118, and 10-122
CL 10-168.	a. $(n-1)(n-2) = n^2 - 3n + 2$ b. $n(n-1) = n^2 - n$	Lesson 10.2.2	Problems 10-78 and 10-91
CL 10-169.	a. 0.0253 b. $\frac{_{26}C_5}{_{52}C_5}$ c. 0.000495 d. $\frac{_{13}C_5}{_{52}C_5}$ e. 0.0019808	Lessons 10.2.3 and 10.2.6 Math Notes box in Lesson 10.2.4	Problems 10-95, 10-118, 10-142, 10-143, and 10-144

Problem	Solutions	Need Help?	More Practice
CL 10-170.	a. 24 b. 12 c. 6 d. When the letters are repeated, we cannot distinguish between them.	Lessons 10.2.1 10.2.2, 10.2.4, and 10.2.5	Problems 10-62, 10-75, 10-120, and 10-125

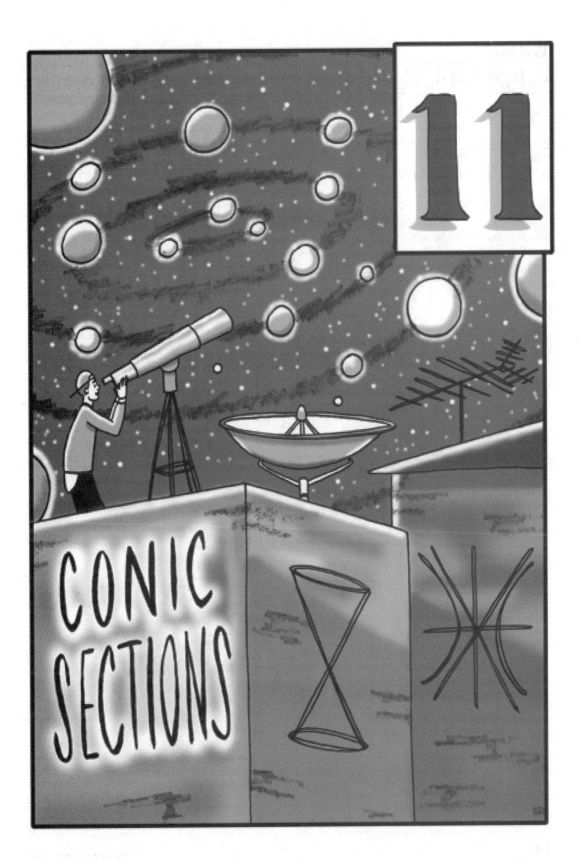

CHAPTER 11

To begin this chapter, you will revisit the parabola by **investigating** the principle that makes a satellite dish work. You will discover a new way to define a parabola and will use that new definition to redevelop its equation.

Then you will analyze the shapes that result from slicing a cone with a plane. These shapes are called **conic sections**. Some of them will already be familiar! You will use your algebraic skills to derive new equations and learn how to sketch graphs of these shapes quickly. Finally, you will see how equations of all conic sections are related to one general equation.

In this chapter, you will:

➤ Learn about the special property of parabolas that makes satellite dishes work.

➤ Name and analyze the shapes that result from slicing a cone with a plane.

➤ Learn new definitions of familiar shapes such as parabolas, hyperbolas, and circles.

➤ Complete the square to change equations of conic sections into graphing form.

Guiding Questions

Think about these questions throughout this chapter:

What is the connection?

What do they all have in common?

How can I transform it?

How can I describe it algebraically?

Chapter Outline

Section 11.1 In this section, you will discover a very useful property of parabolas. You will also learn a new way to create a parabola and derive its equation.

Section 11.2 Here, you will identify and analyze the shapes that result from slicing a cone with a plane. You will use your algebraic skills to derive equations and will develop techniques for graphing them efficiently.

Section 11.3 You will further develop techniques for graphing conic sections and will identify what they all have in common. In this section, you will also create your own conic section and analyze it completely.

11.1.1 What is special about a parabola?

....

A Special Property of Parabolas

In this chapter, you will study new ideas about a group of shapes, some of which you have seen before. In this lesson, you will take a closer look at a parabola and discover a property of parabolas that makes them extremely useful in devices such as high-powered telescopes and satellite dishes.

11-1.   What makes a parabola so special? Discuss this with your team. Have you ever heard of parabolas being useful outside of your math class? If so, what have you heard? If not, think of some parabolas you can see in the physical world.

11-2.   Have you ever wondered how a satellite dish works? If you slice a satellite dish in half, you will find that the cross section of the dish is parabolic. In this activity, you will learn about a special property of parabolas that make a satellite dish work.

Your teacher will provide you and your partner with the Lesson 11.1.1A Resource Page, a viewfinder, a ruler, a set of colored pens or pencils, a flat mirror, a round-topped pin, and possibly a piece of dry spaghetti.

a.   Choose a color and mark a point at the intersection of one of the dotted lines with the **bold** line at the bottom of the resource page. Fold the page so that the colored dot lands on the point shown in the center of the page (called the center point). Make a firm crease, unfold the paper, and use a ruler and the same color to draw a line along the crease.

b.   Use another color to mark another point along the **bold** line where it intersects a dotted line, and make another fold so that the new point lands on the center point. Again, make a firm crease, unfold the paper, and use a ruler and the same color to draw a line along the crease.

c.   Repeat part (b) until you have at least nine lines drawn in as many different colors as possible.

d.   Tape the piece of spaghetti along the line at the top of the page to serve as a guide for the viewfinder, and tape the pin so its head is on the center point. Have one partner place the edge of a flat mirror along one of the colored lines, as shown in the diagram at right. Place the viewfinder behind the piece of spaghetti. The other

partner will look through the viewfinder along the dotted line that intersects the point that is the same color as the line the mirror is on. Adjust the viewfinder and mirror until you can see a clear image of the pinhead in the mirror. When you see it, mark the spot on the dotted line in front of the mirror.

Problem continues on next page.→

11-2.   *Problem continued from previous page.*

    e.   Repeat part (d) for each of the fold lines drawn in pencil. When you are finished, you should have at least nine marks.

    f.   Draw a smooth curve through all of the points you sighted. What shape is formed?

11-3.   Now that you have seen that focusing reflections to one point can form a parabola and you know that the cross section of a satellite dish is a parabola, how are these ideas connected? How does a satellite dish work? What happens to signals that hit the dish on a path parallel to its axis of symmetry? Discuss this with your team.

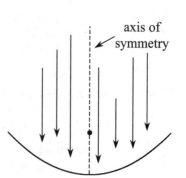

    a.   Draw a diagram like the one at right and complete it to show what happens to the signals that hit the dish.

    b.   If you were building a satellite dish, where would you put the receptor that can read the signals coming in from the satellite? Explain.

    c.   Describe in as much detail as you can why a satellite dish is parabolic. What does the parabolic shape allow it to do?

11-4.   **Investigate** the distance of each point on your parabola from the bold line (called the **directrix**) and compare it to the distance to the marked point on the axis of symmetry (called the **focus**). What do you notice? Create a summary statement about this relationship and be prepared to share it with the class.

11-5.   What is special about a parabola? How can it be used in a telescope or satellite dish? What do all of the points of a parabola have in common? Answer these questions in your Learning Log. Title this entry "Parabolas" and label it with today's date.

11-6. Graph each of the following functions and label the x- and y-intercepts.

   a. $f(x) = 3(x-4)^2 - 5$

   b. $g(x) = 2x^2 - 3x - 5$

11-7. For the function $f(x) = 5x^2 + 4x + 20$, find the roots and the vertex of the graph. Then rewrite the equation in graphing form.

11-8. Solve $\sqrt{x^2 + 6} = x + 2$.

11-9. Find the distance between each of the following pairs of points.

   a. $(-6, 9)$ and $(2, -4)$

   b. (x, y) and $(5, 2)$

11-10. If Emily bought three pounds of oranges and four pounds of bananas for \$8.53 and Beth bought four pounds of oranges and two pounds of bananas for \$7.74, how much should Jenel expect to pay for nine pounds of oranges and seven pounds of bananas?

11-11. For what values of n does the equation $2x^2 + nx + 9 = 0$ have exactly one root?

11-12. Consider the graph of $f(x) = \sin(x)$.

   a. Describe the graph.

   b. Could this graph be an example of any other function? Explain why $f(x) = \sin(x)$ cannot be a polynomial function.

11-13. State the degree of $f(x) = (x+4)(x+1)^2(x-2)$ and sketch its graph.

11-14. Find the equation of a third degree polynomial that has the roots 3, 2, and -1 and passes through the point $(1, 1)$.

11.1.2 How can I describe it algebraically?

Constructing and Analyzing Parabolas

In Lesson 11.1.1 you learned that one way to define a parabola is the set of all points that are an equal distance from a line and a point that is not on the line. In this lesson, you will use that understanding to construct a parabola with your team and analyze it algebraically.

11-15. Obtain the Lesson 11.1.2A Resource Page and a compass from your teacher. Each team member should choose two different distances to work with. For example, if one team member chooses 4 and 8 units, the other three members of your team could choose 6 and 10, 5 and 12, and 3 and 7 units.

   a.   Adjust your compass so its radius measures the first number of units you have chosen, using the grid on the resource page to measure units. Using the focus as the center, sketch an arc with your compass that is the correct number of units from the focus point.

   b.   Now locate the two points on the circle that are exactly one radius length from the directrix. Make sure that the distance you measure from the circle to the directrix is the shortest possible (the perpendicular distance) and is the same as the distance from the circle back to its center. Find these points and darken them on your circle. Then repeat the process for the second length you have chosen. Check to be sure that all of your teammates have done the same on their own papers.

   c.   Obtain a Lesson 11.1.2A Resource Page transparency and an overhead pen from your teacher. Line up the focus and directrix from the transparency with your own focus and directrix and trace your four points onto the transparency. In the same way, collect points from all team members. Use your overhead pen to sketch the curve that passes through all of your team's points.

   d.   There is one length where there is only one point equidistant from the center of the circle and the line. What length is this and what point does it give?

   e.   What should be true of all of the points on your parabola? In other words, what do they all have in common?

11-16.　Now you will use your understanding of the points on the parabola to find its equation. Obtain a Lesson 11.1.2B Resource Page from your teacher.

    a.　With your team, place your transparency parabola on the axes on your resource page such that the vertex of the parabola lies on the origin, it is oriented upward, and it is symmetrical about the y-axis.

    b.　Mark a point on your parabola P (it can be any point on the curve) and label its coordinates (x, y). Draw a line from the point you marked to the focus and another line from your point perpendicular to the directrix. Write an expression that represents the distance from your point P to the focus of your parabola. (Note that you are intentionally using the variables x and y here and not number coordinates. This allows you to **generalize** for any point.)

    c.　Write an expression for the distance between the point (x, y) and the directrix of your parabola.

    d.　What is the relationship between these two distances for a parabola? Use this relationship to write an equation for your parabola. Simplify your equation and solve it for y.

    e.　Does your equation make sense? Use your previous knowledge of parabolas to **justify** your decision.

11-17.　How many equations can you find? Choose at least three different ways to place your parabola over the axes provided. You can even rotate it $90°$. Use the equal distances (as you did in problem 11-16) to find a new equation for each placement. Be prepared to share your **strategies** and your equations with the class.

11-18.　On graph paper, sketch the parabola that is the set of all points equidistant from the focus $(0, 7)$ and the directrix $y = -3$.

    a.　Find and simplify the equation of the parabola.

    b.　Change the equation of this parabola to shift the graph five units to the right. What would the vertex of your new parabola be?

11-19.　On graph paper, sketch the parabola that is the set of all points equidistant from the focus $(3, 0)$ and the directrix $x = -5$.

    a.　Find and simplify the equation of the parabola.

    b.　Change the equation of the parabola to shift the graph up 3 units. What would the vertex of the new parabola be?

11-20. Complete the square to convert each of the following quadratic functions to graphing form. State the vertex and sketch the graph.

    a. $f(x) = x^2 + 6x + 7$ b. $f(x) = x^2 - 10x$

11-21. Solve each system of equations below.

    a. $x - 2y = 7$ b. $\frac{x+4y}{3} - \frac{6y-x}{4} = -3$

          $2x + y = 3$ $\frac{x}{10} + 5y = 2$

11-22. Convert the following degree measures to radians.

    a.   45°   b.   75°   c.   −15°   d.   450°

11-23. Verify that $3 + i\sqrt{2}$ is a solution of $x^2 - 6x + 11 = 0$.

11-24. Show and explain why the equation $2^x = 5 - x$ has only one real solution.

11-25. Compute each complex product.

    a. $(1 + i)^2$ b. $(1 + i)^3$

11-26. Sketch a graph of $y = -x^2(x - 2)^2(x + 2)^2$.

11-27. The mascot for Sacramento High School is the DRAGONS.

    a.   How many ways can the cheerleaders rearrange the letters in the school mascot?

    b.   How many ways can the letters be rearranged if the first and last letters are correctly placed?

11-28. A bag contains eight blue marbles and four gold marbles. If you choose three marbles without looking, what is the probability of getting:

    a.   All blue marbles?   b.   Two blue and one gold?

    c.   All gold marbles?   d.   One blue and two gold marbles?

    e.   Show two different ways to calculate the answer to part (d).

11.2.1 What happens when I slice a cone?

Sections of a Cone

In this lesson, you will **investigate** the shapes that result from slicing a three-dimensional cone with a plane. You will look at these shapes both geometrically, as the intersection of a cone and a plane, and algebraically, as solutions to three-dimensional systems of equations.

11-29.   What will the graph of $z^2 = x^2 + y^2$ look like? Discuss this with your team and make a prediction. Then check your prediction on the class grapher. What shape do you see?

11-30.   What will the graph of $z = 2 - x$ look like? What will happen when the graph of $z = 2 - x$ is graphed on the same set of axes as the graph of $z^2 = x^2 + y^2$?

   a.   Consider the graph of this system on the class grapher. Sketch the graph on your paper.

   b.   What shape do the solutions form?

   c.   Solve the system algebraically. Does your algebraic result make sense when you look at the graph? Explain.

11-31.   Is it possible to get an intersection of a cone and a plane that form a different shape? Discuss this with your team. On your paper, sketch any shapes you think are possible.

11-32.   Now your teacher will change the equation of the plane to $z = 2$, so that it is parallel to the xy-plane.

   a.   What will the intersection look like? Make a prediction with your team.

   b.   Your teacher will graph the system at right on the class grapher. What shape do the solutions form? Was your prediction correct?

$$z^2 = x^2 + y^2$$
$$z = 2$$

   c.   Solve your system algebraically and explain the result.

11-33.   How else could you orient a plane to create a different kind of cross section? Be prepared to share your ideas with the class.

11-34. Now the plane will change again. Consider the graphs of the cone and the plane represented by the system below on the class grapher.

 a. What shape do the solutions form?

 b. Solve the system algebraically.

$$z^2 = x^2 + y^2$$
$$z = 2 - 0.5x$$

11-35. Now your teacher will change the equation of the plane that slices the cone to $z = 2 - 3x$, so it makes a steeper angle than the side of the cone.

 a. What will the intersection look like now? Sketch your prediction.

 b. Consider the graph of the system at right. Does the shape of the solutions look familiar? What is it? Is it similar to your prediction?

$$z^2 = x^2 + y^2$$
$$z = 2 - 3x$$

 c. Solve the system algebraically.

11-36. Are there any other shapes you could generate by making a cone and a plane intersect? As your teacher graphs each of the following systems, sketch the system and describe the intersection.

 a. $z^2 = x^2 + y^2$
    $z = 0$

 b. $z^2 = x^2 + y^2$
    $x = 0$

 c. $z^2 = x^2 + y^2$
    $z = x$

11-37. Your teacher will assign your team one of the conic sections. Create a poster that shows your conic section as a graphical *and* algebraic solution to a system of three-dimensional equations. Use $z^2 = x^2 + y^2$ as the equation of your cone. You can use the planes given in the preceding problems, or you can choose from the planes given below.

Planes parallel to the *xy*-plane:	$z = 4$, $z = 3$, $z = -5$
Planes less steep than the side of the cone:	$z = 3 - 0.5x$, $z = 0.25x + 2$
Planes parallel to the side of the cone:	$z = 3 - x$, $z = 1 - y$, $z = x + 4$
Planes steeper than the side of the cone:	$z = 3 - 3x$, $z = 2x + 3$, $z = 2 - 1.5y$

11-38. Solve the following systems of equations and describe the shapes of the intersections.

a. $z^2 = x^2 + y^2$

$z = x + 2$

b. $z^2 = x^2 + y^2$

$z = 7$

11-39. Find the vertex of the parabola given by each quadratic equation below.

a. $f(x) = x^2 + 8x + 12$

b. $g(x) = x^2 - 2x + 3$

11-40. Where do the graphs of $x^2 - y = 4$ and $y = 2x - 1$ intersect?

11-41. Solve each equation below for x. Show all of your work. (Your answers will contain the variables $a, b,$ and/or c.)

a. $cx - a = b$

b. $\frac{x}{a} - b = c$

c. $(x - a)(x - b) = 0$

d. $ax^2 - acx = 0$

e. $\frac{x}{a+b} = \frac{1}{c}$

f. $\frac{1}{x} + a = b$

11-42. Your midterm exam contains 12 questions and you must answer any 10.

a. How many different combinations of questions are possible?

b. If everyone must answer questions one, two and three, how many different combinations are possible?

11-43. The big math test is tomorrow! You know that if you have time to study there is a 90% chance of getting a good grade, but if you cannot study there is only a 40% chance of earning a good grade. Your family uses a spinner to see who will have to work at the family business tonight. The spinner has five evenly divided sections and your name is on one section. If you have to work tonight there will be no time to study. What is the probability of getting a good grade? An area model or a tree diagram may be helpful in solving this problem.

11-44.   Graph each plane in three dimensions.

   a. $2x - 3y + 4z = 12$ b. $2x - 3y = 12$

11-45.   Use reference angles, the symmetry of a circle, and the knowledge that $\cos(\frac{\pi}{3}) = \frac{1}{2}$ to write three other true statements using cosine and angles that are multiples of $\frac{\pi}{3}$.

11-46.   The Flat Building's roof is 32 feet wide and 60 feet long. An antenna rises 25 feet above the center of the roof, and wires connect from the top of the antenna to each corner of the roof and to the midpoint of each edge, as shown in the picture at right.

   a.   What is the total length of wire needed (without counting any extra needed for attaching it)?

   b.   The wires that attach to the corners of the building form an angle with the roof. Find the measure of that angle.

   c.   Suppose the height of the antenna is x feet (instead of 25 feet). Represent the total length of the wires in terms of x.

11.2.2 How else can I see it?

Multiple Perspectives on Parabolas and Circles

In Lesson 11.2.1, you learned that a parabola is one of the shapes that can result from slicing a cone with a plane. You have many other ideas about parabolas also. In this lesson, you will focus on parabolas and bring together all of the ways you have of looking at this interesting shape. You will then extend one of your newest ideas about a parabola to help you define a circle in a new way.

11-47.   Polly Parabola, CEO of Professional Parabola Productions, is very confused! She has sent your team the following memo.

> *Dear Study Team,*
>
> *My parabola laboratory has been making parabolas for a very long time now, and we thought we were experts! – until recently. I have heard two rumors that suggest that there may be more to a parabola than we had thought: something about making a parabola from a point and a line and something else about a cone and a plane.*
>
> *Please investigate these new rumors for me. If they turn out to be true, they may help us to design more efficient ways to make parabolas and streamline our ordering process, allowing us to offer an even wider variety of parabolas to our customers.*
>
> *Please have a report on my desk by the end of the day with your findings.*
>
> *Thank you,*
> *Ms. Polly Parabola*

Your task: With your team, demonstrate *all* of the mathematical ways you can describe a parabola. Be sure to use complete summary statements to explain your findings clearly, so that Polly Parabola can understand you.

Discussion Points

How can we create the equation of a parabola algebraically?

How can we make a parabola on a two-dimensional graph without using an equation?

How can we make a parabola on a three-dimensional graph?

Are all parabolas functions?

Further Guidance

11-48.   In Chapter 4, you used the equation $y = x^2$ as a parent equation for the family of quadratic functions.

    a.   What was the general equation that you found for the family of quadratic functions?

    b.   You also looked briefly at the family of sleeping parabolas. What was their general equation?

11-49.   In Section 11.1, you learned about a special property of parabolas and a new way to define a parabola.

    a.   Write this new definition of a parabola in your own words.

    b.   Show how you can use this definition to draw a parabola.

11-50.   In Lesson 11.2.1, you learned that the equation of a parabola can be the solution to a three-dimensional system of equations.

    a.   What are the three-dimensional shapes that can form a parabola when they intersect?

    b.   Use algebra to show that a three-dimensional system representing the shapes in part (a) can have a quadratic solution.

Further Guidance
section ends here.

11-51.   The set of all points with a given set of characteristics is called a **locus** of points. A line through the origin is a locus of points where the ratio of the y-coordinate to the x-coordinate is constant. A parabola is a locus of points, and one of the ways to describe a parabola is by using its **locus definition**.

    a.   What is the locus definition of a parabola? In other words, what is true about each and every point of a parabola?

    b.   What do all of the points in a circle have in common? Work with your team to write a locus definition of a circle based on what all points of a circle have in common. Be prepared to share your ideas with the class.

11-52. Draw a circle with its center at the origin and a radius of 5. Mark a point P on the circle and label it with the coordinates (x, y).

a. Write an expression for the distance between point P and the center of the circle.

b. Since you know the radius of the circle, you can turn your distance expression into an equation that describes all of the points in the circle. Write and simplify the equation of this circle.

11-53. Now draw a circle with center $(3, 5)$ and radius 4 units. Again, label a point P with the coordinates (x, y).

a. Write an expression for the distance between point P and the center of the circle.

b. What is the exact distance between any point on your circle and the center of the circle? Use this distance with your expression from part (a) to write an equation and then simplify the result.

11-54. Work with your team to **generalize** this process to find the equation of a circle with any radius r and center (h, k). How does your result compare to your previous understanding of the equation of a circle?

11-55. LEARNING LOG

In your Learning Log, write the locus definitions for a circle and a parabola and show how these definitions can help you find equations. Title this entry "Locus Definitions for a Circle and Parabola" and label it with today's date.

LOOKING DEEPER

Focus and Directrix of a Parabola

A parabola can be defined in relationship to a line (called its **directrix**) and a point (called its **focus**). All of the points that make up the parabola are equidistant from the focus and the directrix. For the parabola shown at right, the directrix is the line $x = -5$ and the focus is the point $(3, 0)$.

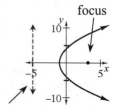

The focus is also the point at which the reflections of parallel rays (perpendicular to the directrix) from a parabolic mirror will intersect. The distance p from the vertex to the focus is called the **focal length** of the parabola, and it is related to the stretch factor. In the parabola shown above, $p = 4$. Below are some equations of parabolas along with their **foci** (plural of focus).

- The parabola described by $y = x^2$ has its focus at $(0, \frac{1}{4})$.

- The parabola described by $y = 3x^2$ has its focus at $(0, \frac{1}{12})$.

- The parabola described by $y = \frac{1}{8}x^2$ has its focus at $(0, 2)$.

- In general, the parabola described by $y = ax^2$ has focal length $p = \frac{1}{4a}$. Its focus is located at the point $(0, \frac{1}{4a})$, and the directrix is $y = -\frac{1}{4a}$.

11-56.   On graph paper, sketch the parabola that is the set of all points equidistant from the focus $(0, -5)$ and the directrix $y = 7$.

a.   Find and simplify the equation of the parabola.

b.   Change the equation of the parabola to shift the graph up 3 units. What would the vertex of the new parabola be?

c.   What would the new focus point be, and what line would be the new directrix?

Algebra 2 Connections

11-57.   Find the equation of a circle with center $(-2, 7)$ that passes through the point $(3, 11)$.

11-58.   Draw a circle and a line tangent to it at any point P on the circle. Now draw a line from the center of the circle through point P.

a.   What do you know about these two lines?

b.   What do you know about the slopes of the lines?

11-59.   Using a graph of $y = \sin x$ as a reference, graph $y = |\sin x|$.

11-60.   Solve each equation below for x.

a. $1234x + 23456 = 987654$ b. $\frac{10}{x} + \frac{20}{x} = 5$

c. $5x^2 - 6x + 1 = 0$ d. $x^3 - 3x^2 + 2x = 0$

11-61.   Factor and simplify each expression below.

a. $\frac{x^2-4}{x^2+4x+4}$ b. $\frac{2x^2-5x-3}{4x^2+4x+1}$

c.   **Justify** each step in simplifying the expression in part (a).

11-62.   For each equation below, state the amplitude, period, and locator point, and then sketch two cycles of the graph.

a. $y = \tan(x)$ b. $y = \tan(x - \pi)$

11-63.   Solve each equation.

a. $\log_5(2x) = 3$ b. $\log_5(x+1) = -1$

c. $\log(4) - \log(x) = 2$ d. $2\log_3(6) + \log_3(y) = 4$

11-64.   Calculate $(2+i)(3-5i) - (1-4i)^2$.

11.2.3 How can I find the equation?

Equations of Ellipses

In Lesson 11.2.2, you wrote locus definitions for a circle and a parabola. An ellipse has a locus definition as well. In this lesson, you will construct your own ellipse and use a locus definition to find its equation.

11-65.   An **ellipse** can be defined as the locus of points for which the sum of their distances from two fixed points remains constant. In this activity, you will use this definition to make your own ellipse.

Directions for constructing an ellipse:

- Obtain a piece of cardboard, tape, two pins, a string, and the Lesson 11.2.3 Resource Page from your teacher.

- Tape the Lesson 11.2.3 Resource Page on top of the cardboard and place your pins on the points $(5,0)$ and $(-5,0)$.

- Make two loops on your string 20 units apart, as shown at right. (Measure this on your resource-page grid.) Put a loop over each pin.

- Use your pencil to stretch the string as far as it will go in any direction.

- Move your pencil as far as you can around the pins, *keeping the string taut.*

The length of the string is the sum of the distances from your pencil to each of the two pins (or **foci**). As long as you do not add or remove any string and the string remains taut, this sum remains constant and the shape you see on your paper is an ellipse.

11-66.   Choose at least five points on the ellipse you have constructed. For each point, measure the distances to each of the foci and calculate the sum. Does the sum truly remain constant?

11-67.   Mark a point P on your ellipse and label it with the coordinates (x, y).

    a.   Write an expression for the sum of the distances from your point P to each of the pins. (These points are called **foci**, which is plural for **focus**.)

    b.   The length of your string is the sum of the distances from any point on the ellipse to the foci. Use this distance with your expression from part (a) to create an equation.

    c.   Work with your team to simplify the equation you wrote in part (b). Be prepared to share your simplification **strategies** with the class.

11-68.   With your team, compare the ellipse you constructed with its equation. How do the numbers in the equation relate to the graph? Be prepared to share all of your ideas about the possible connections between the equation and the graph with the class.

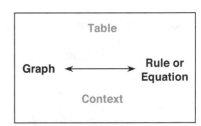

⃝OOKING DEEPER

Foci of an Ellipse

MATH NOTES

Suppose an ellipse has its center at the origin, with x-intercepts at $(\pm a, 0)$ and y-intercepts at $(0, \pm b)$, where $a > b$. Then there are two points on the x-axis at $(\pm c, 0)$, with $c^2 = a^2 - b^2$, which are called the **foci** of the ellipse.

Ellipses also have unique geometric properties; not every oval is an ellipse. To understand the geometric properties of the ellipse, imagine a pool table in the shape of an ellipse, with only one pocket, located at one focus. If you place a ball on the other focus and hit it *in any direction*, it will bank off the rail and go into the pocket. Also, no matter where the ball hits the rail, it will always travel the same distance before reaching the pocket.

11-69. Find the equation of the ellipse you would form using the same process as in problem 11-65 but with a string 15 units long.

Extra challenge: See how far you can get rewriting it to fit the form of your result from problem 11-65.

11-70. Find the distance between each of the following pairs of points.

a. $(8, 4)$ and $(12, 20)$

b. (x, y) and $(-3, -5)$

11-71. Solve each of the following equations.

a. $\frac{x}{x+1} = \frac{5}{7}$

b. $\frac{2}{y} = \frac{3}{y+5}$

c. $\frac{x}{x+1} + \frac{2}{x-1} = \frac{8}{x^2-1}$

d. $\frac{2}{y+5} - \frac{3}{y} = \frac{3}{y+5}$

11-72. Solve for x and y in each system below.

a. $2x + y = 12$
$xy = 16$

b. $2x + y = 12$
$xy = 20$

c. Explain how the graphs of (a) and (b) relate to the solutions to each system of equations.

11-73. Sketch the graph of $y = (x + 2)^3 + 4$.

a. Rewrite the equation $y = (x + 2)^3 + 4$ without parentheses. Remember the order of operations.

b. How would the graph in part (a) differ from the graph of the original equation?

c. What is the parent equation of $y = (x + 2)^3 + 4$? Of $y = x^3 + 6x^2 + 12x + 12$?

Algebra 2 Connections

11-74.   A sequence starts $24, 12, \ldots$ Use that information to complete parts (a) and (b) below.

    a.   If the sequence is arithmetic:

        i.   Find $t(3)$.

        ii.   Find $t(n)$.

        iii. What is the shape of its graph?

        iv. Which term is -624?

    b.   If the sequence is geometric:

        i.   Find $t(3)$.

        ii.   Find $t(n)$.

        iii. What is the shape of its graph?

        iv. Which term is $\frac{3}{128}$?

11-75.   Before radios and satellite communication systems, ships would communicate with each other by using a string of colored flags. With four blue flags and two red flags, how many six flag signals are possible?

11-76.   Use reference angles, the symmetry of a circle, and the knowledge that $\tan(20°) \approx 0.3640$ to write three other true statements using tangent.

11-77.   Use the properties of logarithms to rewrite each equation and then solve. Check for extraneous roots.

    a. $\log(x) + \log(x + 21) = 2$ b. $2\log_4(x) - \log_4(3) = 2$

    c. $\log_2(9x + 5) - \log_2(x^2 - 1) = 2$ d. $\log_7(x + 1) + \log_7(x - 5) = 1$

11.2.4 How can I graph it quickly?

Equation ↔ Graph for Ellipses

In Lesson 11.2.3, you constructed an ellipse and found its equation. In this lesson, you will **investigate** the connections between the equation and the graph of an ellipse and will develop methods that enable you to sketch a graph quickly from an equation.

11-78.   EQUATION ↔ GRAPH

With your team, find as many connections as you can between the graph of the ellipse you constructed in Lesson 11.2.3 and its equation. How could you use the equation to make the graph? Be prepared to share your ideas with the class.

11-79.   Consider the equation $\frac{x^2}{16} + \frac{y^2}{9} = 1$.

a.   Use your ideas from problem 11-78 to help you make a graph.

b.   Work with your team to write a general equation for an ellipse centered at the origin with x-intercepts $(a,0)$ and $(-a,0)$, and y-intercepts $(0,b)$ and $(0,-b)$.

c.   For this equation, the length of the **major axis** of this ellipse is the distance between the two x-intercepts. What is the length of the **major axis** for this graph? What is it in general?

d.   For this equation, the length of the **minor axis** of this ellipse is the distance between the two y-intercepts. What is the length of the **minor axis** for this graph? What is it in general?

11-80.   How could you change the equation $\frac{x^2}{16} + \frac{y^2}{9} = 1$ to make each of the following transformations? Be prepared to share your equations with the class.

a.   The graph moves 3 units to the right.

b.   The graph moves 2 units down.

c.   The center of the ellipse is $(5,1)$.

d.   What information can you get from looking at an equation of *any* ellipse that can help you sketch a graph?

11-81. The 16 and the 9 in the equation $\frac{x^2}{16} + \frac{y^2}{9} = 1$ give useful information about the graph of the ellipse.

    a.   What information do the 16 and the 9 give?

    b.   If the ellipse is shifted so that its center is not on the origin (like $\frac{(x-5)^2}{16} + \frac{(y-1)^2}{9} = 1$), what information do the 16 and the 9 give now?

    c.   The four points on an ellipse, the one farthest to the right, one farthest to the left, one highest, and one lowest are called the **vertices** of the ellipse. Find the coordinates of the vertices of $\frac{(x-5)^2}{16} + \frac{(y-1)^2}{9} = 1$ and sketch the graph. Be prepared to share your strategies with the class.

11-82. Find the equation of the ellipse at right. When you have decided on an equation, test it on the class grapher.

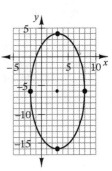

11-83. Use the information from each equation below to make graphs of the ellipses. Label the center and the vertices of each graph.

    a. $\frac{x^2}{9} + \frac{y^2}{64} = 1$
                    b. $\frac{(x-3)^2}{16} + \frac{(y+2)^2}{9} = 1$

    c. $\frac{(x-2)^2}{25} + (y+1)^2 = 1$
             d. $x^2 + \frac{(y-4)^2}{9} = 1$

11-84. Write the general equation for an ellipse centered at (h, k) with a horizontal major axis of length $2a$ and a vertical minor axis of length $2b$.

11-85. LEARNING LOG

In your Learning Log, explain everything you know about the connections between the graph of an ellipse and its equation. Title this entry "Equation $\leftrightarrow$ Graph for Ellipses" and label it with today's date.

METHODS AND MEANINGS

Ellipses and Eccentricity

The line segment that connects the two farthest extremes of the ellipse in the long direction is called the **major axis** of the ellipse, and the distance from the center of the ellipse to one end of the major axis is called the **semi-major axis**. The line segment that connects the two closer extremes is called the **minor axis** of the ellipse, and the distance from the center of the ellipse to one end of the minor axis is called the **semi-minor axis**. If a is the length of the semi-major axis, b is the length of the semi-minor axis, and (h, k) is the center, the equation of the ellipse can be written:

$$\frac{(x-h)^2}{a^2} + \frac{(y-k)^2}{b^2} = 1 \text{, if the major axis is horizontal, or}$$

$$\frac{(x-h)^2}{b^2} + \frac{(y-k)^2}{a^2} = 1 \text{, if the major axis is vertical.}$$

Eccentricity is a term that refers to a measure of the shape of the ellipse. Eccentricity can be calculated with the formula $e = \frac{c}{a}$, where c is the distance from the center to the focus, and $c^2 = a^2 - b^2$. Since $c < a$, the eccentricity of an ellipse is always between 0 and 1. The larger the eccentricity of an ellipse, the more elongated the ellipse appears. The smaller the eccentricity, the more the shape of an ellipse resembles a circle.

11-86. Graph each of the following ellipses.

a. $\frac{x^2}{25} + \frac{y^2}{100} = 1$

b. $\frac{(x-4)^2}{64} + \frac{(y+3)^2}{9} = 1$

11-87. Find the distance from the point $(4, 10)$ to each line or point described below.

a. The line $x = -4$.

b. The line $y = 7$.

c. The point $(3, 7)$.

d. The point $(5, -4)$.

11-88.   Solve the following equations.

a. $\frac{3}{x} + \frac{5}{x-7} = -2$

b. $\frac{2x+3}{4} - \frac{x-7}{6} = \frac{2x-3}{12}$

11-89.   Betty's Quick Stop makes a 15% profit on its lunches and a 22% profit on its dinners. If Betty took in $2700 on Tuesday and made $513.01 profit, how much did Betty take in on lunch? Write one or two equations, then solve.

11-90.   Show how to solve the equations below *without* using your calculator. You will have radicals or logarithms in your answers.

a. $3^x = 17$

b. $x^3 = 17$

11-91.   Write the equation of the line tangent to the graph of $(x-7)^2 + (y-2)^2 = 169$ at the point $(12, 14)$. (Hint: Drawing a diagram will help.)

11-92.   For the polynomial function $f(x) = x^3 - 5x^2 + 11x - 15$, which of the following are possible factors?

a. $(x+1)$ b. $(x-2)$ c. $(x+4)$ d. $(x-3)$

11-93   Using your answers to the previous problem:

a.   Factor $f(x) = x^3 - 5x^2 + 11x - 15$.

b.   Solve $f(x) = 0$.

11-94.   For an object shot into the air, its height h in feet above the ground after t seconds is given by the equation $h = 80t - 16t^2$. Use this equation to answer the following questions.

a.   For what times is the object on the ground?

b.   For what domain is this function reasonable?

c.   How long did it take the object to hit the ground?

d.   For what times is the height greater than 64 feet?

11.2.5 What if I use a constant difference?

A New Conic Section

Imagine mathematicians studying the conic sections before their equations were known. They had just finished studying the ellipse, which has to do with a *sum* of distances. Now they are curious about what would happen, if instead of considering a *sum* of distances, they considered a *difference* of distances. They wondered what shape would result from the set of points where the *difference* of distances from two fixed points to any point on the curve remained constant. In other words, what is the curve that is the locus of points where the *difference* in the distances to two given points is always the same?

11-95. How would the algebraic
analysis of a conic section
change if you were considering
a difference instead of a sum?

    a.   Draw a set of axes on
graph paper and draw two
focus points at $(5,0)$ and
$(-5,0)$. Then mark a
point P somewhere else
and label it (x, y). You
will assume that this point
is on your new curve.

    b.   With your team, write an expression for the difference of distances from any
point P to each of the foci. You can look back at your work with the ellipse in
problem 11-67 to help you.

    c.   Any real number will work for the constant distance, but some numbers are more
convenient than others. A constant difference of 6 units works well. To find out
what will happen, set the expression you got for the difference in part (b) equal to
6 to write an equation.

    d.   Work with your team to simplify the equation you got in part (c). Again, you can
look at the work you did with the equation of the ellipse to help you, but be
careful with the negative signs. Be prepared to share your **strategies** and results
with the class.

11-96.   Now that you have the equation, it is time to figure out what the graph looks like. What information can you get from the equation that can help you draw a graph?

    a.   Can you find the *x*- and *y*-intercepts from the equation? Explain. Do you have enough information to figure out the shape of the graph?

    b.   Make an $x \rightarrow y$ table with enough entries to make a complete and accurate graph. What happens when you try $0, \pm1,$ or ±2 for *x*? Describe the shape of the graph. Does it look like anything you have seen before? What is the domain for this relation?

11-97.   The curve that you have just graphed is a hyperbola, and, as you may recall, it is one of the shapes resulting from slicing a cone with a plane. You may remember from graphing hyperbolas in the past that hyperbolas have asymptotes.

    a.   Sketch a graph of the hyperbola described by $y = \frac{5}{x}$. What are the equations of its asymptotes?

    b.   The hyperbola that you graphed in problem 11-96 is shown at right, along with its asymptotes. How are its asymptotes different from the ones that you have seen before?

    c.   Work with your team to estimate the equations of the asymptotes of the hyperbola described by $\frac{x^2}{9} - \frac{y^2}{16} = 1$. Be prepared to share your **strategies** and results with the class.

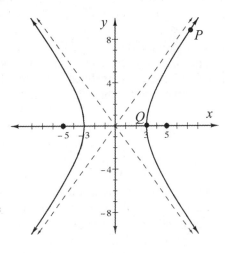

11-98.   With your team, compare your hyperbola with its equation. How do the numbers in the equation relate to the graph? Be prepared to share your ideas about the possible connections between the equation and the graph of a hyperbola.

OOKING DEEPER

Orientation of Conic Sections

Why was the directrix for the parabola always either horizontal or vertical? In other words, why are the parabolas you analyzed oriented either directly up, down, left, or right? What if the directrix were some other line and the parabola was oriented in a different direction?

At right is a parabola with directrix $y = -x$ and focus $(3, 3)$. Notice the point P on the parabola labeled with the coordinates (x, y). The expression for the distance between point P and the focus of the parabola is simple to write; it is $\sqrt{(x-3)^2 + (y-3)^2}$.

The expression for the shortest distance between point P and the directrix, on the other hand, is very challenging to write, because the directrix is neither horizontal nor vertical. Similarly, when analyzing a hyperbola from its locus definition, it is much simpler to orient it directly left-right or up-down.

At right is a sketch of the function $f(x) = \frac{5}{x}$. Notice that its lines of symmetry are $y = x$ and $y = -x$. If the hyperbola were rotated $45°$ clockwise, the new lines of symmetry would be $x = 0$ and $y = 0$.

For simplicity, when you analyze hyperbolas from their locus definition, it is best to orient them horizontally or vertically. Examine the hyperbola at right with foci $(5, 0)$ and $(-5, 0)$ and x-intercepts (or **vertices**) $(3, 0)$ and $(-3, 0)$. Note that the axes of symmetry are the lines $x = 0$ and $y = 0$. Notice that point P is labeled (x, y) and the vertex $(3, 0)$ is labeled point Q.

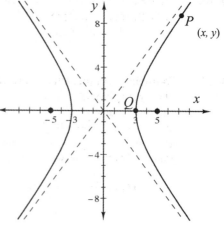

The difference of the distances from point P to each of the focus points is given by $\left| \sqrt{(x+5)^2 + y^2} - \sqrt{(x-5)^2 + y^2} \right|$. The difference of distances from the vertex Q to each of the focus points is 6 units. When you set these differences equal to each other, you get the equation of the hyperbola $\left| \sqrt{(x+5)^2 + y^2} - \sqrt{(x-5)^2 + y^2} \right| = 6$, which simplifies to $\frac{x^2}{9} - \frac{y^2}{16} = 1$.

11-99. Graph each of the following ellipses.

a. $\frac{x^2}{4} + \frac{y^2}{9} = 1$

b. $\frac{(x+2)^2}{25} + \frac{(y-1)^2}{16} = 1$

11-100. Find the equation of the line tangent to the circle $x^2 + y^2 = 25$ at each of the following points.

a. $(5, 0)$

b. $(3, 4)$

11-101. Dolores says that the solutions for $x^2 - x + 1 = 0$ are $\frac{1}{2} \pm \frac{i\sqrt{3}}{2}$. Is she correct? Explain your answer.

11-102. Write a possible equation for the graph at right.

11-103. Find the solutions to the system at right. The solutions may be real or complex.

$$y = x^2 + 2x + 5$$
$$y = 2x^2 + 4x + 7$$

11-104. Without graphing, find where each of the following curves crosses the x-axis. (Find the *exact* points!)

a. $f(x) = x^2 - x - 12$

b. $f(x) = 2x^2 - 3x - 9$

c. $f(x) = 2x^2 + x - 7$

d. $f(x) = 3x^2 - 2x + 7$

e. $f(x) = 3x^3 + 2x^2 - 8x$

f. $f(x) = 2x^3 + 2x^2 + 13x$

11-105. Use properties of exponents to rewrite each expression below so that it involves only multiplication and exponents.

a. $\frac{(-2x)^3 yz^2}{2^{-1}\sqrt{x}y^{-3}}$

b. $\frac{3x^2 y^3}{\sqrt{3x}\sqrt[3]{y}}$

11-106. The graph of $f(x) = x^2 - 3x - 4$ is shown at right. Use the graph to solve:

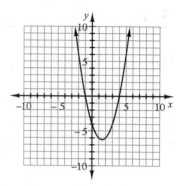

a. $f(x) = 0$

b. $f(x) \geq 0$

c. $f(x) \leq 0$

11-107. Three bouquet styles from Kris's Flower Shoppe are most popular. Style #1 uses three small bunches of carnations, four lilies, and two small bunches of daisies. Style #2 uses five small bunches of carnations and three small bunches of daisies. Style #3 uses one small bunch of carnations, four lilies, and four small bunches of daisies.

a. Organize the information into a *styles* × *flowers* matrix named B.

b. Carnations cost $2.75 for a small bunch, lilies cost $0.60 each, and daisies cost $1.00 for a small bunch. Organize the costs in a matrix named C.

c. Which product, BC or CB, makes sense to find the cost of each bouquet? Find that product.

11.2.6 How can I graph it quickly?

Equation ↔ Graph for Hyperbolas

In this lesson, you will continue to build your understanding of hyperbolas as you explore the relationships between the graphs of hyperbolas and their equations.

11-108.   Is it necessary to make an $x \rightarrow y$ table in order to graph a hyperbola? What information would be enough to allow you to make a reasonably accurate graph without plotting numerous points? Discuss this with your team and be prepared to share your ideas with the class.

11-109.   As you learned in Lesson 11.2.5, hyperbolas have asymptotes. This is shown in the diagram at right. The steps below will help you find the asymptotes for the hyperbola described by $\frac{x^2}{9} - \frac{y^2}{16} = 1$.

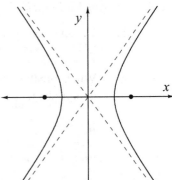

a.   Start by solving the equation of the hyperbola for y.

b.   You can see from the diagram that as the value of x becomes extremely large, the curve of the hyperbola approaches the line of the asymptote. As x becomes very large, which number in the equation has little effect on the value of y?

c.   Try some large numbers for x (such as $x = 100$) with and without subtracting the 1. What do you notice?

d.   Write the equation of the hyperbola without the -1 under the radical. Then simplify the equation. What lines do the branches of the hyperbola approach as x gets very large? These are the asymptotes of the hyperbola.

e.   Add the asymptotes to your graph of $\frac{x^2}{9} - \frac{y^2}{16} = 1$.

f.   What information about the graph of a hyperbola centered at the origin can you find from looking at its equation?

11-110.   Sketch a graph of $\frac{y^2}{36} - \frac{x^2}{25} = 1$ by finding the asymptotes and intercepts.

11-111.   What do you need to know about a hyperbola?

a.   What do you need to know about a hyperbola to sketch a reasonably accurate graph?

b.   What do you need to know about a hyperbola to write its equation?

11-112.   Write the equation and sketch a graph of a hyperbola centered at the origin with intercepts $(4,0)$ and $(-4,0)$ and asymptotes $y = \pm \frac{9}{4} x$.

11-113.   Write the general equation of a hyperbola centered at the origin with intercepts $(a,0)$ and $(-a,0)$ and asymptotes $y = \pm \frac{b}{a} x$.

11-114.   Consider the equation $\frac{x^2}{25} - \frac{y^2}{9} = 1$.

a.   Use the ideas you have developed in this lesson to help you sketch a graph.

b.   How could you change the equation to make each of the following transformations?

i.   The graph moves 4 units to the right.

ii.   The graph moves 3 units up.

iii.   The center of the hyperbola is $(-2,4)$.

iv.   The hyperbola is rotated 90° so that its vertices are on the y-axis.

c.   What information can you get from looking at an equation of *any* hyperbola that can help you sketch a graph?

11-115.   Write the *general equation* of a hyperbola centered at (h,k) with intercepts $(a,0)$ and $(-a,0)$ and asymptotes with slope $\pm \frac{b}{a}$.

11-116.   Graph the hyperbolas described by the equations below.

a. $\frac{(x-2)^2}{4} - \frac{(y+1)^2}{16} = 1$

b. $(y-4)^2 - \frac{(x+2)^2}{9} = 1$

METHODS AND MEANINGS

Equations of Hyperbolas

A hyperbola has relationships similar to those of an ellipse. The line connecting the vertices of the two branches is called the **transverse axis**, and a represents the distance from the center to either vertex.

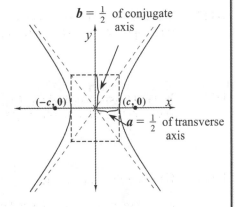

$b = \frac{1}{2}$ of conjugate axis

$(-c, 0)$ $(c, 0)$

$a = \frac{1}{2}$ of transverse axis

If the center of the hyperbola is at the origin and the vertices are on the x-axis, the equation can be written in the form $\frac{x^2}{a^2} - \frac{y^2}{b^2} = 1$.

The vertices are at the points $(\pm a, 0)$, and the asymptotes have equations $y = \pm \frac{b}{a} x$. The foci are on the transverse axis (in this case, the x-axis) at $(\pm c, 0)$, with c given by the equation $c^2 = a^2 + b^2$.

If the vertices of the hyperbola are on the y-axis, the transverse axis is vertical and the equation is shown at right.

$$\frac{y^2}{b^2} - \frac{x^2}{a^2} = 1$$

A hyperbola centered at (h, k) with a horizontal transverse axis of length $2a$ and a vertical **conjugate axis** of length $2b$ is given by the equation at right.

$$\frac{(x-h)^2}{a^2} - \frac{(y-k)^2}{b^2} = 1$$

The **eccentricity** is a measure of the shape of the curve; the larger the eccentricity, the more quickly the branches spread apart. Again, the formula is $e = \frac{c}{a}$. Since $c > a$, the eccentricity of a hyperbola is always greater than 1.

To shift the center of the hyperbola to (h, k), replace x and y in the equations with $(x - h)$ and $(y - k)$, respectively, and adjust the equations of the asymptotes to go through the point (h, k).

11-117.   Which of the following equations is the equation of a hyperbola? How can you tell? What is the shape of the graph of the other equation? After you have decided on the shapes, quickly sketch the graphs.

a. $\frac{(x-1)^2}{9} + \frac{(y+2)^2}{4} = 1$

b. $\frac{(y-3)^2}{16} - \frac{(x+2)^2}{25} = 1$

11-118.   Decide whether each of the following hyperbolas is oriented horizontally or vertically. That is, decide whether the transverse axis is horizontal or vertical. How can you tell?

a. $\frac{x^2}{10} - \frac{y^2}{5} = 1$

b. $\frac{y^2}{6} - \frac{x^2}{16} = 1$

c. $\frac{(y-2)^2}{10} - \frac{(x-5)^2}{7} = 1$

11-119.   Change the equation $x^2 + 8x + y^2 - 12y = 12$ to graphing form and sketch a graph.

11-120.   Sketch a graph of $y = x^3(x-2)(x+2)^2$.

11-121.   Solve the system at right for (x, y, z).

$$2x + y - 2z = 0$$
$$x - y - 4z = -3$$
$$3x + 2y + 2z = -1$$

11-122.   A parabola passes through the points $(0, 5)$, $(2, 1)$, and $(6, 17)$.

a.   What is its equation?

b.   Where is its vertex?

11-123.   After graphing $y = 12x^3 + 55x^2 - 27x - 10$ on a graphing calculator you can easily see that one x-intercept is $(-5, 0)$. Use this information to find all of the x-intercepts.

11-124.   At McDugal's Golden Parabola, Ramona bought four hamburgers and two milkshakes for \$13.50. Inez bought three hamburgers and one milkshake and spent \$9.25. What is the cost of a hamburger? A milkshake?

11-125.   Solve each ratio problem below for x.

a.   Forty-two percent of x is 112.

b.   Forty-two is x percent of 112.

c.   Twenty-seven is x percent of 100.

d.   Twenty-seven percent of 500 is x.

11.3.1 How can I tell which shape?

Identifying and Graphing Conic Sections

In this section, you will learn how to recognize conic sections from their equations and how to sketch graphs quickly. As you work with your team on today's lesson, think about the questions below.

How can we tell what shape the graph will be?

What do we need to know to sketch a graph quickly?

11-126. Carl Conic, cousin of Polly Parabola, was inspired by the success of Professional Parabola Productions and has decided to open his own business, The Courtly Conics Company. He has hired your team to help train his employees to make the right conics according to customers' orders. He has sent your team the following memo:

> *Dear Study Team,*
>
> *My cousin Polly has told me all about your amazing work! I am pleased to hire you to put together the information that I need for the introductory training brochure for my new company, The Courtly Conic Company.*
>
> *Customers will be ordering their conic sections by sending in equations. I need you to explain to my builders how they can tell what type of conic the equation describes and how they can find all of the information from the equation that they need to build the conic correctly.*
>
> *Please have your training instructions on my desk by the end of the day.*
>
> *Thank you,*
> *Mr. Carl Conic*
> *CEO, The Courtly Conics Company*

Your task: Prepare training materials that explain how to recognize what type of equation represents each conic and how to create an accurate graph when given the equation of a conic. Include the general equations for each of the conics in your materials. Use the following equations as examples for the builders.

$$(x-3)^2 + (y-5)^2 = 9 \qquad y = 4(x-2)^2 + 3 \qquad \frac{(x-3)^2}{5} + \frac{(y+2)^2}{16} = 1$$

$$\frac{(x+4)^2}{4} - \frac{(y-2)^2}{25} = 1 \qquad 3(y-1)^2 - x = 4 \qquad \frac{(y+1)^2}{3} - \frac{(x-4)^2}{4} = 3$$

11-127. Organize your training materials into a pamphlet for the builders' use. Use color, arrows, and other math tools to help make your ideas easy to understand.

11-128. For each equation below, identify the shape of the graph, list all of the necessary information, and sketch a graph.

a. $\dfrac{(x-1)^2}{9} + \dfrac{y^2}{4} = 1$

b. $(x-4)^2 + (y+2)^2 = 25$

c. $\dfrac{(y-2)^2}{36} - \dfrac{(x-3)^2}{9} = 1$

d. $3x + (y-2)^2 = 10$

11-129. Complete the square to change the following equations to graphing form. Then sketch the graph of each equation.

a. $f(x) = x^2 + 4x + 6$

b. $x^2 + 6x + y^2 - 8y = 0$

11-130. Two similar triangles are drawn on a piece of paper. The smaller triangle has an area of 600 square mm and the larger triangle had an area of 960 square mm. If the shortest side of the smaller triangle is 26 mm, how long is the shortest side of the larger triangle?

11-131. Find the equation of the line that is perpendicular to $y = \frac{1}{2}x - 3$ and passes through the point $(10, 14)$.

11-132. For the function $f(x) = \dfrac{\sqrt{x+4}}{2} - 1$, complete parts (a) through (d) below.

a. Sketch the graph and the inverse.

b. Find the equation of the inverse function.

c. Determine the domain and range of the inverse.

d. Compute $f^{-1}(f(5))$.

11-133. Solve each equation below.

a. $2^{(x-1)} = 64$

b. $9^3 = 27^{(2x-1)}$

c. $x^6 = 29$

d. $6^x = 29$

11-134.   A small rocket is launched from five meters below ground level reaches a height of 3
          meters above the ground after 4 seconds. On the way down it is 3 meters above the
          ground after 8 seconds.

    a.   What are three data points?

    b.   Draw a rough sketch of the height of the rocket over time.

    c.   Find the equation of the parabola based on the data.

    d.   When will the rocket hit the ground?

    e.   What is the domain for this function?

    f.   For what part of the domain is the rocket below ground?

11-135.   Solve and check each equation.

    a. $|2x+1| = x+1$ b. $|2x+5| = 3x+4$

11-136.   Given the matrices A, B, and C shown at right, calculate each of the
          following (if possible).

    a. AB b. BA

    c. $2A+C$ d. $AC-A$

$$A = \begin{bmatrix} 2 & 3 \\ -1 & 4 \end{bmatrix}$$

$$B = \begin{bmatrix} 1 & 5 & 2 \\ 6 & 3 & 0 \end{bmatrix}$$

$$C = \begin{bmatrix} -3 & 0 \\ 2 & 3 \end{bmatrix}$$

11.3.2 What if it is not in graphing form?

Graphing Form for Conic Sections

In Lesson 11.3.1, you were able to determine the parameters necessary to sketch a graph because the equations were all given in *graphing form*. But what if they are not given in graphing form?

11-137.   In Chapter 4, you developed a method called **completing the square** to change equations of parabolas and circles to graphing form. With your team, review this method and find the center and radius of each circle below.

     a. $x^2 + y^2 + 8x + 6y - 39 = 0$ b. $x^2 + y^2 = 6x - 2y - 5$

11-138.   Norwood is working on conic sections and is trying to change the equation $3x^2 + 24x + 2y^2 - 12y = 6$ to graphing form. He is confused because the x^2 and y^2 terms have coefficients other than 1. He tried rewriting the equation and got $3(x^2 + 8x) + 2(y^2 - 6y) = 6$.

     a.   Did he make any mistakes so far? Is his equation equivalent to the original equation? How can you be sure?

     b.   He brought the work shown below to his friend Noel, but Noel thinks that he has made a mistake. Noel thinks that he should add 48 and 18 to the right side of the equation instead of 16 and 9. Is Noel correct? Why or why not? What is the correct equation?

$$3(x^2 + 8x + \underline{\quad}) + 2(y^2 - 6y + \underline{\quad}) = 6$$
$$\quad\quad\quad\uparrow\quad\quad\quad\quad\quad\uparrow\quad\quad\quad\uparrow\nwarrow$$
$$+16\quad\quad\quad\quad +9\quad\quad +16\quad +9$$
$$3(x + 4)^2 + 2(y - 3)^2 = 31$$

     c.   With your team, find a way to rewrite this equation in graphing form and determine what kind of conic section it is. Then sketch a graph.

11-139. Norwood and Noel decided to try their new expertise on another problem. This time they started with the equation $4x^2 - y^2 - 40x - 4y + 80 = 0$.

a. They rewrote the equation to look like $4(x^2 - 10x) - (y^2 + 4y) = -80$. Check their work by simplifying this result. Is it equivalent to their original equation?

b. Then they worked together to complete the square. Their work is shown at right. Why did they add 100 and subtract 4 from the right side? Is the new equation still equivalent to the original one? How can you be sure?

$$4(x^2 - 10x + \underline{}) - (y^2 + 4y + \underline{}) = -80$$

$$+25 \qquad +4 \qquad +100 \quad -4$$

$$4(x - 5)^2 - (y + 2)^2 = 16$$

c. Finish rewriting the equation and determine the type of conic section it describes. Then sketch a graph.

11-140. Change each of the following equations to graphing form, identify the conic, and sketch the graph.

a. $9x^2 + 4y^2 - 36x + 24y + 36 = 0$ b. $4x^2 - 16x - y + 21 = 0$

c. $16x^2 - 5y^2 - 64x - 30y = 61$ d. $2x^2 + 2y^2 - 12x - 20y = -58$

11-141. LEARNING LOG

In your Learning Log, explain how to change equations of conic sections to graphing form. Be sure to include examples that show how to incorporate negatives correctly. Title this entry "Changing Equations of Conics to Graphing Form" and label it with today's date.

11-142. Change each of the following equations to graphing form, identify the conic, and sketch the graph.

a. $4x^2 - y^2 - 24x - 10y = 5$ b. $x^2 + y^2 + 10x - 4y = -13$

c. $4x^2 + 9y^2 + 24x - 36y = -36$ d. $3x^2 - 12x - y = -17$

11-143. Write a quadratic equation with roots $x = 3 \pm 5i$.

11-144.   In the summer of 1994, a couple was going through their attic and found a $1000 bond issued by the State of Nevada in 1865. It read, "Pay to the Bearer" (whoever has possession). States issue bonds when they need to borrow money. In 1865, Nevada was a new state and in great need of cash, so it issued this bond at an interest rate of 24% compounded annually.

    a.   Do you think it would have been possible to cash in this bond?

    b.   If $1000 were invested in 1865 at an interest rate of 24% compounded annually, how much would the investment be worth in 1994?

    c.   What is the place value of the first digit in the answer to part (b)?

11-145.   Solve the system at right.

$$\frac{z+y}{4} + \frac{z-y}{2} = 1$$
$$\frac{3z-y}{4} + \frac{4z+2y}{11} = 3$$

11-146.   For each equation, state the amplitude, period, vertical shift, horizontal shift, and sketch two cycles of the graph.

    a. $y = 3\cos(2x)$
                                      b. $y = \cos 2(x + \frac{\pi}{4})$

11-147.   Rewrite each equation as an equivalent equation using $\log_{10}$. You do not need to find a numerical answer. These are sometimes known as **change of base** problems.

    a. $\log_2(3) = x$ b. $\log_5(8) = x$ c. $\log_7(12) = x$ d. $\log_a(b) = x$

11-148.   Use the idea of the previous problem to rewrite $y = \log_4(x)$ so that it could be graphed using a graphing calculator.

11-149.   Solve and check each equation.

    a. $\sqrt{x + 20} = x$
                                         b. $\sqrt{x - 2} - \sqrt{2x + 3} = -2$

11-150.   Logarithms are used to measure the "loudness" of sound. Decibels (dB) are logarithmic units used to descrbe a ratio of two levels of intensity or pressure. The difference between two levels of sound pressure (P_1 and P_2) is defined as $10 \log(\frac{P_1}{P_2})$ dB. Usually, when decibels are used to describe just one sound, it is assumed that that sound is being compared to a reference level of 20 micropascals.

    a.   How many decibels correspond to doubling the pressure of a sound?

    b.   What is the sound pressure of a sound described as 60 dB?

    c.   What does 0 decibels mean?

    d.   How many times more pressure is in a sound of 40 dB than of 20 dB?

$11.3.3$ What do they all have in common?

Quadratic Relations

All of the relations you have been studying are members of the family of **quadratic relations**, which are described by the general equation $Ax^2 + By^2 + Cxy + Dx + Ey + F = 0$.

11-151. Carina figured out that when she makes $C = 1$, $F = -5$, and all other coefficients in $Ax^2 + By^2 + Cxy + Dx + Ey + F = 0$ equal to 0, she gets the equation of a familiar function. What function did she find? Write the equation of her function and sketch a graph.

11-152. QUADRATIC-RELATION INVESTIGATION

Carina now wonders how many types of graphs can be found for the quadratic relations when $C = 0$, and she wants your team's help.

Your task: With your team, **investigate** the set of quadratic relations given by the general equation $Ax^2 + By^2 + Dx + Ey + F = 0$. Find all families of graphs that are possible. Decide as a team what different values to try for each of the coefficients (*A, B, D, E,* and *F*). For each family of graphs that you find, provide an example of an equation and a graph of that relation. Then use your function-investigation questions to complete a thorough **investigation**. Use the following questions to guide your **investigation**.

Discussion Points

How can we change the equation to a more useful form?

How can we tell what the shape will be?

What values should we try for the coefficients? Which should we make negative?

Could it be a function? How can we tell?

11-153.   It will help to work backward by starting with equations in graphing form, then changing them to standard form $Ax^2 + By^2 + Dx + Ey + F = 0$. Describe the graph for each of the following equations and then transform each equation into standard form. Compare the standard forms with their graphing forms and with the other standard forms.

a. $\frac{(x-1)^2}{9} + \frac{y^2}{4} = 1$

b. $(x-4)^2 + (y+2)^2 = 25$

c. $\frac{(y-2)^2}{36} - \frac{(x-3)^2}{9} = 1$

d. $3x + (y-2)^2 = 10$

e.   Write equations in graphing form for a different orientation and/or location for each of the conics, and transform those equations into standard form.

f.   What **general** statements can you make about equations in standard form and their graphs?

―――――――   *Further Guidance*   ―――――――
                section ends here.

11-154.   LEARNING LOG

What are all of the conic sections? What do they have in common geometrically? What do they have in common algebraically? Work with your team to answer these questions and then record your ideas in your Learning Log. Title this entry "Similarities Among the Conic Sections" and label it with today's date.

11-155.   Explain why it is useful to make $C = 0$ in the general quadratic relation $Ax^2 + By^2 + Cxy + Dx + Ey + F = 0$.

11-156.   Find values of A, B, D, E, and F in the equation $Ax^2 + By^2 + Dx + Ey + F = 0$ to create each of the following conic sections.

a.   Line

b.   Point

c.   Circle

d.   Ellipse

e.   Parabola

f.   Hyperbola

11-157. Identify the shape of the graph of each equation below, change it to graphing form (if necessary), and sketch a graph.

   a. $2y^2 - x + 4y + 2 = 0$
          b. $5x + 2y - 10 = 0$

   c. $4x^2 + 4y^2 + 4x - 24y + 21 = 0$
          d. $9x^2 - 16y^2 + 54x - 32y + 29 = 0$

   e. $9x^2 + 4y^2 + 54x - 16y + 97 = 0$
          f. $4x^2 - y^2 + 24x + 36 = 0$

11-158. Let $p = 2 + 5i$ and $q = 3 - 4i$. Calculate the following values and simplify to $a + bi$ form.

   a. $p + q$
      b. $p - q$
      c. $p \cdot q$
      d. $\frac{p}{q}$

11-159. Solve the system of equations at right both graphically and algebraically.

$$x^2 + y^2 = 25$$
$$y = x^2 - 36$$

11-160. Compute the value of each expression below.

   a. $(\frac{\sqrt{2}}{2} + \frac{i\sqrt{2}}{2})^2$
          b. $(\frac{-\sqrt{2}}{2} - \frac{i\sqrt{2}}{2})^2$

   c.   Use the results from parts (a) and (b) above to solve $x^2 = i$ for x. (Find the square roots of i.)

   d.   Locate $\frac{\sqrt{2}}{2} + i\frac{\sqrt{2}}{2}$ and $-\frac{\sqrt{2}}{2} - i\frac{\sqrt{2}}{2}$ on a set of complex axes. What do you notice about their locations?

11-161. Solve and graph each inequality.

   a. $|7 - y| \le 3$
          b. $3|2m + 1| - 1 > 8$

11-162. The graphs of $f(x) = 2x^2 + 5x - 3$ and $g(x) = x^2 + 4x + 3$ are shown at right. Use the graphs to solve:

   a. $f(x) = g(x)$

   b. $f(x) > g(x)$

11.3.4 What do I know about conic sections?

Conic Sections Project

. . . .

In this lesson, you will have a chance to demonstrate your understanding of conic sections by making your own conic section and analyzing it completely.

11-163.   CONIC SECTIONS SCULPTURE PROJECT

How much have you learned about conic sections?

Preparation: To prepare the axes, draw a set of *x*- and *y*-axes on graph paper. To prepare the conic section, first obtain modeling compound and a piece of fishing line from your teacher. Then use the modeling compound to make a cone. Your model will be only part of the "double cone" like the one the class used to create conic sections on the class grapher. Be careful to make your cone regular and to give it smooth sides. When your cone is complete, decide on a slicing angle and carefully slice it with the fishing line. Which conic section have you created?

Your task: Work with your partner to create a stand-alone poster that shows everything you know about your conic section. Be sure to make clear summary statements so that anyone reading your poster can understand your thinking. You will need to place your conic section on your axes and trace it with pencil. Consider the following questions to help you get started.

Discussion Points

Where should we place our shape on the axes?

How can we describe it algebraically? Is there more than one way?

How can we describe it geometrically? Is there more than one way?

Further Guidance

11-164.   As you analyze your conic section, consider the following questions. Note that not all questions apply to all of the conic sections.

- Can you find the foci?
- What is the stretch factor?
- What are the lengths of *a* and *b*?
- What are the equations of the asymptotes (if there are any)?
- What is the equation in graphing form?
- What is the equation in standard form?

- What would be the equation if you rotated the graph 90°? 180°?
- How would the equation change if you shifted the graph?
- Is it a function? If not, could you make it a function? How?
- Is this shape useful for anything in the real world? What?

Further Guidance
section ends here.

11-165. Create an equation and its corresponding graph (in any order) for each of the following conic sections.

    a.   Circle   b.   Line   c.   Parabola

    d.   Hyperbola   e.   Ellipse   f.   Two intersecting lines

11-166. Kiesha graphed $y = x(6 - x)$ in a standard calculator viewing window.

    a.   What is the best name for her graph?

    b.   Jamal has bet Kiesha that with his graphing calculator he can make the graph look like a horizontal line without changing, adding, or deleting functions. Kiesha doesn't think he can do this, but Jamal is sure he can. What **strategy** does Jamal have in mind?

11-167. Find the equation of the line passing through the point $(-2, 5)$ that is perpendicular to the line $y = -5x + 2$.

11-168. Solve the system of equations at right.

$$x^2 + y^2 = 16$$
$$y = x^2 - 4$$

11-169. Multiply and simplify each expression.

    a. $(3 + 2i)(4 + i)$ b. $(2 + 3i)(2 - 3i)$

    c. $(5 - 2i)(5 + 2i)$ d. $(a + bi)(a - bi)$

11-170. Graph at least one full cycle of each graph.

    a. $y = 2 \sin x$ b. $y = \cos (2x)$

    c. $y = -1 + 2 \cos(x)$ d. $y = -1 + 2\sin(x + \frac{\pi}{2})$

11-171.   If $f(x) = x^2 + 7x$, calculate the values described below.

    a. $f(2)$ b. $f(-3)$

    c. $f(i)$ d. $f(-3.5 + 1.5i)$

    e.   Solve $f(x) = 0$.

11-172.   Sketch a graph, $f(x)$, that has the numbers and types of roots for each situation described below.

    a.   5 real roots   b.   3 real and 2 complex roots

    c.   4 complex roots   d.   4 complex and 2 real roots

11-173.   Simplify each expression. Assume the denominator does not equal zero

    a. $\frac{3x+2}{x+2} + \frac{x-5}{2x+4}$ b. $\frac{5}{x^2-4} - \frac{3}{x+2}$

    c. $\frac{2x^2+3x+1}{x^2-4} \div \frac{2x+1}{x+2}$ d. $\frac{x^3-125}{3x^2-13x-10}$

Chapter 11 Closure What have I learned?

Reflection and Synthesis

The activities below offer you a chance to reflect on what you have learned in this chapter. As you work, look for concepts that you feel very comfortable with, ideas that you would like to learn more about, and topics you need more help with. Look for connections between ideas as well as connections with material you learned previously.

①   TEAM BRAINSTORM

With your team, brainstorm a list for each of the following categories. Be as detailed as you can. How long can you make your list? Challenge yourselves. Be prepared to share your team's ideas with the class.

Topics: What have you studied in this chapter? What ideas and words were important in what you learned? Remember to be as detailed as you can.

Connections: How are the topics, ideas, and words that you learned in previous courses connected to the new ideas in this chapter? Again, make your list as long as you can.

MAKING CONNECTIONS

Below is a list of the vocabulary used in this chapter. Make sure that you are familiar with all of these words and know what they mean. Refer to the glossary or index for any words that you do not yet understand.

asymptote	circle	complete the square
cone	conic section	conjugate
directrix	ellipse	equidistant
foci	focus	function
graphing form	hyperbola	intersection
line	locus	major axis
minor axis	parabola	perfect square
plane	point	quadratic
relation	system	standard form
transverse		

Make a concept map showing all of the connections you can find among the key words and ideas listed above. To show a connection between two words, draw a line between them and explain the connection, as shown in the example below. A word can be connected to any other word as long as you can **justify** the connection. For each key word or idea, provide a sketch of an example.

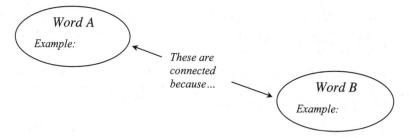

Your teacher may provide you with vocabulary cards to help you get started. If you use the cards to plan your concept map, be sure either to re-draw your concept map on your paper or to glue the vocabulary cards to a poster with all of the connections explained for others to see and understand.

While you are making your map, your team may think of related words or ideas that are not listed above. Be sure to include these ideas on your concept map.

③   SUMMARIZING MY UNDERSTANDING

This section gives you an opportunity to show what you know about certain math topics or ideas.

With your team, make a list of the **big ideas** of this chapter. Discuss the important ideas of the chapter and try to agree on a short list of no more than five big ideas. Be prepared to share your list in a whole class discussion. When the class has reached agreement on a list, continue with parts (a) and (b) below.

a.   Write your own description of each big idea.

b.   For each big idea, provide one or two representative example problems. Solve each problem completely, using multiple representations, if applicable.

Your teacher may give you a "GO" page to work on (or you can download this from www.cpm.org). "GO" stands for "Graphic Organizer," a tool you can use to organize your thoughts and communicate your ideas clearly.

④   WHAT HAVE I LEARNED?

This section will help you evaluate which types of problems you feel comfortable with and which you need more help with. This section will appear at the end of every chapter to help you check your understanding. Even if your teacher does not assign this section, it is a good idea to try these problems and find out for yourself what you know and what you need to work on.

Solve each problem as completely as you can. The table at the end of this closure section has answers to these problems. It also tells you where you can find additional help and practice on similar problems.

CL 11-174. Find the vertices and sketch a graph of each ellipse.

a. $\frac{x^2}{16} + \frac{y^2}{5} = 1$ b. $5x^2 + 4y^2 = 100$

c. $\frac{(x+2)^2}{9} + \frac{(y-3)^2}{4} = 1$

CL 11-175. Find the equation of each ellipse.

a.

b.

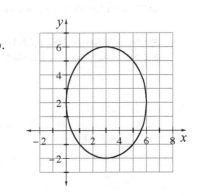

CL 11-176. Using the vertices and slope of the asymptotes as a guide, graph each hyperbola.

    a. $\frac{y^2}{4} - \frac{x^2}{25} = 1$ b. $x^2 - y^2 = 9$ c. $\frac{(x-3)^2}{9} - \frac{y^2}{4} = 1$

CL 11-177. Find the equation of the hyperbola with vertices $(0, \pm 5)$ and asymptotes $y = \pm 2x$.

CL 11-178. Show how to rewrite the equation of the parabola $x^2 + 2x - 8y + 17 = 0$ into the graphing form $(y - 2) = \frac{1}{8}(x + 1)^2$ and then draw the graph.

CL 11-179. For each of the following equations, identify the curve, write the equation in graphing form, and list the following information: center, vertex or vertices, and asymptotes (if there are any).

    a. $2x^2 + y^2 - 4x + 6y - 7 = 0$ b. $3y^2 - x^2 + 12y = 0$

    c. $12x^2 + 8y^2 + 48x - 48y + 24 = 0$

CL 11-180. Find the equation of the parabola that is the set of all points equidistant from the focus $(-3, 1)$ and the directrix $x = -1$.

CL 11-181. Solve each of the following equations, accurate to the nearest 0.001.

    a. $1.8^x = 10$ b. $\log_2 x = 6$

CL 11-182. Find an equation of the parabola that passes through $(2, 11)$, $(-1, -4)$ and $(0, -5)$.

CL 11-183. Sketch a graph of each of the following functions.

    a. $f(x) = \frac{2}{x-1} + 3$ b. $g(x) = -0.5(x + 2)^3 - 3$

    c. $h(x) = |x + 5| - 4$ d. $k(x) = 2\sqrt{x + 1} + 3$

CL 11-184. Find the equation of the exponential function (with an asymptote of $y = 0$) that passes through the points $(-1, 0.6)$ and $(1, 15)$.

CL 11-185. Check your answers using the table at the end of this section. Which problems do you feel confident about? Which problems were hard? Have you worked on problems like these in math classes you have taken before? Use the table to make a list of topics you need help on and a list of topics you need to practice more.

⑤ **HOW AM I THINKING?**

This course focuses on five different **Ways of Thinking**: justifying, generalizing, choosing a strategy, investigating, and reversing thinking. These are some of the ways in which you think while trying to make sense of a concept or attempting to solve a problem (even outside of math class). During this chapter, you have probably used each Way of Thinking multiple times without even realizing it!

Review each of the five Ways of Thinking described in the closure sections of Chapters 1 through 5. Then choose three of these Ways of Thinking that you remember using while working on this chapter. Show and explain where and how you used each one. Describe why thinking in this way helped you solve a particular problem or understand something new. Be sure to include examples to demonstrate your thinking.

Answers and Support for Closure Activity #4
What Have I Learned?

Problem	Solutions	Need Help?	More Practice
CL 11-174.	a. $(\pm 4, 0)$ $(0, \pm\sqrt{5})$ b. $(\pm 2\sqrt{5}, 0)$ c. $(0, \pm 5)$	Lessons 11.2.3 and 11.2.4 Math Notes box in Lesson 11.2.4	Problems 11-81, 11-83, 11-86, 11-99, 11-117, 11-126, 11-128, and 11-153

c. $(-5, 3)$, $(1, 3)$, $(-2, 1)$, and $(-2, 5)$

CL 11-175.	a. $\dfrac{(x+2)^2}{16} + \dfrac{(y-1)^2}{4} = 1$ b. $\dfrac{(x-3)^2}{9} + \dfrac{(y-2)^2}{16} = 1$	Lessons 11.2.3 and 11.2.4 Math Notes box in Lesson 11.2.4	Problems 11-80 and 11-82

Problem	Solutions	Need Help?	More Practice
CL 11-176.	a. b. c.	Lessons 11.2.5 and 11.2.6	Problems 11-110, 11-114, 11-115, 11-116, 11-117, 11-126, 11-128, and 11-153
CL 11-177.	$\dfrac{y^2}{25} - \dfrac{x^2}{6.25} = 1$	Lessons 11.2.5, 11.2.6, Math Notes box in Lesson 11.2.6	Problems 11-112, 11-113, 11-115, and 11-116
CL 11-178.	$8y - 17 = x^2 + 2x$ $8y - 17 + 1 = x^2 + 2x + 1$ $8y - 16 = (x+1)^2$ $8y = (x+1)^2 + 16$ $y = \tfrac{1}{8}(x+1)^2 + 2$	Lesson 11.1.2	Problems 11-20, 11-129, 11-140, 11-142, and 11-157

CL 11-179.	a. ellipse, center $(1,-3)$,
	    vertices $(-2,-3)$, $(4,-3)$, and
	    $(1,-3\pm 3\sqrt{2})$
	    $\dfrac{(x-1)^2}{9} + \dfrac{(y+3)^2}{18} = 1$
	
	b. hyperbola, center $(0,-2)$,
	    vertices $(0,0)$ and $(0,-4)$,
	    asymptotes $y = \pm\dfrac{\sqrt{3}}{3}x - 2$
	    $\dfrac{(y+2)^2}{4} - \dfrac{x^2}{12} = 1$
	
	c. ellipse, center $(-2,3)$,
	    vertices $(-2\pm 2\sqrt{2},3)$ and
	    $(-2,3\pm 2\sqrt{3})$
	    $\dfrac{(x+2)^2}{8} + \dfrac{(y-3)^2}{12} = 1$
		Lesson 11.3.2
		
		Math Notes boxes in Lessons 11.2.4 and 11.2.6
			Problems 11-138, 11-139, 11-140, 11-142, 11-157

Problem	Solutions	Need Help?	More Practice
CL 11-180.	$x = -\frac{1}{4}(y-1)^2 - 2$	Lesson 11.1.2 Math Notes box in Lesson 11.2.2	Problems 11-18, 11-19, and 11-56
CL 11-181.	a. $x \approx 3.917$ b. $x = 64$	Lessons 7.2.1 and 7.2.2 Math Notes box in Lesson 7.2.1	Problems 7-111, 7-133, 7-139, 7-140, 7-223, CL 7-230, 8-84, and 9-62
CL 11-182.	$y = 3x^2 + 2x - 5$	Lesson 7.1.5 Learning Log entry from problem 7-63	Problems 7-62, 7-64, 7-67, 7-72, 7-80, and 7-178
CL 11-183.	a. b. c. d.	Lesson 4.2.1 Math Notes box in Lesson 4.3.2 Parent Graph Tool Kit	Problems CL 4-157, 5-100, and 8-59
CL 11-184.	$y = 3 \cdot 5^x$	Lesson 7.2.3 Checkpoint 15	Problems 7-125, 7-127, 7-164, CL 7-232, 8-21, and 8-68

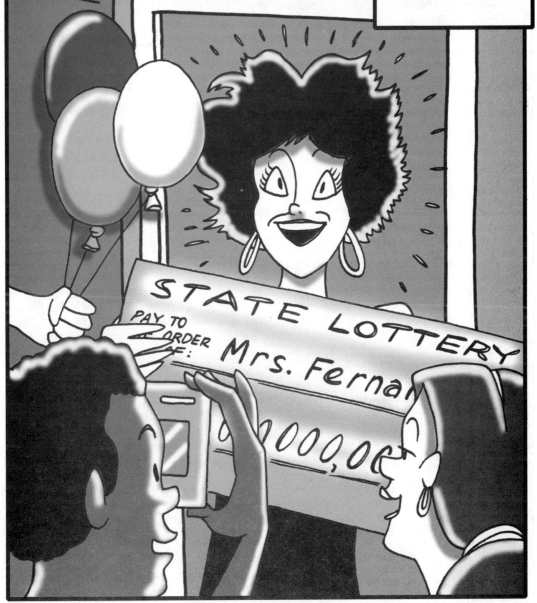

CHAPTER 12   Series

In this chapter you will revisit and add to what you learned about arithmetic and geometric sequences. In Sections 12.1 and 12.3 you will use what you know about sequences and multiple representations to write series and find their sums.

In Section 12.2 you will learn a new way to write a mathematical proof called mathematical induction, and in Section 12.4 you will use what you learned about combinations to develop the Binomial Theorem, which is useful for simplifying some algebraic manipulations, as well as solving some probability problems. In Section 12.5, you will use what you learned about series and the Binomial Theorem to approximate a special number, e, the base of the natural logarithms.

In this chapter, you will learn how to:

➢ Recognize the differences between sequences and series.

➢ Find the sum of an infinite geometric series.

➢ Find sums of arithmetic and geometric series for a known value of n.

➢ Use Pascal's triangle and combinations to rewrite certain algebraic expressions.

➢ Apply the Binomial Theorem to some probability problems.

➢ Find an approximation for e.

➢ Use proof by induction.

Guiding Questions

Think about these questions throughout this chapter:

Is there another way to solve this?

How can I represent it?

How can I **generalize** this?

How can I **justify** this generalization?

Chapter Outline

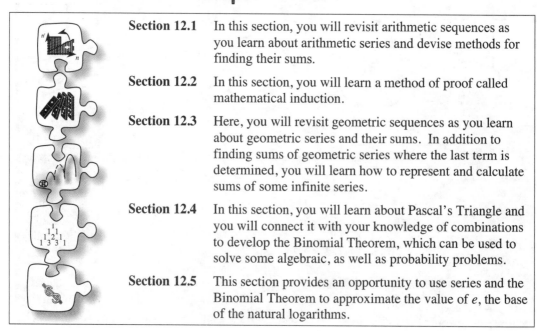

Section 12.1	In this section, you will revisit arithmetic sequences as you learn about arithmetic series and devise methods for finding their sums.
Section 12.2	In this section, you will learn a method of proof called mathematical induction.
Section 12.3	Here, you will revisit geometric sequences as you learn about geometric series and their sums. In addition to finding sums of geometric series where the last term is determined, you will learn how to represent and calculate sums of some infinite series.
Section 12.4	In this section, you will learn about Pascal's Triangle and you will connect it with your knowledge of combinations to develop the Binomial Theorem, which can be used to solve some algebraic, as well as probability problems.
Section 12.5	This section provides an opportunity to use series and the Binomial Theorem to approximate the value of e, the base of the natural logarithms.

12.1.1   How can I find the sum?

Introduction to Arithmetic Series

A popular amusement park notices that the number of people entering the park every minute increases steadily as the morning passes and the time for the park's famous parade approaches. Assuming no one leaves the park, how many people will be in the park by noon to see the parade? Answering this question requires finding the sum of a sequence of numbers, each number representing the number of people for a particular period of time.

Today your team will consider different ways to find the sum of a sequence of terms. As you work, use the following questions to focus and advance your mathematical discussions.

What do the terms (of the sequence) represent? What does the sum represent?

Is there another way to find the sum?

How can we verify our result?

12-1.   JACKPOT FEVER!

Tonight is the long-anticipated drawing for the largest lottery jackpot in the history of your state. Luckily, there is still time to buy a ticket! Because of the growing jackpot, the number of tickets being sold each hour is climbing, as more people are eager to win.

Lottery officials have been monitoring ticket sales carefully. As the morning progresses, the number of tickets sold each hour are listed in the table below.

Number of hours stores have been open	1	2	3
Number of tickets sold during that hour	1,500,000	1,650,000	1,800,000

a.   The drawing will occur 12 hours after the stores open. Assuming that the number of tickets sold each hour will continue to grow at the same rate until the drawing, how many tickets will be sold before the drawing?

b.   If you have not already done so, look for a shortcut to find this sum. What if, instead of 12 hours, the drawing was going to be 37 hours later? How could you find the total number of tickets sold without adding all 37 numbers by hand? Discuss this with your team and be prepared to share your ideas with the class.

c.   When the stores opened this morning, the jackpot was $23,000,000 and each ticket sold increases the jackpot by $1. How big will the jackpot be when the drawing occurs?

12-2. SERIES

In problem 12-1, the total number of tickets sold before the drawing is the sum of an arithmetic sequence, where each term in the sequence represents the number of tickets sold in one hour. When the terms of a sequence are added instead of listed, the result is called a **series**. When a sequence is arithmetic, its corresponding series is called an **arithmetic series**. So, the series in problem 12-1 would be written:

$$1,500,000 + 1,650,000 + 1,800,000 + \ldots + 3,150,000$$

Knowing that there is a difference between arithmetic sequences and series, how can you tell which one to use to represent a situation?

A **matrioska**, a set of Russian nested dolls, can help illustrate the difference. These dolls are special because each doll fills the space inside the doll of the next larger size. When the dolls are placed one-inside-the-other, as in the picture, they are "nested."

a. One way to think of a sequence is as a list of terms that help you relate each term to the other and learn about how the terms are changing. For example, when the dolls are nested, their diameters steadily increase. (Note: Only the top of the innermost doll is shown in the picture.)

If the smallest doll in the diagram has a diameter of 5 cm, and each doll has a diameter that is 1 cm longer than the next-smallest doll, find a sequence that represents the diameters from shortest to longest.

b. If the diameters of the nested dolls can represent a sequence, how could the dolls be arranged so that the sum of their diameters is meaningful? In other words, so a series would be an appropriate representation?

Discuss these questions with your team members and draw a picture of your favorite idea. Then, using the measurements provided in part (a), write the corresponding series and find the sum.

c. Some sets of Russian dolls have as many as 20 dolls! If the diameters (in millimeters) of a set of 20 dolls can be represented with the sequence below, write the corresponding series and find its sum.

$$t(n) = 5 + 3n$$

12-3.   FINDING THE SUM

When an arithmetic series has many terms, finding its sum can be tedious. It is useful to have **strategies** to find the sum other than just adding all the terms together. To look for a **strategy**, consider a new context.

Flo is preparing to run the 100 meter race at her next track meet. Her coach decides to collect data to learn how well Flo is accelerating (speeding up) at the beginning of the race. The sequence below records how far Flo travels during each second of the first six seconds during practice, in meters.

$$1, 3, 5, 7, 9, 11$$

a.   Find the rule, $t(n)$, for the terms of this sequence.

b.   What does the series in this situation represent? What does the total sum represent?

c.   Flo decided to use square tiles below to represent her distance from the starting line as time passed.

She thought it might help to rearrange her tiles to fit a graph, like the one at right. How is her sequence of rates (in meters per second) shown in this graph? How is her series of increasing distances represented?

d.   Using the length and width to find the area of the rectangle in part (c) requires adding all the terms in order to find the length. How can the columns in Flo's graph be rearranged to form one big rectangle so the dimensions can be found without having to add *all* of the terms? Discuss this with your team and be prepared to share your ideas with the class.

12-4. For each arithmetic series graphed below, find the sum. Verify your solution.

a.

b.

c.

d.

12-5. TEAM CHALLENGE

How much information do you need to be able to write an arithmetic series and find its sum? For each arithmetic series described below, work with your team to write the series, find its sum, or both. If it is not possible, explain why not.

a. What if you know that the first term is 18, the last term is 72, and the common difference is 4.5? What is the series? What is the sum?

b. What if you know that the last term is 21, there are 6 terms, and the sum is 336? What is the series?

c. What if you know that the series has 9 terms and the last term is 18? What is the series? What is the sum?

d. What if the third term of an 18-term series is 29 and the terms are increasing by 10? What is the series? What is the sum?

12-6. The 300 people who were lined up outside the amusement park had all entered by 8:15, and by 8:30, 550 more had entered. The number who entered each 15 minutes increased steadily by 250 after that, and all were planning to stay for the parade.

    a. How many people entered between 11:45 and 12:00 noon, just in time for the parade?

    b. Represent the problem as a series and write a formula for the nth term.

12-7. Write a formula for the nth term of each of the following series.

    a. $3+10+17+...$ b. $20+11+2+...$

12-8. If the third term of an arithmetic sequence is 13 and the seventeenth term is –29, what is the eighth term?

12-9. Change the relation below into graphing form, find the locator point (h, k), and sketch a graph of the relation.

$$x = 2y^2 - 12y + 13$$

12-10. Divide. $(x^4 - 7x^2 + 3x + 18) \div (x + 2)$

12-11. Simplify.

    a. $(2 + 3i)(2 - 3i) + (2 + 3i)^2$ b. $\frac{2+3i}{2-3i}$

12-12. Find the sum.

    a. $\frac{a}{b} + \frac{c}{d}$ b. $\frac{a}{b} + \frac{c}{d} + \frac{e}{f}$

12-13. What do you notice about the two problems below when you simplify them?

a. $\dfrac{x^{1/2}}{x^{-3/2}}$

b. $\sqrt{x} \div \left(\dfrac{1}{\sqrt{x}}\right)^3$

12-14. Solve and check your solutions.

a. $\dfrac{4}{m} + \dfrac{3m}{5} = \dfrac{4m+1}{5}$

b. $\dfrac{z}{5} + 4 = \dfrac{3z}{z-2}$

12-15. Use the symmetry of the unit circle and the knowledge that $\cos\frac{\pi}{4} = \frac{\sqrt{2}}{2}$ to write three other true statements using cosine.

12-16. One angle of a triangle measures $70°$ and the opposite side has length of 37.2 feet. Another angle of the triangle measures $30°$. Find the measures of the remaining angle and the two remaining sides of the triangle.

12-17. How many people were in the amusement park in problem 12-6 to watch the noontime parade?

12-18. Chloe wants to place her matrioska dolls in a row on a windowsill that is 92 cm long. Will her entire set of 20 dolls fit if their diameters in *millimeters* are given by the formula $t(n) = 10 + 3n$?

12-19. Find the sum of $1 + 6 + 11 + 16 + 21 + ...$ if the series has 10 terms.

12-20. A series has 9 terms, the last term is 18, and the fifth term is 6. What is the series?

12-21. Is 435 a term in the sequence 3, 11, 19, ...? If so, which term is it? If not, **justify** why not.

12-22. Given the points A (3, 2) and B (–21, 0), determine each of the following.

  a. The slope of the line $\overrightarrow{AB}$.

  b. The length of $\overline{AB}$.

  c. The midpoint of $\overline{AB}$.

  d. An equation of $\overrightarrow{AB}$.

12-23. A cannon shoots a cannon ball into the air. The barrel of the cannon is located six feet above the ground. After two seconds the ball is 102 feet above the ground. After four seconds it is 70 feet above the ground. Find the equation of the parabola that models the path of the cannon ball.

12-24. Factor each of the following expressions completely.

  a. $24x^2 - 14x - 20$

  b. $16x^4 - 1$

12-25. The graph of $y = \frac{1}{x^2}$ is shown at right.

  a. What is the domain of the function?

  b. What is the range of the function?

  c. Solve $\frac{1}{x^2} = 4$

  d. Solve $\frac{1}{x^2} < 4$

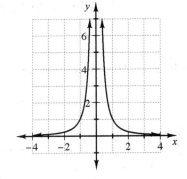

12.1.2 How can I find the sum?

More Arithmetic Series

In Lesson 12.1.1, you explored ways to use a graph of a series to find its sum without adding every term. Can the **strategies** you developed help you find the sum of a series when you do not have a graph? As you work with your team to answer that question, remember to talk together about how to describe a term or series **generally** and to ask each other if the answers you find make sense.

12-26. While trying to find the sum of an arithmetic series, Antonio rearranged the terms so that the last term is combined with the first term, the second-to-last term is combined with the second term, etc. (as shown at right). Use his graph to answer the questions below.

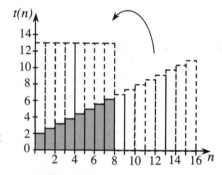

a. How can Antonio be sure that the result of stacking the terms this way will be a rectangle?

b. What is the sum of his series? How do you know?

c. Which terms of the series form the first column? What is the height of this column?

d. Write out Antonio's series.

12-27. With your team, create a series that has an odd number of terms. How could you apply Antonio's method to this series? Be prepared to share your ideas with the class.

12-28. Will Antonio's method work for all arithmetic series? Why or why not? Use an example to explain your conclusion.

12-29. How can Antonio's method be altered to help you find the sum of an arithmetic series without a graph? Work with your team to find the dimensions of the transformed rectangle for each arithmetic series below without graphing the series. Then find the sum.

a. $11 + 18 + 25 + \ldots + 74$

b. 14 terms with $t(1) = 8$ and $t(14) = 151$

c. $t(n) = 6n - 2$, for integer values of n starting at 1 and ending at 25

12-30.   Decide if each situation below involves a series or a sequence and give a reason for your choice. Then answer the question.

a.   Hornets build nests by constructing hexagonal cells around a center, as shown at right. As this hexagonal pattern forms, the first ring of cells has 6 cells, the next has 12, and the next has 18. If a colony of hornets builds 10 rings, how many cells will they have?

b.   Thanks to fundraising, the balance of the math club's savings account grows by $55 each month. The balance during the first month of the school year was $190. At the end of the year, the club's treasurer produced a report showing the balance for each month of the school year. What was the balance after the 8th month?

c.   Starting on his birthday, Evan's allowance increases $0.25 each week. He decides to save his money in order to buy a new πPod, which costs $180. If his allowance on his birthday is $1.50, will he have enough savings by his next birthday to buy the πPod?

12-31.   JACKPOT FEVER RETURNED!

As Ms. Fernandez was standing in line to buy her lottery ticket (see problem 12-1), she noticed that a different state has a jackpot that may go even higher. Then she realized that because of a time difference, it has more hours to grow! She has already predicted that the jackpot in her state will be $50,900,000 when tickets are drawn, and she has to decide quickly if she should buy tickets in the other state.

On a nearby television screen, she sees a news report explaining that the other state started the day with a jackpot of $29,000,000. The news also mentioned that 1,800,000 tickets were sold in the first hour and hourly ticket sales have steadily increased by 20,000 tickets per hour throughout the day. If the drawing in that state occurs 14 hours after stores have opened, which state will have the largest jackpot? Show how you found your answer.

12-32.   With your team, find the sum of the arithmetic series $t(1)+t(2)+t(3)+...+t(n)$?

12-33.   LEARNING LOG

Describe how to find the sum of an arithmetic series in your Learning Log. Be sure to include examples in your description. Title this entry "Arithmetic Series" and label it with today's date.

ETHODS AND MEANINGS

Series

MATH NOTES

The sum of the terms of a sequence is called a **series**. If the terms have a constant difference (meaning that they increase linearly), then it is an **arithmetic series**. If the terms instead have a constant multiplier (meaning that they increase exponentially), then it is a **geometric series**.

Examples of arithmetic and geometric series are shown below.

arithmetic series: $2 + 6 + 10 + 14 + \ldots + (4n - 2)$

geometric series: $1 + \frac{1}{2} + \frac{1}{4} + \frac{1}{8} + \ldots + \frac{1}{2^n}$

Review & Preview

12-34. Examine each of the series below.

Odd numbers: $1 + 3 + 5 + \ldots + 149$

Even numbers: $2 + 4 + 6 + \ldots + 150$

a. Write an expression for the nth term of each series.

b. What is the sum of each series?

12-35. Consider the series $21 + 17 + 13 + \ldots + -99$ as you answer the questions in parts (a) through (c) below.

a. Write an expression for the nth term.

b. How many terms are in the series? How can you tell?

c. What is the sum of this series?

12-36.   Given that $(x+1)$ is one of the factors of $3x^3 - 8x^2 - 5x + 6$, find all of the factors.

12-37.   Simplify.

    a. $(1-i)^2$

    b. $(1-i)^3$

12-38.   Write the expressions in simplest form.

    a. $(9b^{-6})^{-3/2}$

    b. $\frac{x}{(\sqrt{x})^{-1}}$

12-39.   Solve.

    a. $5^{x-3} = 120$

    b. $\log(2x+1) = -1$

12-40.   Use the symmetry of the unit circle and the knowledge that $\sin \frac{\pi}{3} = \frac{\sqrt{3}}{2}$ to write three other true statements using sine.

12-41.   Graph each ellipse.

    a. $5x^2 + 4y^2 = 100$

    b. $\frac{(x-2)^2}{25} + \frac{(y+3)^2}{9} = 1$

12-42.   Twelve horses raced in the CPM Derby. In how many orders could they finish?

12.1.3 How else can I see it?

General Arithmetic Series

So far, you have developed **strategies** that help to find the sum of a given series for a given number of terms. However, what if the possible number of terms is unknown? For example, in the lottery example from Lessons 12.1.1 and 12.1.2, what if the time of the drawing has not yet been set? How can you find a **general** expression that would represent the total number of tickets sold after any number of hours?

As you work with your team today, pay attention to the different ways to study a series. Many of the **strategies** introduced today may be helpful in the future when thinking about the sum of other types of series. When your team finds a new way to "see" the sum of a series, be sure to share the idea with your classmates.

12-43. Consider the series $1 + 2 + 3 + 4 + ... + n$.

a. What is the sum of the first 3 terms? The first 10 terms?

b. What is the sum of the first n terms? That is, find $1 + 2 + 3 + 4 + ... + n$. **Justify** your answer.

c. Legend has it that long ago, when famous mathematician Carl Gauss was a young student, his teacher tried to keep him busy by giving him the task of finding the sum $1 + 2 + 3 + 4 + ... + 99 + 100$. He stunned his teacher and his classmates by finding the sum quickly without assistance. What is the sum?

12-44. In problem 12-43, you found a **general** rule that gives the sum of the first n counting numbers, but what about other types of numbers? For example, what is the sum of the first n odd numbers? Or the first n even numbers? Find rules for both of these cases below. Look for new **strategies** and **justify** your answer.

a. Sum of the first n even numbers: $\quad 2 + 4 + 6 + 8 + ... + 2n$

b. Sum of the first n odd numbers: $\quad 1 + 3 + 5 + 7 + ... + (2n - 1)$

c. Use your rules from parts (a) and (b) to find the sum of the first 100 even numbers and then the sum of the first 100 odd numbers.

12-45. Terrell noticed that if he adds the first terms, second terms, third terms, etc. of the two arithmetic series at right, he gets a brand new series!

original series $\longrightarrow$ $\begin{cases} 1 + 2 + 3 + 4 + ... + n \\ 2 + 4 + 6 + 8 + ... + 2n \end{cases}$

new series $\longrightarrow$ $3 + 6 + 9 + 12 + ... + 3n$

Problem continues on next page. →

12-45.   *Problem continued from previous page.*

   a.   Describe his new series. Is it arithmetic? How many terms does it have?

   b.   Use the expressions for the sums of the original series to find an expression for the sum of the new (resulting) series.

   c.   Is there another way you could have found the expression for the sum of the series $3+6+9+\ldots+3n$? Be prepared to explain your **strategy** to the class.

   d.   If you have not done so already, verify that your **strategy** in part (c) resulted in an expression equivalent to your expression from part (b).

12-46.   In problem 12-45, you used the sums of two different series to find the sum of a new series. How else can the sum of one series be used to find the sum of another series? Consider this as you work on the problems below.

   a.   How can the sum of $1+2+3+4+\ldots+n$ be used to find the sum of $2+4+6+8+\ldots+2n$? Test your idea algebraically using the expressions for the sums of these series.

   b.   How can the sum of $2+4+6+8+\ldots+2n$ be used to find the sum of $1+3+5+7+\ldots+(2n-1)$? Test your idea algebraically using the expressions for the sums of these series.

12-47.   Flo saw the sum of odd numbers from part (b) of problem 12-44 differently. She decided to represent the arithmetic series with the tile pattern below, where the area of each figure is equal to the term of the series.

Fig. 1   Fig. 2   Fig. 3   Fig. 4   Fig. n

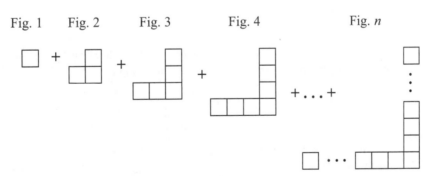

   a.   How many tiles are in the nth term? **Justify** your conclusion.

   b.   What is the sum of the first 3 terms? The sum of the first 5 terms? How can you represent this sum with the tiles?

   c.   What is the sum of the first n terms? Represent the sum algebraically in terms of n and with a diagram with tiles.

   d.   Based on Flo's representation, what is the sum of the first $(n+1)$ odd numbers? **Justify** your answer.

12-48. Use one or more of the series below to create a new series you have not summed before. Then use the algebraic expressions for the sums to generate an expression for the sum of your new series. Be ready to share your new series and explain its sum to the class.

$$1 + 2 + 3 + 4 + \ldots + n$$

$$2 + 4 + 6 + 8 + \ldots + 2n$$

$$1 + 3 + 5 + 7 + \ldots + (2n - 1)$$

MATH NOTES

METHODS AND MEANINGS

Arithmetic Series

An arithmetic sequence can be represented in general by a formula for its nth term:

$$t(n) = a + (n - 1)d$$

The first term (when $n = 1$) is a, and the common difference is d.

An arithmetic series is the sum of the terms of an arithmetic sequence.

$$t(1) + t(2) + t(3) + \ldots + t(k)$$

The total sum of this series can be found by adding the first and last terms, multiplying by the number of terms k and dividing by 2,

$$S(k) = \frac{k(t(1) + t(k))}{2}$$

The sum of a series can be represented with the area in the diagram at right, where each column represents a term of the series.

Note that when the diagram is rearranged as shown, the region becomes a rectangle with a height of $t(1) + t(k)$ and a width of $\frac{k}{2}$.

12-49.   Find the sum of the arithmetic series below.

a. $5 + 10 + 15 + 20 + \ldots + 400$ b. $3 + 8 + 13 + 18 + \ldots + 398$

c. $80 + 74 + 68 + 62 + \ldots + 14$

12-50.   Consider the sequence of multiples of 11 that are less than 100. Write them as a series and find the sum.

12-51.   Lorna is looking at the series $5 + 3 + 10 + 8 + 15 + \ldots + 400 + 398$.

"The sequence definitely isn't arithmetic, but it does have a pattern," Lorna told her team, *"I wonder if we can still find the sum of the series?"*

a.   What patterns do you see in Lorna's series? Describe them as completely as you can.

b.   Do you agree with Lorna's statement that this sequence is not arithmetic? **Justify** your conclusion. Do you think it is still possible to find a sum for the series?

c.   *"I think I see it!"* Lorna exclaimed. *"I think we can separate the terms into the two different arithmetic series shown below, kind of like unzipping a zipper."* Her work is shown below.

$$5 + 10 + 15 + \ldots + 395 + 400$$
$$3 + 8 + 13 + \ldots + 393 + 398$$

How can you use Lorna's two series to find the sum of the original series? State the sum and describe your process.

12-52.   A polynomial graph has a double root at $(-2, 0)$, a single root at $(2, 0)$, and passes through $(-1, 6)$. Find the exact equation of the function.

12-53. Solve each of the following equations without a calculator.

a. $\log_x 17 = 1$

b. $x = \log_4\left(\frac{1}{2}\right)$

c. $\log_4 x = \frac{1}{2}$

d. $\log_3 81 = x$

12-54. Solve $\sqrt{x+18} + 2 = x$ and check for extraneous solutions.

12-55. Solve each equation for $0° \le \theta < 360°$.

a. $2\sin\theta = -1$

b. $\cos^2\theta + 5\cos\theta + 4 = 0$

12-56. If B is the midpoint of $\overline{AC}$, $A = (-3, 2)$ and $B = (5, -2)$, what are the coordinates of point C?

12-57. Ernie and Lisa were trying to find the roots of a quadratic function $g(x)$ by solving $g(x) = 0$. Ernie's answer was $-3 \pm \sqrt{\frac{17}{2}}$; Lisa's answer was $\frac{-6 \pm \sqrt{34}}{2}$. Without using a calculator, show that both answers are equivalent and figure out what their original quadratic function $g(x)$ might have been.

12-58. Write an equation of the ellipse with the given information.

a. x-intercepts at $(\pm 3, 0)$ and y-intercepts at $(0, \pm 6)$.

b. x-intercepts at $(\pm\sqrt{5}, 0)$ and y-intercepts at $(0, \pm 1)$.

12-59. Twelve students will be chosen at random from the 900 students at Rolling Meadows High School to serve as the Judicial Board for minor student infractions.

a. How many different Judicial Boards are possible?

b. Mariko hopes to be on the board. How many possible boards include her?

c. What is the probability that Mariko is chosen for the board?

Algebra 2 Connections

12.1.4 How else can I express it?

Summation Notation and Combinations of Series

In this chapter you have focused your work on arithmetic series represented by graphs, algebraically, and geometrically. Today you will be introduced to a new notation for arithmetic series and you will look at methods for writing equations to find sums.

As you work today, keep the following questions in mind to focus your team discussions:

How does this connect to what we have done before?

How can we simplify it?

How can we describe it?

12-60. Remember the mathematician Gauss, from Lesson 12.1.3, whose teacher tried to keep him busy by asking him to add up the numbers from 1 to 100? Legend has it that Gauss did not show any of his work (shocking!), but he is commonly said to have used a method that starts with the steps below:

$$S = 1 + 2 + 3 + \ldots + 98 + 99 + 100$$
$$S = 100 + 99 + 98 + \ldots + 3 + 2 + 1$$
$$2S = 101 + 101 + 101 + \ldots + 101 + 101 + 101$$

a. Examine his work. What is he doing? Discuss this with your team, and then summarize each step on your paper.

b. How can you simplify his resulting equation to find the sum of the series $1 + 2 + 3 + \ldots + 100$? Show and explain on your paper.

c. How is the process from parts (a) and (b) related to how you have used a graph to find the sum of a series? Discuss with your team and write your conclusions.

d. Show how to use this **strategy** to find the sum of the series below. Show all of your work.

$$S = 2 + 5 + 8 + 11 + \ldots + 59$$

12-61. The series in part (d) of problem 12-60 can also be represented using **summation notation**, as shown below:

$$\sum_{c=1}^{20} (-1+3c)$$

The symbol "Σ" is the Greek letter "sigma," and indicates that the terms generated as c changes from 1 to 20 are summed. The expression $-1+3c$ is the rule for the terms of the series. As you can see in the table at right, when $c=1$, $t(1) = -1 + 3(1) = 2$, and so on. So, as c changes from 1 to 20, the series below appears:

c	$t(c)$
1	2
2	5
3	8
:	:
20	59

$$2+5+8+\ldots+59$$

c is referred to as an **index**, which temporarily represents the term number as the series terms are determined. The same series could be written:

$$\sum_{p=1}^{20} (-1+3p)$$

It is also possible for the series to be written with a different starting value, such as:

$$\sum_{p=0}^{19} (2+3p)$$

a. Use summation notation to represent the series $15 + 19 + 23 + 27 + 31$.

b. Expand the series $\sum_{t=1}^{6} t^2$ and find its sum.

12-62. In problem 12-51 you separated Lorna's complicated series into two different arithmetic series, as shown below.

$$5 + 3 + 10 + 8 + 15 + \ldots + 400 + 398 = 5 + 10 + 15 + \ldots + 400$$
$$+ 3 + 8 + 13 + \ldots + 398$$

a. Write each arithmetic series using summation notation.

b. How could you use your expressions from part (a) to write an expression for Lorna's series using summation notation?

12-63. Find the sum of each arithmetic series described below.

a. $\displaystyle\sum_{t=1}^{10} -5 + 13t$

b.

c. $4 + 10 + 16 + 22 + \ldots + (6n - 2)$

d. $\displaystyle\sum_{t=1}^{30} 10 - 5t$

ⓂETHODS AND MEANINGS

Summation Notation

The capital Greek letter **sigma**, Σ, (equivalent to "S" in English) is used in mathematics as a shorter way to indicate the sum of a series. For example:

$$\sum_{k=1}^{5} (2k - 3) = -1 + 1 + 3 + 5 + 7 = 15$$

Translated, this expression means the sum from $k = 1$ to $k = 5$ of the terms $2k - 3$ equals 15.

Also, the sum of the series $1^2 + 2^2 + 3^2$ can be written $\sum_{k=1}^{3} k^2$.

Note: We call k the **index** and k^2 the **argument** of this summation. The values of the index are consecutive integers only, so the values of k in this second example are 1, 2, and 3.

Review & Preview

12-64.   Write each series in sigma notation and find the sum or an expression for the sum.

   a. $47 + 34 + 21 + ... + (-83)$

   b. $3 + 10 + 17 + ... + (7n - 4)$

12-65.   Use any method to find the sum of the integers from 100 through 1000. Describe your **strategy**.

12-66.   Use algebra to demonstrate that each pair of expressions in parts (a) and (b) below are equivalent.

   a. $\frac{k(k+1)}{2} + k + 1$ and $\frac{(k+1)(k+2)}{2}$

   b. $\frac{k(7k-1)}{2} + 7(k+1) - 4$ and $\frac{(k+1)(7k+6)}{2}$

12-67.   For many years mathematicians tried to come up with a formula to generate prime numbers. One candidate was the expression $n^2 + n + 41$, where n is a positive integer. Try at least 3 or 4 numbers. What do you think of the formula? Does it work? Could you prove it?

12-68.   Write each expression in a shorter form.

   a. $3(7 \cdot 3^{n-1})$

   b. $0.6(10(0.6)^{n-2})$

12-69. Graph each complex number and find its absolute value. Remember that the absolute value of a complex number is the same as its distance from the origin.

    a. $-2i$ b. $-3+4i$ c. $-2-2i$ d. 4

12-70. Without a calculator, estimate the value of $2 \log 50$. Explain your logic clearly.

12-71. What is the solution for the system of equations at right?

$$\frac{7}{13}x + \frac{4}{15}y = 0$$
$$\frac{5}{8}x + \frac{12}{7}y = 0$$

12-72. Brianna is working on her homework and is asked to state the domain and range for $y = \tan\theta$. She enters the equation on her graphing calculator and sets her Xmin to $-\pi$ and her Xmax to 2π. After looking at its graph, Brianna is still unclear how to state the tangent's domain because of the asymptotes.

    a. Explain to Brianna the domain of $y = \tan\theta$ and how to use the graph to make sense of it.

    b. The second part of Brianna's problem asked her to graph the transformed equation $y = \tan(\theta - \frac{\pi}{2})$. As she entered the equation into her graphing calculator, the screen went blank. (Her batteries were dead.) Explain to Brianna how she can use her first graph to sketch her transformed graph $y = \tan(\theta - \frac{\pi}{2})$. Include a labeled sketch.

    c. Does this transformation have a different domain from that in part (a)? If so, how is it different? What is the range for each function $y = \tan\theta$ and $y = \tan(\theta - \frac{\pi}{2})$? Justify your answers completely.

12-73. Use the graph at right to solve $2^x + 1 < 3^x$.

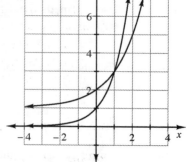

12-74. Find the equation for an ellipse with vertices $(-2, -3)$, $(10, -3)$, $(4, -2)$, and $(4, -4)$.

12-75. Ten points lie on a circle.

    a. How many chords can be drawn using the given points as endpoints?

    b. How many triangles can be drawn using the points as vertices?

12.2.1 How can I prove it?

Mathematical Induction

In Section 12.1, you generated expressions that represented the sums of series with n terms. For example, you determined that the series $1 + 3 + 5 + 7 + \ldots + (2n - 1) = n^2$. But is this expression true for all values of n? How can you be convinced? How can you convince others? Your peers? Your teacher? Other math teachers? A mathematician?

Today, you will develop a new way to convince yourself and others that the sum of an indeterminate series (a series with n terms) is valid for any value of n.

12-76. One way to represent the sum of the series $1 + 3 + 5 + \ldots + (2n - 1)$ is geometrically, using the tile pattern below (from problem 12-44).

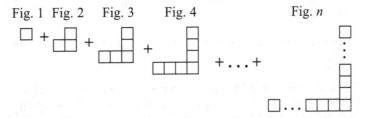

Fig. 1 Fig. 2 Fig. 3 Fig. 4 Fig. n

a. What is the sum of the first n terms of this series? **Justify** your answer.

b. Does the sum you found in part (a) work when $n = 1$? What about for $n = 5$? $n = 8$? For each case, write out the corresponding series and test the expression for the sum.

c. Khalil wonders, *"What if my expression for the sum works for some values of n but not all? It seems to work... but does it always work? How can we show that it must work for all integer values $n \geq 1$?"* Discuss these questions with your team and brainstorm ways to convince yourselves and others that this expression represents the sum of the series $1 + 3 + 5 + \ldots + (2n - 1)$ for all integer values $n \geq 1$.

12-77. PROOF BY INDUCTION

A **proof** is a convincing logical argument. One form of mathematical proof is called **proof by mathematical induction**. This type of argument is used to demonstrate that a conclusion is true for an infinite set of possibilities (such as an infinite number of values of n). Use the questions below to help you understand the logic behind proof by mathematical induction.

Problem continues on next page. →

12-77. *Problem continued from previous page.*

a. In problem 12-70, you demonstrated that $1+3+5+\ldots+(2n-1)=n^2$ when $n=1$, $n=5$, and $n=8$. These demonstrated values can be represented with points on a number line, such as the one below. Is it reasonable to prove that n^2 works for all positive integer values for n by testing them all? Why or why not?

b. What if you know that whenever the relationship $1+3+5+\ldots+(2n-1)=n^2$ is true for one integer value (we call this value k), it always is true for the value that is one larger ($k+1$)? Discuss with your team how you could use this knowledge to help you prove the relationship must be true for all integer values greater than a demonstrated value. The diagram below may help your discussion.

c. If you know that the relationship in part (b) is true, what value of n do you need to test in order to use mathematical induction to prove a relationship is true for all positive integers? Why?

12-78. The core aspect of mathematical induction is proving that whenever a relationship is true for $n=k$, it must be true also for $n=k+1$. This requires starting with an *assumption* that the relationship is true for k in order for it to be proven that the relationship is true for $k+1$. The questions below will help you prove that $1+3+5+\ldots+(2n-1)=n^2$ is true for all $n\geq 1$.

a. This sum of the first k odd numbers can be represented with the diagram below. One way to extend the series to include the $(k+1)^{\text{th}}$ term is to add the $(k+1)^{\text{th}}$ figure to both sides. Study the diagram with your teammates. How many tiles are being added to both sides of the equation? That is, how many tiles does the $(k+1)^{\text{th}}$ figure have?

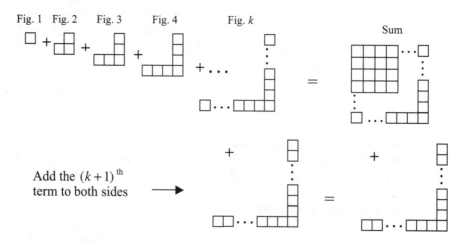

Problem continues on next page. →

12-78.   *Problem continued from previous page.*

   b.   The right side of the sum above can be represented algebraically with $k^2 + (2k+1)$. Does this sum confirm that the expression $1+3+5+\ldots+(2n-1) = n^2$ is true when $n = k+1$? Show how you know algebraically and geometrically.

   c.   Since you found that the relationship is true when $n = 1$ (in part (b) of problem 12-76), and you showed that the relationship is true for $n = k+1$ whenever $n = k$ is true, then what conclusion can you draw?

   d.   Review the Math Notes box in this lesson for more information about mathematical induction. Add an entry in your Learning Log describing the process of induction. Title this entry "Proof by Induction" and label it with today's date.

12-79.   Does this process work for other finite series, such as $1+2+3+\ldots+n = \frac{n(n+1)}{2}$? What if you do not have a geometric representation? Review the process of mathematical induction as you answer the questions below.

   a.   According to the relationship $1+2+3+\ldots+n = \frac{n(n+1)}{2}$, what should be the sum of the first $(k+1)$ terms?

   b.   If you want to prove $1+2+3+\ldots+n = \frac{n(n+1)}{2}$ is true for all natural numbers (that is, all positive integers), for what value of n should you demonstrate the relationship is true first? Discuss this with your team, and then show that the relationship is true for that specific value of n.

   c.   Assume that the relationship is true for some value k. That is, assume the following:
$$1+2+3+\ldots+k = \frac{k(k+1)}{2}$$

With your team, extend the series to include the $(k+1)^{\text{th}}$ term by adding it to both sides of the equation. Then demonstrate that the result on the right is equivalent to the sum of the first $(k+1)$ terms of the series that you found in part (a) above.

   d.   Conclude your proof with a statement of what has been proven. Often, these concluding statements begin with "Therefore … ."

12-80.   Prove the following relationships are true for $n \geq 1$ using mathematical induction.

   a. $2 + 4 + 6 + \ldots + 2n = n(n+1)$

   b. $5 + 8 + 11 + \ldots + (3n+2) = \frac{n(3n+7)}{2}$

   c. $1^2 + 2^2 + 3^2 + \ldots + n^2 = \frac{n(n+1)(2n+1)}{6}$

12-81.   EXTENSION

   In problem 12-48, you generated a unique series and found an expression for its sum. Now, use mathematical induction to prove that the expression you found will find the sum for any $n \geq 1$.

12-82.   Demonstrate that $\frac{3k^2+7k}{2} + 3k + 5$ is equivalent to $\frac{3k^2+13k+10}{2}$.

12-83.   Find the sum of the first 11 terms of the sequence $21, 26, 31, 36, 41, \ldots$

12-84.   Use summation notation to represent the sum of first ten terms of the arithmetic series $2 + 4 + 6 + \ldots$. Then find the sum.

12-85.   Use what you know about series to find the sum of all of the multiples of 7 that are between 0 and 500.

12-86.   Factor each of the expressions below, if possible.

   a. $3x^2 - 18x$ b. $3k^2 + 13k + 10$

   c. $6m^2 - 13m - 5$ d. $9t^2 - 25$

12-87.   Sketch the graph of $f(x) = 5\log(x - 2) + 3$.

12-88.   Find a polynomial function of degree four with roots: $x = -1, 3, \pm\sqrt{5}$.

12-89.   If Michele knows that $\sin(\frac{7\pi}{6}) = -\frac{1}{2}$ and $\cos(\frac{7\pi}{6}) = -\frac{\sqrt{3}}{2}$, how can she use this information to find the exact value for $\tan(\frac{7\pi}{6})$? What is it?

12-90.   Graph each hyperbola.

   a. $x^2 - y^2 = 9$ b. $\frac{(x-2)^2}{4} - \frac{(y+1)^2}{9} = 1$

12-91. The booster club sells meals at basketball games. Each meal comes with a choice of hamburger, pizza, hot dog, cheeseburger, or taco, and a choice of root beer, lemonade, milk, tea, or cola. How many different meals can be made?

12-92. In how many ways can five different French books and three different Spanish books be arranged on a shelf if all the books of one language must remain together?

12-93. Use mathematical induction to prove that the relationship below is true for $n \geq 1$.

$$9 + 14 + 19 + \ldots + (4n + 5) = n(2n + 7)$$

12-94. Examine Kari's proof by induction below.

I know $3 + 6 + 9 + \ldots + 3n = \frac{3}{2}n(n+1)$ is true for $n = 2$ because $3 + 6 = \frac{3}{2}(2)(2+1) = 9$. If I assume that $3 + 6 + 9 + \ldots + 3k = \frac{3}{2}k(k+1)$ is true, then:

$$3 + 6 + 9 + \ldots + 3k + 3(k+1) = \frac{3}{2}k(k+1) + 3(k+1)$$
$$= \frac{3}{2}k^2 + \frac{3}{2}k + 3k + 3$$
$$= \frac{3}{2}k^2 + \frac{9}{2}k + 3$$
$$= \frac{3}{2}(k^2 + 3k + 2)$$
$$= \frac{3}{2}(k+1)(k+2)$$

Therefore, the relationship is true for $n = k + 1$ whenever it is true for $n = k$.

a. What did she prove?

b. How could she adjust her proof so that she can know for sure that the relationship is true for all $n \geq 1$?

12-95. For the sequence: 5, –2, –9, –16, …

a. Find $t(50)$, the 50th term.

b. Find $S(50)$, the sum of the first 50 terms.

12-96. Use summation notation to write this series: $1 + 4 + 7 + 10 + 13 + 16$.

12-97.   Simplify each of the following expressions.

      a. $5(2 \cdot 5^{n-1})$ b. $0.3(1000(0.3)^{n-3})$

      c. $\frac{1}{3}(2(\frac{1}{3})^{n-5})$ d. $r(ar^{n-2})$

12-98.   Describe the possible values of x that would make each of the following statements true.

      a. $\log x > 3$ b. $\log x < 1$ c. $\log 100 < x$ d. $\log_x 27 > 3$

12-99.   Solve the system of equations at right.

$$x^2 + y^2 = 25$$
$$y = x^2 - 13$$

12-100.   Find the exact value for each of the following trig expressions:

      a. $\cos(\frac{3\pi}{4})$ b. $\tan(\frac{4\pi}{3})$ c. $\sin(\frac{11\pi}{6})$

12-101.   For each equation, identify the curve, write the equation in graphing form, state the locator point, and draw the graph.

      a. $2x^2 + y^2 - 4x + 6y - 7 = 0$ b. $3y^2 - x^2 + 12y = 0$

12-102.   How many committees of three juniors and three seniors can be formed from the student government class of eight juniors and 10 seniors?

12-103.   A bag contains four red pens, six green pens, and two blue pens. If three pens are chosen at random, what is the probability that one of each color is picked?

12.3.1 What about geometric series?

Geometric Series

In this lesson you will work with **geometric series** and develop a method for representing and calculating their sums. Being able to find the sum of a geometric series makes it easy to calculate how much a long-term loan will really cost or how much you will end up paying for something when you buy it on credit. As you work with your team on the problems in this lesson, keep the following discussion questions in mind:

Can we use any of the **strategies** we already know?

How can we use what we know about systems of equations?

How can we describe what we have done?

How can we **generalize** what we have done?

12-104.   PICKING A PAYOUT

With a record-setting lottery jackpot projected for noon tomorrow, Hank stood in a very long line to buy a ticket. The man behind him in line tapped him on the shoulder to ask, *"Hey, have you thought about how you'd spend the money if you won?"* Before he could answer, the woman in front interrupted to say, *"First, you have to decide whether you want to get your winnings in one lump sum right away, or if you want to receive them spread out over time. I'm sure one option must be a better deal, but I haven't figured out which one!"*

When Hank got home he immediately went on the Internet and learned that lottery winners do have a choice: receive the winnings in a single payment of 51% of the jackpot right away, or spread payments of the jackpot over 20 years. He also learned that the jackpot is projected to be $50 million! He knew that if he took the single payment he could invest it right away and earn 4% interest on that money.

If he chose to receive the payout over 20 years, the Lottery Commission would invest for him. They guarantee to pay $1,500,000 the first year, and to increase the amount they pay by 5% each year to keep up with inflation.

At lunchtime, Hank called his brother and told him that if his algebra class could figure out the difference between the totals for the two payment methods, he would give that amount to the class if he won the lottery.

a.   If Hank wins the lottery and takes the payments over time, the amounts he will receive each year form a geometric sequence. What is the initial term? What is the growth factor? Write an equation to represent a term in this sequence.

Problem continues on next page. →

12-104. *Problem continued from previous page.*

    b.   If Hank takes the payments over time, how much will his payout in the 20th year be?

    c.   When you add up the terms of this sequence to find the total over 20 years, you are finding the sum for the geometric series. Show the geometric series.

    d.   With your team, discuss finding a **strategy** for calculating the sum without having to calculate and add all 20 terms. Consider the graphical method of creating rectangles that you used with arithmetic series. Would that work for this kind of series? Explain your thinking.

12-105.   While working on a strategy to solve the lottery problem, Luann's team decided to look at an easier sequence and use fewer terms:

$$t(n) = 2 \cdot 5^{n-1}$$

They wrote out the series for six terms, represented the sum of the series as $S(6)$, and then wrote the series in an equation:

$$2 + 10 + 50 + 250 + 1250 + 6250 = S(6)$$

Then Luann remembered the algebraic **strategy** she used for finding the sum of an arithmetic series where she added the sequence to itself, and manipulated the equations. Is there a similar method you can use for geometric series? Work on this as a team. Is there a way to write the equation down twice and then rewrite the second equation to eliminate some of the terms when the two equations are combined?

12-106.   *"I'm sure that this can be simplified,"* Luann reported to her team. *"But when I try to add the series to itself, like we did with the arithmetic series, it just gets bigger, and there's no clear pattern. If I subtract it from itself I'm left with $0 = 0$."*

    a.   What are some techniques for rewriting an equation that you use when solving systems of equations by elimination? Could these techniques be applied in this situation?

    b.   *"Aha!"* Luann almost shouted.

        "Shhh!" her teammate cautioned, *"What have you got?"*

        "Look! I multiplied both sides of the equation by the multiplier." Luann was really excited about the result. How can you use her results and combine the equations to find the sum $S(6)$?

12-107.   Luann wondered if they could use the same method to write an expression for the general sum of any number of terms of the series:

$$2 + 10 + 50 + ... + 2 \cdot 5^{n-1} = S(n)$$

Show how to use her method to write a general expression for the sum. Make a note of what you multiplied by, what was left when you subtracted, and what you finally divided by to get the result.

12-108.   Antonio is working with a new geometric series generated by the equation $t(n) = 30(1.2)^{n-1}$. His sister has challenged him to find the sum of the first 15 terms. He needs your help.

   a.   Show Antonio how he can figure out the sum without adding up all of the terms.

   b.   Antonio knows his sister will not be satisfied with his answer and she will give him another number of terms to add up. Show him how to write a formula for the sum of the terms of this series.

12-109.   PICKING A PAYOUT . . . continued

Look back to your work on problem 12-104. For your convenience, the two payment options are reprinted below. Recall that the jackpot in question is $50,000,000.

Option 1: Receive a single payment of 51% of the jackpot right away. Invest the money and earn 4% interest compounded annually.

Option 2: Receive payments once a year for 20 years. The first payment would be $1,500,000 and the payments would increase by 5% each year.

Your task: Work with your team to determine which is the best way to collect the money. Should Hank take his winnings immediately and invest the money himself? Or should he choose the guaranteed payout each year for 20 years? In which way would he receive the most money? Be prepared to **justify** your decision with explanations and calculations.

Discussion Points

How will the amount increase over time if he invests it himself?

How can we represent the amount he would receive each year algebraically if he chooses the annual payout?

How much will there be in total after 20 years in each situation?

Further Guidance

12-110.   Imagine taking the single payment of 51% of the jackpot.

    a.   How much will you receive?

    b.   If you invest all of the money at a rate of 4% compounded annually, how much can you expect to have after 20 years?

    c.   Is the answer to part (b) the sum of a series?

12-111.   If instead, you choose to take payments spread over 20 years, starting with $1,500,000 in year 1 and growing by 5 percent each year,

    a.   How much money would you receive in year 2? In year 5?

    b.   Write an equation to show how much money you receive in any given year.

    c.   How much money will you have received after 20 years? Be ready to explain your thinking to the class.

12-112.   Which way would you receive more money? How much more? Which way would you choose to receive the funds? Why?

————————   *Further Guidance*   ————————
section ends here.

12-113.   Scott and Greg are looking for summer jobs. Their father, head of the neighborhood beautification committee, says that if they pick up litter from around the neighborhood for a whole day he will pay them $0.15 per piece. Scott realizes that the more litter they pick up the more difficult it will be to find more pieces, so he proposes a different payment scheme. *"How about you give us $0.10 for the first piece, and increase our pay by 2% for each piece after that? Then we'll get paid more for the pieces we work harder to find."*

    a.   Write an equation to generate the series Scott is proposing.

    b.   With Scott's plan, how much will his dad have to pay him for the 100th piece of litter he finds? For the 200th?

    c.   If Scott collects 150 pieces of litter, how much will he have earned in total? What if he picks up 200 pieces?

Problem continues on next page. →

12-113.   *Problem continued from previous page.*

    d.   Greg thinks Scott is crazy to propose an increase of just 2% per piece. After all 2% of 10 cents is just $\frac{2}{10}$ of a cent! Instead, he plans to ask for a one-cent increase for every piece. If their father agrees to this, how much would Greg get paid for the 100th piece he collects? For the 200th piece?

    e.   If the boys each collect 150 pieces of litter, which payment scheme will earn them the most money?

    f.   What if they each pick up a total of 200 pieces?

12-114.   Drought-conscious Darcy is collecting rainwater in order to water her garden through the hot, dry summer. During the last big rainstorm she filled 12 buckets full to the rim! She plans to use one bucket of water each week.

However, Darcy did not count on evaporation. In the sun, each uncovered bucket loses 0.35 gallons of its water volume each week.

    a.   If each bucket starts with 15 gallons in it, how many gallons will be in each of the unused buckets after 2 weeks in the sun? After 7 weeks?

    b.   Is the series arithmetic, geometric, or something else?

    c.   At the end of the 12th week, how many total gallons of water will Darcy have poured on her plants?

12-115.   Hannah is very interested in genealogy, the study of family history. She has traced her family back many years and knows the names of her biological parents, grandparents, great-grandparents, great-great-grandparents, and so on.

    a.   How many people are in each of the first three generations on Hannah's chart? (Assume Hannah herself is the first generation.)

    b.   What kind of sequence does the number of names in each generation form? Is it arithmetic, geometric, or something else? **Justify** your conclusion.

    c.   If Hannah is successful in tracing her true biological ancestors for the last 12 generations, how many names will she have?

12-116.   For each of the problems below, decide if the series is arithmetic, geometric, or
something else. Then, find the sum of the series.

a. $\displaystyle\sum_{t=0}^{15} 5(2)^t$

b. $\displaystyle\sum_{p=1}^{17} (20 - 4p)$

c. $4 + 8 + 12 + \ldots + 392$

d. $\displaystyle\sum_{q=1}^{312} 11q$

e. $2 + 8 + 4 + 10 + 6 + \ldots + 84 + 90$

f. $5 + \frac{10}{4} + \frac{10}{8} + \ldots + \frac{10}{4096}$

12-117.   Lucy is working with a series that has 12 as its first term and is generated by the
expression $t(n) = -9 + 21n$. The sum of her series is 3429. How many terms are in
her series?

12-118.   LEARNING LOG

Write an entry in your Learning Log describing what you learned
during this lesson. Include information about the differences between
geometric sequences and geometric series, and about how to find the
sum of a geometric series. What questions do you have about
geometric series? Title this entry "Geometric Series" and label it with
today's date.

METHODS AND MEANINGS

MATH NOTES

Geometric Series

A geometric sequence can be represented by a formula for its nth term:
$$t(n) = ar^{n-1}$$

The first term, for which $n = 1$, is a, and the common multiplier (or
ratio) is r.

A **geometric series** is the sum of the terms of a geometric sequence:
$$t(1) + t(2) + t(3) + \ldots + t(k)$$

The total can be found by multiplying the last term by the common
multiplier r, subtracting the first term, and then dividing by $r - 1$.

$$S(k) = \frac{r \cdot t(k) - t(1)}{r - 1}$$

12-119.   Antonio and Luann were trying to explain their strategy for finding the sum of a geometric series to their homework group. They decided to generate a sequence that would be easy to add up so they could convince the other students that their **strategy** really worked: $t(n) = 3 \cdot 10^{n-1}$.

a.   The sum of the first six terms of the series is easy to calculate. You can do it in your head. Write out the first six terms and find the sum.

b.   Now explain Luann and Antonio's **strategy** for finding the sum and use your answer to part (a) to check your result.

c.   Represent the first n terms of the series in summation notation, and write an expression for the total sum of n terms.

12-120.   According to the school secretary, the size of the graduating class of Gauss High has steadily increased since it has opened. She claims that the number of graduates each year forms the sequence $t(n) = 30 + 12n$, where n is the number of years the high school has had students graduate. At the end of the year, the administration mails out invitations to all previous graduates to attend the upcoming graduation ceremony.

a.   In this situation, what does a sequence represent? What does a series represent?

b.   After the 10th graduation ceremony, how many total graduates should there be? Explain how you found your answer.

c.   The total number of Gauss High graduates after n years can be represented by the graph at right. If the alumni relations committee wants to invite all graduates to a party to celebrate the nth anniversary of the school, how may invitations will they need to send?

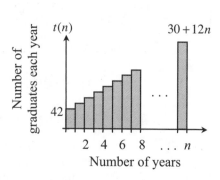

12-121.   Consider the series $8 + 1 + (-6) + (-13) + ... + (-90)$.

a.   How many terms are there?   b.   What is the sum?

12-122.   Evaluate the sum of the series $\sum\limits_{n=3}^{9}(5n)$. Is the series arithmetic or geometric?

12-123.   Find a polynomial function of degree four with roots: $x = \pm i,\, 2 \pm \sqrt{3}$.

12-124.   Solve each of the equations below.

   a. $3^x = 141$ b. $2 \cdot 7^{(x-5)} = 12$

12-125.   Give the exact value(s) for each of the unknowns ($0 \le \theta < 2\pi$) in the equations below.

   a. $\sin(\frac{3\pi}{4}) = ?$ b. $\cos(\frac{5\pi}{4}) = ?$ c. $\tan\theta = 1$ d. $\tan(\theta) = -1$

12-126.   State the domain and range for the sine, cosine and tangent functions. Include a sketch as part of your answer.

12-127.   For each equation below, identify the curve, write the equation in graphing form, state the locator point, and draw the graph.

   a. $12x^2 + 8y^2 + 48x - 48y + 24 = 0$ b. $4x^2 + 4y^2 + 16x - 16y + 22 = 0$

12-128.   A bag contains five green marbles and four white marbles. You pick three marbles, one at a time, without replacing them.

   a.   What is the probability of getting white, another white, and then green?

   b.   What is the probability of getting two white and a green in any order?

12-129.   Joe's dad is only 40, but he's already thinking about retiring. If he retires early at age 55, he will receive an annual pension starting at $30,000 and increasing at a rate of 3% each year to account for inflation. If he waits until he is 65, his pension will be a larger percentage of his salary at that time. He figures that it will be about $60,000 to start and the same 3% increase after that for inflation. He wants to know which plan will pay out the largest total by age 80. Show him how to find out the answer to his question.

12-130.   **RETURN OF THE BOUNCING BALL**

Remember the bouncing ball back in Chapter 2? What if you tossed the ball straight up to a height of 10 meters and then let it bounce 15 times up and down?

a.   How far does the ball travel up and down on the initial toss (before the first bounce)?

b.   If the rebound ratio for the ball is 0.6, write a geometric series to represent the distance it travels up and down by the 15th bounce.

c.   What is the total distance the ball will travel up and down?

12-131.   Ms. Fernandez invested $50,000 of her lottery winnings into two different mutual funds. At the end of one year, both funds together were worth $53, 550. One of the funds had produced a return of 8% while the second fund had produced a return of 6.5%. How much money was invested in each fund?

12-132.   Find the exact value for each of the following trig expressions:

a. $\frac{\sin(\frac{\pi}{3})}{\cos(\frac{\pi}{3})}$

b. $\tan(\frac{\pi}{3})$

c.   Explain the relationship between the answers from part (a) and (b) above.

12-133.   Find the exact value, if possible, for each of the following trig expressions:

a. $\tan(0)$

b. $\tan(\frac{\pi}{2})$

c. $\tan(\pi)$

d. $\tan(\frac{3\pi}{2})$

e. $\tan(2\pi)$

f. $\tan(4\pi)$

g.   Explain each of your answers as it relates the graph of $y = \tan\theta$.

12-134.   In $\triangle ABC$, if $AB = BC$ and $m\angle ABC = 70°$, then what is $m\angle BAC$?

12-135.   Solve the system of equations at right.

$$\frac{x}{4} + \frac{y}{3} = 1$$
$$2x - \frac{y}{3} = 17$$

12-136.   An exponential function has an asymptote at $y = -10$ and passes through the points $(2, 8)$ and $(4, 30.5)$. Find its equation.

12-137.   Prove $5 + 8 + 11 + ... + (3n + 2) = \frac{n(3n+7)}{2}$ by induction.

12.3.2 What if n is very large?

Infinite Series

What if a bouncing ball continued to bounce forever? How far would it travel? Of course we know that the ball cannot bounce forever, but thinking about the possibility has led to some interesting discoveries. If the ball could bounce forever, the distance for each bounce would be getting smaller and smaller as the number of bounces grew larger and larger. Would the total distance continue to grow to be infinitely large?

12-138. HOW FAR IS IT?

While we know that a ball cannot bounce forever, imagine that the ball in problem 12-130 could. Or instead, imagine starting at 0 on a number line and moving according to the following rule: move 20 units to the right, and then continue making moves to the right with each move being 0.6 times as long as the previous move.

Your task: With your team, investigate the question below.

How far along the number line will you travel if you keep going and going and going and … ?

Use what you have learned about geometric sequences and try out different values for n. When your team agrees you have answered the question, make up some new infinite geometric series and **generalize** your results to write a **strategy** for finding sums of any infinite geometric series. Prepare a poster to share your team's findings. Include your examples, **generalizations**, and **justifications**. As you work with your team, keep the following discussion questions in mind:

Discussion Points

What patterns do we see as n increases?

What happens when we multiply or divide by numbers smaller than one?

How can we represent this?

Is there a simpler equivalent expression?

Further Guidance

12-139.   You already calculated the distance for 15 bounces of the ball in problem 12-130. Calculate the distance for 25 moves along the number line and for several larger values of n. What do you notice about the results as you use larger values for n?

12-140.   Calculate the sums of each of the following geometric series for at least two values of n, say $n = 10$ and $n = 30$. What do you notice about the results?

   a. $200 + 100 + 50 + ... + 200(\frac{1}{2})^n$ b. $16 + 24 + 36 + ...16(\frac{3}{2})^n$

   c.   What makes the difference in the results for the series in parts (a) and (b)?

12-141.   Replace $t(n)$ and $t(1)$ in the general formula for the sum of a geometric series with $t(n) = ar^{n-1}$ and $t(1) = a$ in order to rewrite the formula in a more convenient form.

$$S(n) = \frac{r \cdot t(n) - t(1)}{r - 1} = \frac{r(ar^{n-1}) - a}{r - 1}$$

   a.   Rewrite the numerator of the new expression for the sum in a simpler form.

   b.   Multiply both numerator and denominator by -1, and rearrange the terms. Will this new expression be equivalent to the original? How do you know?

   c.   Use the distributive property to rewrite the numerator as a product using a as a factor.

12-142.   Be sure your result for problem 12-141 is equivalent to the equation $S(n) = \frac{a(1-r^n)}{1-r}$.

   a.   In problem 12-138, $a = 20$ and $r = 0.6$. What happens to the value of r^n as you use larger and larger values for n? And what happens to the value of the expression $1 - r^n$? Discuss these questions with your team.

   b.   For infinite series, the formula can be rewritten as shown below. Use this formula to recalculate the sums of the series in problem 12-139 and part (a) of problem 12-140 part (a), if they were to continue without ending.

$$S(n) = \frac{a}{1-r}$$

   c.   Compare your results for part (b) with your original answers and discuss this with your team.

=====   *Further Guidance*   =====
         section ends here.

12-143. LEARNING LOG

Write an entry in your Learning Log describing what you learned during this lesson. Include information about infinite geometric series and their sums. What questions do you have about series? Title this entry "Infinite Geometric Series" and label it with today's date.

ETHODS AND MEANINGS

Infinite Geometric Series

For an **infinite geometric series** with an initial value of a and a multiplier (or common ratio) r, and $0 < |r| < 1$, the sum of the series can be represented:

$$\sum_{n=1}^{\infty} ar^{n-1} = \frac{a}{1-r}$$

For example: When $a = 100$ and the multiplier is $r = 0.2$:

$$100 + 20 + 4 + .8 + \ldots = \frac{100}{1-0.2} = 125$$

Review & Preview

12-144. A hiker decided to spend his days walking around the country. On the first day he walked 25 miles, but on the following days he found he could not keep up that pace. On average he traveled 5% less each day. If he could walk forever, how far would he go?

12-145. Find the infinite sum: $0.9 + 0.09 + 0.009 + 0.0009 + \ldots$.

12-146. Why does the formula for the sum of an infinite geometric series contain the condition that $0 < |r| < 1$?

12-147.　Find the sum of the first five terms of this series: $3 + 1 + \frac{1}{3} + \ldots$

12-148.　Solve and check.

　　a.　$\frac{5}{x-1} = 4 + \frac{x}{2}$　　　　　　　　b.　$2x = \sqrt{10 + 6x}$

12-149.　Consider the table at right for the function $f(x) = \log_b x$.

　　a.　Complete the table.

　　b.　Extend the table to include six more x-values of your choice. Show how you calculated the $f(x)$ values for each.

　　c.　Find the base of this logarithmic function and explain how you found it.

x	$f(x)$
1	
2	0.2702
3	0.4283
4	
5	0.6275
6	
7	0.7587
8	
9	
10	
11	0.9349

12-150.　Let $p = 2 + 5i$ and $q = 3 - 4i$. Calculate each of the following and give your answer in the form $a + bi$.

　　a.　$p - q$　　　　b.　$p \cdot q$　　　　c.　$\frac{p}{q}$　　　　d.　p^2

12-151.　Where is the $\tan\theta$ undefined? Use the unit circle to support your answer.

12-152.　State the sign (+ or −) of the tangent in each quadrant of the unit circle. **Justify** your answer.

12-153.　Prove by induction: $1 + 3 + 5 + \ldots + (2n - 1) = n^2$

12-154.　From a batch of 500 light bulbs, how many ways can three be tested to see if they are defective?

12.4.1 How can I use combinations?

Pascal's Triangle and the Binomial Theorem

In Chapter 10, you explored several kinds of counting problems:

- *Combinations*: counting where order does not matter and results are not repeated,
- *Permutations*: where order does matter, and results are not repeated,
- *Decision charts*: where order matters and results can be repeated, and
- *A fourth kind of problem*: where order did not matter and results could be repeated, which required considering several subproblems.

You also worked on some problems that did not fit any of these categories exactly. Today you will use combinations as a way of thinking about repeated situations involving *two* alternatives: to choose or not to choose. These situations can be viewed as **binomial.**

For example, when you flip a coin five times, for each flip there are two choices, heads or not heads, and a decision chart gives you $2 \cdot 2 \cdot 2 \cdot 2 \cdot 2$ for the total number of outcomes. But if you want to answer the question, "What is the probability of getting exactly three heads?" or "How many ways are there to get exactly three heads?" you need to think about the number of ways three of the five flips can be heads (and the other two are not heads).

Several of today's problems involve binomial situations where two choices are possible for each of several repeated trials, but first you will consider a problem that may appear to be completely unrelated, looking for patterns in Pascal's Triangle.

12-155.   The array of numbers at right is known as Pascal's Triangle. Copy the triangle and add several more rows.

n						
0				1		
1			1		1	
2			1	2	1	
3		1	3		3	1
4	1	4	6		4	1
5	1	5	10	10	5	1

a.   There are many patterns in the triangle, which continues to grow indefinitely. With your team, find and describe as many patterns as you can. You should be able to describe at least three.

b.   Discuss with the class the patterns you found. Write down any patterns your classmates found that your team did not find.

c.   The lone number 1 at the top of the triangle is called Row 0. Add rows to your triangle down to row 10, and describe a rule for writing any new row in the triangle.

12-156. Now consider what may appear to be a completely different problem: the algebraic expansion of the binomial expression $(a+b)^n$. Use what you know about polynomial multiplication to complete parts (a) through (d) below.

    a.   Write $(a+b)^2$ in expanded form. In other words, multiply $(a+b)(a+b)$. How many terms are there in the resulting polynomial? What are the coefficients of the terms?

    b.   Write $(a+b)^3$ in expanded form. How many terms are there and what are their coefficients? What did you do to expand the polynomial? With your team, discuss possible ways to carry out the polynomial multiplication quickly.

    c.   How many terms do you think $(a+b)^4$ will have when expanded? Write it in expanded form. What are the coefficients of these terms?

    d.   Based on the patterns in the preceding problems, discuss with your team a possible short cut for writing the answers for parts a-c without multiplying. Use your method to write out the expansion of $(x+y)^5$.

    e.   Describe a method for using Pascal's Triangle to expand $(a+b)^n$.

12-157. Donna has four bracelets in her wardrobe. They can all be worn together, but each is different from the others. Before she goes to bed at night, she sets out the outfit she will wear the next day, including her accessories. How many different ways can she choose the following: 0 bracelets? 1 bracelet? 2 bracelets? 3 bracelets? 4 bracelets?

    a.   How do these possible combinations compare to the 4th row ($n = 4$) of Pascal's Triangle?

    b.   If Donna bought two new bracelets, how many combinations of four bracelets can she choose for her outfit? How can you figure this out without multiplying or using your calculator?

12-158. The Spirit Club (remember them from Chapter 10), recently got a call from the school executive council. They now have 10 volunteers and will need to choose a three-person committee. They need to calculate $_{10}C_3$, the number of possible committees, but they have no calculator with them.

    a.   Al had a thought: *"I remember that the number of three-person committees you can select from 9 is 84. This would be the number of committees the new volunteer will NOT be on because they would be selected from the other nine members."* How would you calculate this number?

Problem continues on next page. →

12-158.   *Problem continued from previous page.*

    b.   *"And I also know how many committees the new volunteer WILL be on because I can just add his name to each of the two-member committees I had already selected from 9."* How many possible committees would include the new volunteer?

    c.   Without using a calculator (and without multiplying or dividing), explain how Al used parts (a) and (b) to calculate $_{10}C_3$.

    d.   How is this related to Pascal's Triangle?

12-159.   Use Pascal's Triangle to expand $(a+b)^3$.

    a.   Pascal's Triangle can be used to expand any binomial raised to a power. Use it to expand the expression $(2x+3)^3$, by substituting $2x$ for a and 3 for b.

    b.   Now use Pascal's Triangle to expand $(x-1)^5$. What will you need to substitute for a and b?

12-160.   **LEARNING LOG**

Write an entry in your Learning Log explaining Pascal's Triangle and why it is useful. Title this entry "Pascal's Triangle" and label it with today's date.

12-161.   Use Pascal's Triangle to expand $(x+y)^7$.

12-162.   Use the pattern for $(a+b)^3$ to expand $(2x-3)^3$.

12-163.   Use the pattern for $(a+b)^5$ to write the fourth term of $(w-4z)^5$.

12-164.   George starts a chain letter by sending it to four friends who then send it to four more friends and so on. If George counts as round one and his four friends as round two, how many people will have received the letter after round six?

12-165.   Evaluate these infinite geometric series if possible. If it is not possible, explain.

   a. $8 + 4 + 2 + \ldots$

   b. $3 + 9 + 27 + 81 + \ldots$

12-166.   Given the polynomial equation $x^3 - 2x + 1 = 0$, answer the following questions.

   a.   What integer is a clear solution?

   b.   What is a factor of $x^3 - 2x + 1$?

   c.   Solve $x^3 - 2x + 1 = 0$.

12-167.   Solve the equations below.

   a. $(x+2)^2 - (x-2)^2 = 8$

   b. $(x+2)^2 + (x-2)^2 = (2x)^2$

12-168.   Explain everything you know about the tangent, including its relationship to the sine and cosine. Be complete using examples and sketches to support your statements.

12-169.   Explain each transformation below in terms of the parent graph $y = \tan\theta$.

   a. $y = \tan\theta + 1$

   b. $y = \tan(\theta + \frac{\pi}{4})$

   c. $y = -\tan(\theta)$

   d. $y = 4\tan\theta$

12-170.   Suppose $|x| < 1$. Consider the infinite sequence $1 + x + x^2 + x^3 + \ldots$.

   a.   Write an expression for the sum of the sequence.

   b.   What is the result when you use polynomial division to divide 1 by $1 - x$? Show the first five terms of the quotient.

12.4.2 How can I use the Binomial Theorem?

Applying the Binomial Theorem

Knowing the Binomial Theorem not only helps with some algebra multiplication problems, but it can be very useful in solving some probability problems that involve repeated decisions between two alternatives such as True or False, Win or Lose, Heads or Tails, and Hit or Miss.

12-171.   Cheryl is playing a game where she tosses four coins in the air. If she has an equal number of heads and tails, she wins. Below is the sample space of all 16 possible outcomes from the tosses.

HHHH	*HTHH*	*THHH*	*TTHH*
HHHT	*HTHT*	*THHT*	*TTHT*
HHTH	*HTTH*	*THTH*	*TTTH*
HHTT	*HTTT*	*THTT*	*TTTT*

a.   How many ways can Cheryl win? What is the probability that she wins?

b.   The number of ways two heads can be tossed could have been found without the list but instead by using $_4C_2$. How do the 4 and the 2 relate to the problem?

c.   How many ways will the coin tosses result in:

   i.   4 heads?   *ii.*   3 heads?   *iii.*   2 heads?   *iv.*   1 head?   *v.*   0 heads?

d.   How do your results from part (c) compare to Pascal's Triangle?

e.   What is the sum of your answers in part (c)? Why does the result make sense?

12-172.   Cheryl wants to know if she could have a better chance of getting two heads if she tossed five coins.

a.   Help her answer this question by showing her how to calculate the probability.

b.   What if she tossed n coins? What would be the total number of possible results? What would be the probability of two heads?

c.   What is the probability of getting k heads with n coins? ($k = 0, 1, 2, 3, ..., n$)

12-173. Cheryl decided to rewrite her list using a shortcut. When she had three heads and a tail as an outcome, she wrote it as H^3T^1. Her rewritten list is below.

H^4	H^3T	H^3T	H^2T^2
H^3T	H^2T^2	H^2T^2	HT^3
H^3T	H^2T^2	H^2T^2	HT^3
H^2T^2	HT^3	HT^3	T^4

Greg rewrote Cheryl's list as $1H^4, 4HT^3, 6H^2T^2, 4HT^3, 1T^4$. Then they both said, *"Wow, that looks almost like what you'd get if you used H and T for variables and expanded the algebraic expression $(H+T)^4$! How can that be?"*

What would you get if you expanded this expression? Why is the 4th row of Pascal's Triangle a key to the solution of both of these very different problems?

12-174. In his homework assignment, Andrew had to expand $(a+b)^9$. He just realized that he did not have the coefficient for the term a^3b^6. He started writing out the first nine rows of Pascal's Triangle when his friend Robbie said he could find the value using combinations. What combination should Andrew use, and what is the coefficient?

12-175. Rebecca needs to write the 5th term in the expansion of $(a+b)^{11}$.

a. How many terms are in the expansion?

b. What is the 5th term of the expansion? (The term is of the form $\_\_a^7b^4$.)

c. Now Rebecca needs to know the 5th term of $(x-2)^{11}$. How can you use your result from part (b)?

12-176. In problem 12-173, Greg used $6H^2T^2$ to label the number of ways of tossing two heads out of four coin flips.

a. If h is the probability of a coin showing heads, and t is the probability of a coin showing tails, what does $6h^2t^2$ represent when $h = \frac{1}{2}$? How does the result compare to your result in part (a) of problem 12-171?

b. Greg had some trick coins that were weighted so the probability of getting heads was 0.57. What would be the probability of getting two heads using four of Greg's weighted coins?

12-177.   Carrie is the top batter on her softball team. Carrie has a 0.400 batting average, which means she gets a hit 40% of the time (A walk does not count as a time at bat). Carrie comes up to bat 5 times in a game. What is the probability that she will not get a hit?

    a.   If h represents the probability of a hit and m represents the probability of not a hit (an out). Write an expression using h and m that represents the probability of all of the ways that Carrie can get exactly 3 hits in 5 at bats and then calculate the probability.

    b.   Carrie wants to know the probability that she gets at least 3 hits in a game, so she needs to know her probability for 3, 4, or 5 hits. Show her how to calculate the probability of at least 3 hits.

    c.   What is the probability that Carrie gets fewer than 3 hits in a game? You can use your answer to part (b) or calculate this result separately. Discuss which **strategy** to use with your team.

12-178.   Jake was walking across the room carrying 8 dice when he suddenly tripped and the dice went flying. When he went to pick up the dice, he discovered that 5 of them came up 6! What is the probability of rolling exactly 5 sixes with 8 dice?

12-179.   In part (c) of problem 12-172 the probability of getting k heads when flipping n fair coins was represented by $\frac{nC_k}{2^n}$. Using the method of part (a) of problem 12-176, how could you represent the probability of getting k heads when flipping n fair coins? Are the two representations equivalent? Explain why or why not?

METHODS AND MEANINGS

Binomial Theorem

The **Binomial Theorem** can be used to write the expansion of binomial expressions of the form $(a+b)^n$, and to calculate binomial probabilities. For example:

$$(x+3y)^4$$

$$=_4C_4x^4(3y)^0 +_4C_3x^3(3y)^1 +_4C_2x^2(3y)^2 +_4C_1x^1(3y)^3 +_4C_0x^0(3y)^4$$

$$= 1x^4 + 4x^3(3y) + 6x^2(9y^2) + 4x(27y^3) + 81y^4$$

$$= x^4 + 12x^3y + 54x^2y^2 + 108xy^3 + 81y^4$$

In general, $(a+b)^n = {}_nC_na^n + {}_nC_{n-1}a^{n-1}b + {}_nC_{n-2}a^{n-2}b^2 + \cdots {}_nC_1ab^{n-1} + {}_nC_0b^n$.

Probabilities for situations in which there are only two possible outcomes are called **binomial probabilities**. If a and b are binomial probabilities, then $b = 1 - a$.

12-180. Five coins are tossed. What is the probability that exactly two are heads?

12-181. What is the third term of $(2x + \frac{1}{4x})^7$?

12-182. Find the sum of the first six terms of the series $2 + 6 + 18 + 54 + \ldots$.

12-183. Use the pattern for $(a + b)^4$ to expand $(3x + 1)^4$.

12-184. **Challenge:** Use the general form for the Binomial Theorem to show that the sum of the elements of the nth row of Pascal's Triangle is 2^n.

$$_nC_n + {_n}C_{n-1} + {_n}C_{n-2} + \ldots + {_n}C_2 + {_n}C_1 + {_n}C_0 = 2^n$$

12-185. Solve $\dfrac{x}{2x+1} - \dfrac{1-x}{2x-1} = \dfrac{2x+7}{4x^2-1}$ for x.

12-186. Rewrite the expression $(x^{-2} - 5y^{-1})^{-1}$ so that it does not have negative exponents.

12-187. Duong noticed that $_1C_0 + {_1}C_1 = 2^1$. He tried $_2C_0 + {_2}C_1 + {_2}C_2 = 2^2$ and found that it worked also.

   a. Does $_3C_0 + {_3}C_1 + {_3}C_2 + {_3}C_3 = 2^3$?

   b. Does $_4C_0 + {_4}C_1 + {_4}C_2 + {_4}C_3 + {_4}C_4 = 2^4$?

   c. Explain why $_nC_0 + {_n}C_1 + {_n}C_2 + \ldots + {_n}C_n = 2^n$.

12-188. Sketch the graph of $y = 2^{(x+3)}$. Then write the equation of the graph that is four units to the right and five units down from this one.

12-189. You know that $_nC_r = \dfrac{n!}{(n-r)!r!}$ and $_nC_r = \dfrac{_nP_r}{r!}$. Show that the formulas are equivalent.

12-190. In the past, many states had license plates composed of three letters followed by three digits (0 to 9). Recently, many states have responded to the increased number of cars by adding one digit (1 to 9) ahead of the three letters. How many more license plates of second type are possible? What is the probability of being randomly assigned a license plate containing ALG 2?

12.5.1 What is *e*?

The Number *e*

What you have learned in this chapter about sums of infinite series and the Binomial Theorem will help you with this exploration of the number decimal representation of *e* is 2.718281828..., but this is only an approximation. Like π, the number *e* has been proven to be a **transcendental** number, with a decimal representation that continues infinitely and does not form a repetitive pattern. The number *e* is the base of logarithms known as **natural logarithms** and is important in many areas of science as well as in business and economics.

An approximation for *e* resulted from the work of several mathematicians early in the seventeenth century, about the time that John Napier was in the process of developing logarithms. At that time there was tremendous growth in international trade and increasing involvement in financial deals that involved compound interest. In problem 12-191, you will consider a problem that involves compounding interest over shorter and shorter time intervals.

12-191. Tabitha's uncle gave her $10,000 on her thirteenth birthday. She wants to invest it in a college savings fund. The banker tells her that interest rates have dropped to 3%, but at their bank they will compound the interest at any time interval, daily, even hourly, so their customers can still get a good deal. Tabitha decided to make a table to see how good a deal she could get.

    a.   Tabitha knows that a one year compounding period will result in $10000(1 + .03)^1 = \$10300$, and she can get the amount for semiannual periods by dividing the rate by 2 and then squaring to compound, or $10000(1 + \frac{0.03}{2})^2 = \$10302.25$. Make a table for shorter and shorter compounding periods, quarterly, monthly, daily, and hourly.

    b.   What do you notice about the results? Be prepared to share your observations with the class.

12-192. Tabitha was disappointed, but she decided the daily compounding would have to do. Her friend Veronica was more of a dreamer. She asked, *"What if you could earn 100% interest and compound that?"*

"Wow, that should grow fast!" said Tabitha. *"I've got my calculator. Let's just start with one dollar to make it easy, and we can multiply by any initial amount later."*

Veronica added, *"Yes, and that makes our formula easier."*

    a.   What is the easier version of the formula Veronica is thinking of?

    b.   With your team, make a table for at least 12 values of *n*, including some very large ones.

    c.   Did you try 1,000,000? What do you notice as you use larger numbers for *n*?

12-193.   Team Challenge: Investigate the function $f(x) = (1 + \frac{1}{x})^x$.

METHODS AND MEANINGS

MATH NOTES

Compound Interest

The formula for compound interest is generally written:

$$A = P(1 + \frac{r}{n})^{nt}$$

Where A is the total amount of money at any time, P is the principle or initial value, r is the annual rate of interest, t is the number of years, and n is the number of times per year the interest is compounded.

For example, if you invest $5,000 for 20 years at an annual interest rate of 4.8%, compounded monthly:

$$A = \$5000(1 + \frac{0.048}{12})^{12 \cdot 20} = \$5000(1.004)^{240} = \$13,033.50$$

Review & Preview

12-194.   Robin and Teryll each have $8,000 to invest and they disagree about the best place to start a savings account. Teryll found a savings and loan company that will guarantee a rate of 3.9% compounded monthly for the next 10 years. Robin says her bank is much better because they will give her 4% interest compounded semi-annually for the next ten years. In ten years, which account will end up with the greatest amount and how much difference is there?

12-195.   Use the Binomial Theorem to write the expansion of each of the following expressions.

a. $(1 + \frac{1}{n})^3$

b. $(1 + \frac{1}{n})^5$

12-196.   Rewrite the expression on the left side of the equation so that it is the same as the one on the right. Explain each algebraic step you take.

$$\frac{(1 - \frac{5}{y})(3 + \frac{2}{z})}{x} = \frac{(y - 5)(3z + 2)}{xyz}$$

12-197. Prove that the expressions in each of the following pairs are equivalent by showing the algebraic steps needed to rewrite the one on the left so it is the same as the one on the right.

a. $\dfrac{a(a-1)}{7} \cdot \dfrac{1}{a^2}$, $\dfrac{1-\frac{1}{a}}{7}$

b. $\dfrac{x(x-1)(x-b)}{c^2} \cdot \dfrac{1}{x^3}$, $\dfrac{(1-\frac{a}{x})(1-\frac{b}{x})}{c^2}$

c. $\dfrac{n(n-1)}{3!} \cdot \dfrac{1}{n^2}$, $\dfrac{1-\frac{1}{n}}{2!}$

d. $\dfrac{n(n-1)(n-2)}{3!} \cdot \dfrac{1}{n^3}$, $\dfrac{(1-\frac{1}{n})(1-\frac{2}{n})}{3!}$

12-198. Assuming normal conditions, atmospheric pressure P (in lbs. per square inch) can be approximately calculated by using the formula below, where h represents number of feet above sea level.

$$P = 14.7e^{-0.00003h}$$

a. What is normal pressure at sea level?

b. Use the formula to calculate the atmospheric pressure under normal conditions in the mile-high city of Denver, Colorado.

c. The lowest point in Death Valley is 285 feet below sea level. What is the atmospheric pressure in Death Valley under normal conditions?

12-199. You know that the solutions of the general quadratic equation $ax^2 + bx + c = 0$ are

$x = \dfrac{-b \pm \sqrt{b^2 - 4ac}}{2a}$.

a. Find the sum $\dfrac{-b+\sqrt{b^2-4ac}}{2a} + \dfrac{-b-\sqrt{b^2-4ac}}{2a}$.

b. Find the product $\left(\dfrac{-b+\sqrt{b^2-4ac}}{2a}\right)\left(\dfrac{-b-\sqrt{b^2-4ac}}{2a}\right)$.

c. How is the sum of the solutions related to the original quadratic equation?

d. How is the product of the solutions related to the original quadratic equation?

12-200. Use what you just proved about the sum and product of the roots of a quadratic equation, in problem 12-199, to write a quadratic equation for each of the following pairs of roots.

a. $-3+5i$, $-3-5i$

b. $\frac{1}{2} \pm \frac{3}{2}i$

c. $7 \pm \sqrt{3}$

d. $7, -6$

e. $\frac{2}{3}, -\frac{3}{4}$

12.5.2 What is e?

Calculating e and Using Natural Logarithms

The Binomial Theorem provides another way to think about the number e. This particular approach turned out to be very useful because later on it led to some surprising connections with other areas of mathematics.

The beginning of the binomial expansion for $(1+\frac{1}{n})^n$ is written below:

$$(1+\tfrac{1}{n})^n = {}_nC_n(1) + {}_nC_{n-1}(\tfrac{1}{n}) + {}_nC_{n-2}(\tfrac{1}{n^2}) + {}_nC_{n-3}(\tfrac{1}{n^3}) + {}_nC_{n-4}(\tfrac{1}{n^4}) + \ldots$$

In problem 12-201 you will use this expansion to further explore the value of e.

12-201.   From your work in Chapter 10 you learned that there are several ways to represent combinations. One way is to use the formula:

$$_nC_r = \frac{n!}{(n-r)!\,r!}$$

a.   Rewrite each of the first five terms of the expansion for $(1+\frac{1}{n})^n$ using the combinations formula given above. Check with your team to see that you are all coming up with the same results.

b.   Simplify each of the first two terms completely. Then simplify the other terms by using what you know about dividing factorial expressions to reduce them as far as possible.

c.   By rewriting each term one more time, you will have a version that will help you reason about what will happen for infinitely large values of n. Rewrite the third and fifth terms based on the way the fourth term is shown below. Discuss a **justification** for each step with your team, and rewrite the other two.

$$\frac{(n-1)(n-2)}{3!} \cdot \frac{1}{n^2} = \frac{\frac{(n-1)(n-2)}{n^2}}{3!} = \frac{\frac{(n-1)}{n} \cdot \frac{(n-2)}{n}}{3!} = \frac{(1-\frac{1}{n})(1-\frac{2}{n})}{3!}$$

12-202.   In problem 12-201, you should have written the beginning of the binomial expansion of $(1+\frac{1}{n})^n$ as the following expression:

$$1 + 1 + \frac{1-\frac{1}{n}}{2!} + \frac{(1-\frac{1}{n})(1-\frac{2}{n})}{3!} + \frac{(1-\frac{1}{n})(1-\frac{2}{n})(1-\frac{3}{n})}{4!} + \ldots$$

a.   What happens to each factor in the numerators as the value of n gets very large? If n could be infinitely large, what would each numerator equal? Explain your reasoning.

b.   Rewrite the series of fractions, changing the numerators to what they would be if n became an infinitely large number.

12-203.   Euler made the discovery that when n becomes infinitely large $e = \sum\limits_{n=0}^{\infty} \frac{1}{n!}$.

a.   Is this series arithmetic or geometric? Explain why or why not.

b.   Calculate the sum of the first 5 terms and then the sum of the first 7 terms. What do you notice?

c.   Use your calculator to compute the sum $\sum\limits_{n=0}^{12} \frac{1}{n!}$.

12-204.   Consider the function $f(x) = e^x$.

a.   What is its inverse function, $f^{-1}(x)$?

b.   Investigate $f(x)$ and $f^{-1}(x)$.

c.   For what integer values of n is the graph of $f^{-1}(x)$ between the graphs of $y = \log_n x$ and $y = \log_{n+1} x$?

d.   For what values of x is the graph of $f^{-1}(x)$ above each of the graphs in your answer to part (c)? For what values is it below?

12-205.   The use of e provides a shortcut for calculation of continuously compounding interest. The formula for continuous compounding is $A = Pe^{rt}$, where A is the total amount at any time, P is the original principle, r is the rate of interest, and t is the time period.

a.   Use this new formula to calculate the amount Tabitha had after investing her $10,000 for one year at 3% annual interest, compounded continuously. How does this compare with her daily compounding result of $10,304.56?

b.   Suppose a large investment group invested 10 billion dollars at 8% annual interest. Compare the amount they would have in one year if the interest were compounded continuously with the amount they would earn if the interest were compounded daily.

c.   Which investors might benefit from continuous compounding, rather than daily compounding?

12-206. Natural logs and exponential functions in base e are often used in formulas. For many problems you can use either the [LOG] or the [LN] key on your calculator. Solve each of the following problems, first using base 10 logs and then using natural logs.

   a. $10,000(1.08)^x = 20,000$

   b. $30,000(0.8)^x = 15,000$

   c.   Interpret the answer for part (a) if the equation represents an amount of money invested at 8% annual interest.

   d.   Interpret the answer to part (b) if the equation represents the price paid for a car that depreciates at 20% per year.

12-207. Given $\ln 2 \approx 0.69315$ and $\ln 3 \approx 1.0986$, why is $\ln 2 < 1$ and $\ln 3 > 1$? For what value of x does $\ln x = 1$?

12-208. Use the values for $\ln 2$ and $\ln 3$ given in problem 12-207 to evaluate each of the following expressions. Do **not** use a calculator.

   a. $\ln 6$

   b. $\ln 12$

   c. $\ln 16$

   d. $\ln \frac{1}{3}$

12-209. If $p = \ln 2$ and $q = \ln 3$, solve for x in terms of p and/or q.

   a. $e^x = 2^{10}$

   b. $4e^x = 27$

12-210. Omar was 8 years old when he received $25,000 dollars from his grandmother's will. His father invested it for him in a fund that earned 6% annual interest compounded quarterly. He was hoping to see the investment double by the time Omar was ready for college. Another fund offered the same interest rate but the interest would compound continuously. This second fund was a little riskier, however.

   a.   Write an equation to represent each situation.

   b.   Which method of compounding the interest will double his money faster?

   c.   Is the difference in doubling time worth the extra risk?

12-211. The sum of the digits of a two-digit number is 11, and when the digits are reversed the difference between the new number and the original is 27.

    a. If you use t to represent the tens digit, and u to represent the units digit, how can you represent one of the numbers?

    b. How can you represent the number with its digits reversed, still using t and u?

    c. Use the information from the problem and parts (a) and (b) to write two equations that can be used to solve this problem.

    d. What are the two numbers?

12-212. Maia had 130 coins, all nickels, dimes, and quarters, in her change jar. Their value totaled $20.80 and she noticed that there were 15 more dimes than nickels. How many of each type of coin did she have?

12-213. Without a graphing calculator, sketch the graph of $f(x) = x^3 + x^2$.

    a. On another set of axes, sketch the graphs of $g(x) = x^3$ and $h(x) = x^2$ and show how to combine these two graphs to get $f(x)$.

    b. On a third set of axes, sketch the graphs of $p(x) = x^2$ and $q(x) = x + 1$ and show how to combine the graphs to get the graph of $f(x)$.

12-214. Sketch the graph of $g(x) = (x-2)^2 - 1$.

    a. On the same set of axes (in a different color) sketch the graph of $|g(x)| = |(x-2)^2 - 1|$.

    b. On a new set of axes sketch the graph of $g(|x|) = (|x| - 2)^2 - 1$.

    c. Describe how each of the graphs in parts (a) and (b) are related to the original graph of $g(x)$.

Chapter 12 Closure What have I learned?

Reflection and Synthesis

The activities below offer you a chance to reflect on what you have learned in this chapter. As you work, look for concepts that you feel very comfortable with, ideas that you would like to learn more about, and topics you need more help with. Look for connections between ideas as well as connections with material you learned previously.

① TEAM BRAINSTORM

With your team, brainstorm a list for each of the following categories. Be as detailed as you can. How long can you make your list? Challenge yourselves. Be prepared to share your team's ideas with the class.

Topics: What have you studied in this chapter? What ideas and words were important in what you learned? Remember to be as detailed as you can.

Connections: How are the topics, ideas, and words that you learned in previous courses and chapters connected to the new ideas in this chapter? Again, make your list as long as you can.

② **MAKING CONNECTIONS**

Below is a list of the vocabulary used in this chapter. Make sure that you are familiar with all of these words and know what they mean. Refer to the glossary or index for any words that you do not yet understand.

arithmetic	binomial theorem	e
geometric	index	infinite
natural logarithm	Pascal's Triangle	proof by induction
series	sigma	summation notation

Make a concept map showing all of the connections you can find among the key words and ideas listed above. To show a connection between two words, draw a line between them and explain the connection, as shown in the example below. A word can be connected to any other word as long as you can **justify** the connection. For each key word or idea, provide a sketch of an example.

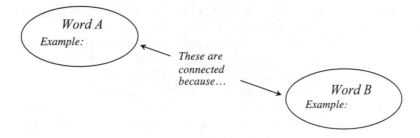

Your teacher may provide you with vocabulary cards to help you get started. If you use the cards to plan your concept map, be sure either to re-draw your concept map on your paper, or to glue the vocabulary cards to a poster with all of the connections explained for others to see and understand.

While you are making your map, your team may think of related words or ideas that are not listed above. Be sure to include these ideas on your concept map.

③   SUMMARIZING MY UNDERSTANDING

This section gives you an opportunity to show what you know about certain math topics or ideas.

With your team, make a list of the **big ideas** of this chapter. Discuss the important ideas of the chapter and try to agree on a short list of no more than five big ideas. Be prepared to share your list in a whole class discussion. When the class has reached agreement on a list, continue with parts (a) and (b) below.

a.   Write your own description of each big idea.

b.   For each big idea, provide one or two representative example problems. Solve each problem completely, using multiple representations, if applicable.

④   WHAT HAVE I LEARNED?

This section will help you evaluate which types of problems you feel comfortable with and which you need more help with. This section will appear at the end of every chapter to help you check your understanding. Even if your teacher does not assign this section, it is a good idea to try these problems and find out for yourself what you know and what you need to work on.

Solve each problem as completely as you can. The table at the end of this closure section has answers to these problems. It also tells you where you can find additional help and practice on similar problems.

CL 12-215. Find the sum of each series.

a. $11 + 12 + 13 + ... + 40$

b. $90 + 84 + 78 + ... + 24$

CL 12-216. For this series: $3 + 3.3 + 3.6 + 3.9 + 4.2 + ... + 63$,

a.   How many terms are there?

b.   What is the sum of the series?

CL 12-217. A rubber ball is thrown 20 feet into the air. If it rebounds $\frac{3}{5}$ of the height, how far will it have traveled after the fifth bounce?

CL 12-218. Write each series using summation ($\sum$) notation.

a. $3 + 9 + 12 + ... + 30$

b. $-7 + -4 + -1 + 2 + 5 + 8 + 11$

CL 12-219. Consider the series $\sum\limits_{n=0}^{\infty} 4\left(-\frac{2}{3}\right)^n$.

        a.   Is it arithmetic or geometric? Explain.

        b.   Does it have a finite sum? Explain.

        c.   If it has a sum, find it.

CL 12-220. Prove by induction: $2 + 4 + 6 + ... + 2n = n(n+1)$

CL 12-221. Use the pattern for $(a+b)^4$ to expand $(2m + \frac{1}{m})^4$.

CL 12-222. What term of $(a-b)^8$ contains a^5? What is the whole term?

CL 12-223. For a certain family, the probability of any child having red hair is 25%. If the family has four children what is the probability that exactly one has red hair?

CL 12-224. Check your answers using the table at the end of this section. Which problems do you feel confident about? Which problems were hard? Have you worked on problems like these in math classes you have taken before? Use the table to make a list of topics you need help on and a list of topics you need to practice more.

⑤   HOW AM I THINKING?

This course focuses on five different **Ways of Thinking**: justifying, generalizing, choosing a strategy, investigating, and reversing thinking. These are some of the ways in which you think while trying to make sense of a concept or attempting to solve a problem (even outside of math class). During this chapter, you have probably used each Way of Thinking multiple times without even realizing it!

Review each of the five Ways of Thinking described in the closure sections of Chapters 1 through 5. Then choose three of these Ways of Thinking that you remember using while working on this chapter. Show and explain where and how you used each one. Describe why thinking in this way helped you solve a particular problem or understand something new. Be sure to include examples to demonstrate your thinking.

Answers and Support for Closure Activity #4
What Have I Learned?

Problem	Solutions		Need Help?	More Practice
CL 12-215.	a. 765	b. 684	Lessons 12.1.1, and 12.1.2 Math Notes box in Lesson 12.1.3	Problems 12-19, 12-29, 12-34, 12-35, 12-49, 12-61, 12-63, and 12-83
CL 12-216.	a. 201	b. 6633	Lesson 12.1.1 Math Notes boxes in Lessons 12.1. and 12.1.3	Problems 12-19, 12-20, 12-29, 12-34, 12-35, 12-49, 12-63, 12-64, 12-83, and 12-121
CL 12-217.	92.224 feet		Math Notes box in Lesson 12.3.1	Problems 12-129 and 12-130
CL 12-218.	a. $\displaystyle\sum_{n=1}^{10}(3n)$	b. $\displaystyle\sum_{n=1}^{7}(3n-10)$	Math Notes box in Lesson 12.1.4	Problems 12-61, 12-62, 12-64, 12-84, 12-96, and 12-119
CL 12-219.	a. Geometric, $r=-\frac{2}{3}$ b. yes, $|r|<1$ c. $\frac{12}{5}$		Math Notes boxes in Lessons 12.1.4 and 12.3.2	Problems 12-138, 12-139, 12-144, 12-145, 12-146, 12-147, and 12-165
CL 12-220.	$2 = 1(1+1) \Rightarrow n = 1$ is true $2 + 4 + \cdots + 2k + 2(k+1) = k(k+1) + 2(k+1)$ $\qquad\qquad\qquad\quad = k^2 + k + 2k + 2$ $\qquad\qquad\qquad\quad = k^2 + 3k + 2$ $\qquad\qquad\qquad\quad = (k+1)(k+2)$ $\qquad\qquad\qquad\quad = (k+1)((k+1)+1)$		Lesson 12.2.1	Problems 12-80, 12-93, 12-137, and 12-153
CL 12-221.	$16m^4 + 32m^2 + 24 + \frac{8}{m^2} + \frac{1}{m^4}$		Lesson 12.4.1	Problems 12-159, 12-162, 12-163, 12-183, and 12-195
CL 12-222.	$-56a^5b^3$		Lesson 12.4.2 Math Notes box in Lesson 12.4.2	Problems 12-174, 12-175, and 12-181
CL 12-223.	$_4C_3(\frac{1}{4})^1(\frac{3}{4})^3 = \frac{27}{64} \approx 0.423$		Lesson 12.4.2	Problems 12-177, 12-178, 12-179, and 12-180

CHAPTER 13   Analytic Trigonometry

In Chapter 8, you began your study of trigonometric functions as you learned about radians and how to transform the graphs of $y = \sin(x)$, $y = \cos(x)$ and $y = \tan(x)$. In this chapter, you will continue your study of trigonometry, this time **investigating** solutions to trigonometric equations. You will learn about three new trigonometric ratios (secant, cosecant, and cotangent) and their corresponding functions.

By the end of this chapter you will be able to solve a wide variety of trigonometric equations and make statements about how many solutions there are and why, based on the unit circle and the graph.

In this chapter, you will:

➤ Learn about the inverse trigonometric functions and relations.

➤ Learn about the reciprocal trigonometric functions.

➤ Recognize the number of solutions to trigonometric equations for a given domain.

➤ Understand solutions to trigonometric equations algebraically, from the graphs of the functions, and based on the unit circle.

➤ Further develop your algebraic manipulation skills as you rewrite trigonometric expressions and equations.

Guiding Questions

Think about these questions throughout this chapter:

When is it true?

How can I rewrite it?

How many solutions are there?

Is it a function?

How can I solve it?

Chapter Outline

Section 13.1   In this section, you will solve trigonometric equations. You will learn about inverse and reciprocal trigonometric functions. You will also learn how to determine the number of solutions a trigonometric equation has.

Section 13.2   Here, you will identify trigonometric identities (statements that are always true). The identities will allow you to rewrite trigonometric equations, which will expand the range of equations that you are able to solve.

13.1.1 When is it true?

True?
When?

Evaluating Trigonometric Equations

Throughout your study of algebra, you have encountered algebraic statements that are always true, sometimes true, and never true. Then, in Chapter 8, you learned about the trigonometric functions $y = \sin(x)$, $y = \cos(x)$, and $y = \tan(x)$. You learned how to represent these functions in a table, on a graph, and with a unit circle. In this chapter, you will expand your understanding of trigonometric functions and develop **strategies** to determine when trigonometric equations are true. Throughout this chapter all answers should be given in radians unless otherwise stated in the problem.

13-1. How can you tell which values of x make an algebraic statement is true? For each of the following statements, work with your team to decide if it is always true, sometimes true, or never true. If it is always true, **justify** how you know; if it is sometimes true, give the exact values of x that make it true; and if it is never true, explain why it is never true.

   a. $5(x - 7) = 5x - 35$

   b. $2x^2 = 50$

   c. $4x - (3x + 2) = x - 7$

   d. $\frac{2}{3}(x - 9) = \frac{3}{4}(2x + 5)$

13-2. WHEN IS IT TRUE?

   Your teacher will assign your team one of the following equations. Your task is to decide whether the equation is always true, sometimes true, or never true, and to **justify** your decision using as many representations as you can.

   • If the equation is always true, **justify** how you know. Then decide how you could change the equation so that it would never be true.

   • If the equation is sometimes true, find the exact values of x that make it true. Then decide how you could change the equation to make it never true.

   • If the equation is never true, **justify** how you know. Then decide how you could change the equation so that it would be sometimes true.

   a. $\sin(x) = \frac{1}{2}$

   b. $\cos(x) = 2$

   c. $\sin(x) = \cos(\frac{\pi}{2} - x)$

   d. $\sin(x) = \sin(\frac{\pi}{2} - x)$

   e. $\tan(x) = 0$

   f. $2\sin(x) = \sqrt{3}$

   g. $\sin(x) = \frac{3}{2}$

   h. $\cos(x) = \sin(\frac{\pi}{2} - x)$

13-3.   Organize your work from problem 13-2 into a poster that will serve as a visual aid for a presentation. Be sure to include all of your **justifications** and reasoning. Use colors, arrows, and other math tools to help make your thinking clear. When you have prepared your poster and presentation, go back to problem 13-2 and evaluate the equations your team did not work on.

13-4.   With your team, discuss the meaning of solutions. Record what you know about the solutions of an equation that are:

a.   Always true.   b.   Sometimes true.

c.   Never true.

13-5.   Decide if each of the following statements are always true, sometimes true, or never true. If a statement is always true, **justify** how you know; if it is sometimes true, give the exact values of x that make it true; and if it is never true, explain why it is never true.

a. $3x - 2 - 4(x+1) = -x - 6$ b. $3x - 5 = 2(x+1) + x$

c. $\sin(x) = \cos\left(\frac{\pi}{2} - x\right)$ d. $\tan(x) = 1$

13-6.   Factor each of the following expressions.

a. $x^2 - 4$ b. $y^2 - 81$ c: $1 - x^2$ d. $1 - \sin^2(x)$

13-7.   Solve for x in each of the following triangles. What methods can be used for finding unknown parts of triangles?

a.   b.   c.

13-8.   Show that $\cos(2x) \neq 2\cos(x)$.

13-9.   Given the function $f(x) = 2 + \sqrt{2x - 4}$, find each of the following.

a.   The domain and range.   b.   The inverse equation.

c.   The domain and range of the inverse.

13-10.   Consider the function $f(x) = 3 \sin (x + \frac{\pi}{2}) - 4$.

      a.   How is its graph different from $f(x) = \sin(x)$?

      b.   Sketch the graph.

13-11.   Find the sum of the integers $-10 + -9 + -8 + ... + 40$.

13-12.   Find the infinite sum (if possible).

      a. $6 + 3 + \frac{3}{2} + ...$ b. $\sum_{k=1}^{\infty} (\frac{1}{3})^k$

13-13.   Graph $\frac{(x-2)^2}{16} + \frac{(y-3)^2}{25} = 1$.

      a.   What are the coordinates of the four relocated intercepts? These points, at the top, bottom, left, and right extremes of the ellipse, are called the **vertices** of the ellipse.

      b.   Choose two of the four points you found in part (a) and substitute their coordinates into the equation to show that they check.

13-14.   If the PEP squad has 12 members, in how many ways can five students:

      a.   Line up for a picture in the school newspaper?

      b.   Be chosen to visit the rival school before the big game?

13-15.   List 3 possible values for h that will make the equation $\cos(x - h) = \sin(x)$ true.

13-16.   If $\pi \leq \theta \leq \frac{3\pi}{2}$, what must be true about the sign of:

      a. $\sin(\theta)$ b. $\cos(\theta)$

      c. $\tan(\theta)$ d. $\frac{1}{\cos(\theta)}$

13-17.   Find all values of a for which the equation $ax^2 + 5x + 6 = 0$ has a solution that is a real number. Express a in terms of one or more inequalities.

13-18.   Using a graph of $f(x) = \cos(x)$ for reference, graph $f(x) = |\cos(x)|$.

13-19.   Factor and reduce the rational expression $\frac{5x+10}{x^2+6x+8}$ to simplify. **Justify** each step.

13-20.   Solve each equation.

    a. $\sqrt{x+7} + 5 = x$ b. $\frac{a}{a^2-36} + \frac{2}{a-6} = \frac{1}{a+6}$

13-21.   Change the angle measures below from radians to degrees or degrees to radians.

    a. $108°$ b. $320°$ c. $\frac{7\pi}{9}$

    d. $\frac{19\pi}{12}$ e. $\frac{17\pi}{2}$ f. $260°$

13-22.   Using the intercepts and slopes of the asymptotes as a guide, graph each hyperbola without using a graphing calculator.

    a. $\frac{y^2}{4} - \frac{x^2}{25} = 1$ b. $x^2 - y^2 = 9$

13-23.   A jar contains five red, four white, and three blue balls. If three balls are randomly selected, find the probability of choosing:

    a.   Two red and one white.   b.   Three white.

    c.   One of each color.   d.   All the same color.

    e.   One red and two white.   f.   Two of one color and one of another.

13-24.   Expand.

    a. $(a+b)^3$ b. $(2m+5)^3$

13.1.2 How many solutions are there?

True?
When?

Solutions to Trigonometric Equations

In Lesson 13.1.1, you recognized that equations can be always true, sometimes true, or never true. In the next few lessons you will focus on trigonometric equations that are sometimes true, as you learn how to solve them and how to determine the number of solutions they have.

13-25.　When is the equation $\cos(x) = \frac{1}{2}$ true?

　　a.　What do the solutions to this equation represent?

　　b.　Solve the equation graphically. How many solutions can you find on the graph?

　　c.　Draw a unit circle showing the solutions to $\cos(x) = \frac{1}{2}$. How many solutions do you see?

13-26.　Just as taking the square root ($\sqrt{\ }$) can be used to undo a square to solve an equation algebraically, there is an undo (inverse) operation for cosine.

　　a.　With your team, see if you can find the undo operation for cosine on your calculator. What does it look like? How can you be sure that it is undoing cosine?

　　b.　Use the undo operation for cosine on your calculator to solve the equation $\cos(x) = \frac{1}{2}$. Show where the solution given by the calculator can be seen on the graph and on the unit circle.

13-27.　With your team, decide how many solutions there are to the equation $\cos(x) = \frac{1}{2}$. **Justify** your decision using as many representations as you can. How can you write all of them?

13-28.　How do all of the solutions to $\cos(x) = \frac{1}{2}$ relate to the one given by $\cos^{-1}(\frac{1}{2})$ on your calculator?

13-29.　Find all of the solutions for each equation below. You may use your calculator, but you must represent your solutions graphically and on a unit circle. After you have found all of the solutions, identify which ones lie in the domain $0 \le x \le 2\pi$.

　　a.　$2\cos(x) + 1 = 0$　　　　　　　　b.　$\tan(x) = 1$

13-30. Jeremy used the $\sin^{-1}$ button on his calculator to solve a trigonometric equation and got the solution $37°$. He knows that there must be more than one solution. What are the rest of the solutions to Jeremy's equation? Explain how you found them. Use a unit circle and a graph in your explanation.

13-31. For each of the following equations, find the solutions that lie in the domain $0 \le x \le 2\pi$.

a. $2\sin(x) - 1 = 0$

b. $2\cos(x) = -\sqrt{3}$

c. $2\sin(x) = \sqrt{2}$

d. $\cos(x) = 1$

13-32. Salina, Tamara, and Traci are working on their homework together. Salina tells her friends that she got $\theta = 52°$ for the inverse cosine problem she is working on and asks if they got the same answer. Tamara says she got $\theta = 128°$, and Traci volunteers her answer of $\theta = 308°$. Is it possible that these are all solutions to the same problem? **Justify** your answer.

13-33. Graph $f(x) = 1 + \tan\left(x - \frac{\pi}{4}\right)$.

13-34. What is the inverse of $f(x) = -x + 6$? **Justify** your answer.

13-35. Simplify then add $\frac{x-2}{x+2} + \frac{2x-6}{x^2-x-6}$. **Justify** each step.

13-36. Josephina thinks that she has discovered a new pattern, shown at right.

$\dfrac{x-1}{x-1} = 1$

a. Check her equations by multiplying. Does her pattern work?

$\dfrac{x^2-1}{x-1} = x + 1$

$\dfrac{x^3-1}{x-1} = x^2 + x + 1$

b, Based on her pattern, what does $\frac{x^5-1}{x-1}$ equal? Is it true? **Justify** your answer.

$\dfrac{x^4-1}{x-1} = x^3 + x^2 + x + 1$

c. Make a conjecture about how to represent the result for $\frac{x^n-1}{x-1}$. You will probably need ", ...," in the middle of your expression.

13-37. From a class of 28 students, how many different four-person study teams can be formed?

13-38. Three light bulbs are chosen at random from 15 bulbs, of which five are defective. What is the probability that:

a. None of the three are defective.   b. Exactly two are defective.

13-39. For the sequence $0.52, 0.55, 0.58, ..., 2.02$:

a. How many terms are there?

b. What is the sum of the associated series?

13-40. Find the equation of each ellipse shown below.

a.

b.
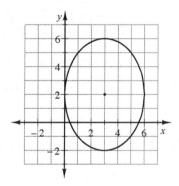

13.1.3 Is it a function?

Inverses of Trigonometric Functions

In Lesson 13.1.2, you learned about using the inverse trigonometric functions to undo operations and solve trigonometric equations. You also learned that the keys for the inverse trigonometric functions on your calculator give you only one of the possible solutions to these equations. In this lesson, you will **investigate** the inverse trigonometric functions more thoroughly. You will determine whether the inverses are also functions.

13-41.   Obtain the Lesson 13.1.3 Resource Page from your teacher.

a.   Make a careful graph of $y = \sin(x)$. Is it a function? What are its domain and range?

b.   Graph the line $y = x$.

c.   Reflect the graph of $y = \sin(x)$ across the line $y = x$ to make a graph of its inverse, $x = \sin(y)$. Is it a function? What are its domain and range?

d: Discuss with your team the restriction you would need to make on the domain of $y = \sin(x)$ so that its inverse is a function.

13-42.   Now graph $y = \sin^{-1}(x)$ on your graphing calculaor. How is the result different from the graph that you made? Does it make sense in terms of your answer to part (d) in the problem above? Highlight the portion of your graph that represents the inverse function and label it with its domain and range. Also highlight the portion of the unit circle provided that shows the restriction on the domain of $y = \sin(x)$ required to make its inverse a function.

13-43.   Consider the equation $\sin(x) = -\frac{\sqrt{3}}{2}$.

a.   How many solutions does the equation have?

b.   Without using a calculator, find the solutions and show them on the unit circle.

c.   Which solution do you predict your calculator will give? How do you know? Once you have made your prediction, use your calculator to solve $\sin(x) = -\frac{\sqrt{3}}{2}$. Were you correct? (Note that this solution can be written as $\sin^{-1}(-\frac{\sqrt{3}}{2})$.)

13-44. Obtain two more copies of the Lesson 13.1.3 Resource Page from your teacher. Sketch $y = \cos(x)$ and $y = \tan(x)$ on separate axes and label the domain and range of each.

a. Reflect each graph across the line $y = x$ to generate graphs of the inverse relations.

b. Find the domain and range of the relations $x = \cos(y)$ and $x = \tan(y)$.

c. Use your graphing calculator to graph the functions $y = \cos^{-1}(x)$ and $y = \tan^{-1}(x)$. Highlight the portion of your graph that represents the inverse function. Find the domain and range for each function. Also highlight the portion of the unit circle provided that it shows the restrictions on the domain required on $y = \cos(x)$ and $y = \tan(x)$ to make their inverses a function.

13-45. For each of the following problems, find all of the solutions without using a calculator. Use a graph or unit circle to support you answers. Then predict the solution that your calculator will give and use your calculator to check your prediction.

a. $2\cos(x) - 1 = 0$ b. $\tan(x) = \sqrt{3}$

c. $2\sin(x) = \sqrt{3}$ d. $4\sin^2(x) - 3 = 0$

13-46. Solve each equation for $0° \le \theta \le 360°$, or if you prefer, $0 \le \theta \le 2\pi$. You may need your calculator, but remember that your calculator only gives *one* answer.

a. $\sin(\theta) = 0.5$ b. $\cos(\theta) = -0.5$

c. $4\tan(\theta) - 4 = 0$ d. $3\sin^2(\theta) = 1$

13-47. State the domain and range for each graph below. Then state whether or not it is a function.

a.   b.

c.   d.

13-48.   Solve each equation. Check for extraneous solutions.

       a. $\sqrt{x+7} = x+1$

       b. $\frac{2}{x+3} - \frac{1}{x} = \frac{-6}{x^2+3x}$

13-49.   Graph.

       a. $(-2, 3, -2)$

       b. $3x - 2y - 3z = -6$

13-50.   Solve each system.

       a. $\frac{x}{2} + \frac{y}{4} = 4$

              $\frac{x}{4} - \frac{3y}{8} = -2$

       b. $x + 2y + z = -1$

               $4x - y - z = -1$

               $-3y = 2z$

13-51.   Divide $(2x^5 - 6x^4 - 2x^2 + 7x - 4) \div (x - 3)$.

13-52.   Find an equation for the ellipse with vertices at $(-4, -5)$, $(1, 7)$, $(6, -5)$, and $(1, -17)$.

13-53.   For the sequence: $7, -2, -11, -20, \ldots$

       a.   Find $t(40)$, the 40th term.

       b.   Find $S(40)$, the sum of the first 40 terms.

13-54.   Find the infinite sum (if possible.)

       a. $8 - 6 + \frac{9}{2} - \frac{27}{8} + -\ldots$

       b. $\sum_{k=0}^{\infty} \frac{1}{8}(2)^k$

13-55.   Hector missed the beginning of this lesson and he is confused about domains for inverse functions. Describe how the domain for each trigonometric function (sine, cosine, and tangent) is restricted in order to find its inverse function, and explain why this restriction is needed.

13-56.   For each of the following problems, find all of the solutions without using a calculator. Use a graph or unit circle to support you answers. Then predict the solution that your calculator will give and use your calculator to check your prediction.

a. $4\sin(x)+2=0$ b. $2\cos(x)=\sqrt{3}$

c. $\tan(x)+1=0$ d. $4\cos^2(x)-4=0$

13-57.   Explain each transformation below in terms of the parent graph $f(\theta)=\tan\theta$.

a. $f(\theta)=\tan\theta+1$ b. $f(\theta)=\tan(\theta+\frac{\pi}{4})$

c. $f(\theta)=-\tan(\theta)$ d. $f(\theta)=4\tan\theta$

13-58.   Quickly sketch each of the following functions.

a. $f(x)=(x-1)^2(x-3)^3(x-5)^2$ b. $g(x)=-(x-1)^2(x-3)^3(x-5)^2$

c.   Express $g(x)$ in terms of $f(x)$.

13-59.   Rewrite each sum below as a single expression.

a. $\frac{1}{2}+\frac{1}{3}$ b. $\frac{3}{2x}+\frac{4}{x^2}$ c. $\frac{x}{x+1}+\frac{3}{x-1}$ d. $\frac{\sin\theta}{\cos\theta}+\frac{1}{\sin\theta}$

13-60.   Rewrite $f(x)=2x^2-4x+1$ in graphing form. State its domain, range, vertex and line of symmetry. Include a labeled sketch as part of your solution.

13-61.   Solve the following equations. Be accurate to three decimal places. Be sure to check your answers.

a. $7=4.2^x$ b. $3x^5=126$ c. $14=2\cdot4^x-10$

13-62.   Expand.

a. $(a+b)^4$ b. $(3m-2)^4$

13-63.   From a new shipment of 100 video games, how many ways can three games be tested to see if they are defective?

13.1.4 What is the reciprocal?

Reciprocal Trigonometric Functions

In this lesson, you will **investigate** the reciprocal trigonometric functions and their graphs.

13-64.   Your team will **investigate** the graph of the reciprocal of $y = \sin(x)$. Obtain a Lesson 13.1.4A Resource Page from your teacher.

　　a.   Using the values on the x-axis as your inputs, complete the table on your resource page and make a careful graph of $y = \sin(x)$.

　　b.   Now you will use the values in your table to help you make a graph of the reciprocal of $y = \sin(x)$, which can be written as $y = \frac{1}{\sin(x)}$. Label the third column in your table $\frac{1}{\sin(x)}$. To find the values that go in this column, calculate the reciprocal of each value for $\sin(x)$.

　　c.   Where are the outputs for $\sin(0)$, $\sin(\frac{\pi}{2})$, and $\sin(\pi)$ located on the graph? What is true about the reciprocal function at these locations in your table? How would they appear on your graph?

　　d.   Now, using a colored pencil, graph $y = \frac{1}{\sin(x)}$ carefully.

　　e.   This ratio that is the reciprocal of sine is named **cosecant**. The cosecant function can be abbreviated by $f(x) = \csc(x)$. Label your graph with its name, "Cosecant."

13-65   Is $y = \csc(x)$ a function?

　　a.   What are its domain and range?

　　b.   What are the intercepts?

　　c.   Are there asymptotes? If so, what are their equations?

　　d.   Describe the relationship between the sine and cosecant graphs.

13-66.   Use your graph to solve each of the following equations in the domain $0 \le x \le 2\pi$. What do you notice about each of the solutions?

a. $\sin(x) = \frac{1}{2}$

b. $\csc(x) = 2$

c. $\sin(x) = 1$

d. $\csc(x) = 1$

e. $\sin(x) = \frac{\sqrt{3}}{2}$

f. $\csc(x) = \frac{2}{\sqrt{3}}$

13-67.   Is there an inverse cosecant button on your calculator? How could you use your calculator to solve $\csc(x) = 3.5$?

13-68.   Obtain the Lesson 13.1.4B and Lesson 13.1.4C Resource Pages from your teacher. Use the same process as you did in problem 13-64 to create graphs of the reciprocal of the cosine function (named **secant** and abbreviated $f(x) = \sec(x)$) and the reciprocal of the tangent function (named **cotangent** and abbreviated $f(x) = \cot(x)$). What are the domains and ranges for these functions?

13-69.   For each of the following equations, work with your team to decide if it is always true, sometimes true, or never true. If it is always true, **justify** how you know; if it is sometimes true, give the exact values of x that make it true; and if it is never true, explain why it is never true. Hint: Use what you have learned above and the idea of rewriting to get started.

a. $\sin^2(x) \csc(x) = \frac{\sqrt{3}}{2}$

b. $\sec^2(x) = \frac{2}{\cos(x)}$

c. $\tan(x) \sec(x) \sin(x) = 0$

d. $\sec^2(x) \cos(x) = 0$

e. $\cos(x) \sec(x) = 1$

METHODS AND MEANINGS

Inverses of Trigonometric Functions

To find an inverse function for a trigonometric function, the domain of the original function had to be restricted. For each function the restriction is different.

For sine, restricting the domain to $-\frac{\pi}{2} \le x \le \frac{\pi}{2}$ leads to the inverse function, $y = \sin^{-1} x$ with domain $-1 \le x \le 1$ and range $-\frac{\pi}{2} \le y \le \frac{\pi}{2}$.

For cosine, restricting the domain to $0 \le x \le \pi$ gives a good piece of the graph close to the origin, and gives an inverse function $y = \cos^{-1} x$, with domain $-1 \le x \le 1$ and range $0 \le y \le \pi$.

For tangent, the restriction is $-\frac{\pi}{2} < x < \frac{\pi}{2}$, so the domain for the inverse tangent $y = \tan^{-1} x$ is all real numbers and the range is $-\frac{\pi}{2} < y < \frac{\pi}{2}$.

13-70. Using the triangle on the right, find:

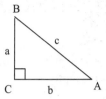

 a. $\sin A$ b. $\sec A$

 c. $\csc B$ d. $\tan B$

13-71. Solve each equation below for x if $-2\pi \le x \le 2\pi$.

 a. $4\sin^2(x) = 1$ b. $3\tan^2(x) = 1$

13-72. Solve $2\sin(x)\cos(x) + \cos(x) = 0$. Give your answers in degrees or radians.

13-73. Solve for x in the figure at right.

13-74. If the cost of a CD now averages $15.95 and in 4 years will cost $21.95, what is the annual multiplier and the annual percent increase?

13-75. Multiply the expressions in parts (a) through (d).

 a. $(a+b)(a^2 - ab + b^2)$ b. $(x-2)(x^2 + 2x + 4)$

 c. $(y+5)(y^2 - 5y + 25)$ d. $(x-y)(x^2 + xy + y^2)$

 e. What did you notice about these products?

 f. Make up another multiplication problem that will follow the same pattern.

13-76. Parts (a) through (d) of problem 13-75 represent a general pattern known as the **sum and difference of cubes**. Use this pattern to factor each of the following polynomials.

 a. $x^3 + y^3$ b. $x^3 - 27$ c. $8x^3 - y^3$ d. $x^3 + 1$

 e. Make up another problem involving the sum or difference of cubes and show how to factor it.

13-77.   Find the equation of a cubic function that has $y = x^3$ as its parent graph, a locator point at $(-6,-10)$, and passes through the origin.

13-78.   For each of the following equations, identify the curve, write the equation in graphing form, and describe any of the following terms that apply: center, vertex or vertices, and asymptotes.

   a. $9x^2 - 16y^2 - 32y = 160$ b. $y^2 - 2y + 3x = 5$

   c. $16 + 6x - x^2 - y^2 = 0$

13-79.   Find the equation of a hyperbola with vertices $(0, \pm 7)$ and asymptotes $y = \pm 2x$.

13-80.   From the 13 spades in a deck of cards, four are selected. Find the probability that:

   a.   Exactly one card is a "face" card (Jack, Queen, or King).

   b.   The cards form a sequence (A, 2, 3, 4; 2, 3, 4, 5; ...; J, Q, K, A).

13-81.   Using the triangle on the right, find:

   a.   sec B b.   tan A

   c.   cot A d.   csc A

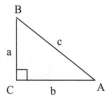

13-82.   Solve $2\sin(x)\cos(x) - \sin(x) = 0$ in the domain $0 \le x \le 2\pi$. Give answers in degrees or radians.

13-83.   If $f(x) = 2x^2 - 3$ and $g(x) = x + 1$, find $f(g(x))$.

13-84.   Without using a calculator, simplify and evaluate each of the following log expressions. Your result should be an expression without logarithms.

   a. $\log(4) + \log(25)$ b. $\dfrac{7^{\log_7(3)}}{\log_5 5^4}$

13-85.   Use the sum or difference of cubes and what you already know about factoring to factor the following expressions as completely as possible.

a. $x^5 + 8x^2y^3$

b. $8y^6 - 125x^3$

c. $x^6 - y^6$ (Note: This is tricky. If you start it as the difference of two cubes, you will not be able to factor it completely. Think of it as the difference of two squares and then factor the factors as the sum and difference of two cubes.)

13-86.   Write an equation for the curve at right. Then sketch the graph of the inverse of this graph and write its equation.

13-87.   An exponential function has an asymptote at $y = 5$ and passes through the points $(2, 5.64)$ and $(-1, 15)$. Find the equation of the function.

13-88.   What is the fifth term of each expansion?

a. $(a+b)^9$

b. $(2x+y)^8$

13-89.   Sure Shot Jane can hit the bull's eye with a bow and arrow 90% of the time. If she shoots five arrows, what is the probability that three or more arrows hit the bull's eye?

13.2.1 How can I rewrite it?

Trigonometric Identities

To solve many trigonometric equations, it is first necessary to rewrite the equation in a simpler form. In this lesson, you will solve trigonometric equations graphically and will develop methods for rewriting those equations so that you can solve them algebraically.

13-90. Consider the equation $2 \sin(x) \cos(x) = \frac{1}{2}$ for the domain $0 \le x \le 2\pi$.

a. Do you have tools to solve this equation algebraically?

b. Use your graphing calculator to graph $y = 2\sin(x)\cos(x)$ and $y = \frac{1}{2}$ in the domain $0 \le x \le 2\pi$. Copy the graph onto your paper and use it to approximate the solutions to $2\sin(x)\cos(x) = \frac{1}{2}$. How many solutions are there in this domain?

c. Crystal was working on this problem and noticed that the graph of $y = 2\sin(x)\cos(x)$ looked just like the graph of a regular cyclic function. She thought it must be possible to write a different equivalent equation for this graph. Work with your team to write a cyclic equation for this graph. Is there more than one? If so, which is the simplest?

d. Using your equivalent equation from part (c), rewrite the equation $2\sin(x)\cos(x) = \frac{1}{2}$ and solve it algebraically. How do your solutions compare to those you approximated from your graph?

e. Write an algebraic statement showing that these two expressions are equivalent. This is called the **Double Angle Identity** for the sine.

13-91. DISCOVERING IDENTITIES GRAPHICALLY

The graphs of some other trigonometric functions can be used to rewrite the functions and create new identities. Use a method similar to the method used in problem 13-90 to rewrite each of the following equations. Then use your result to write a new identity.

$y = \cos(-x)$	$y = \sin(-x)$	$y = \cos(\frac{\pi}{2} - x)$	$y = \sin(\frac{\pi}{2} - x)$
$y = \sin^2(x)$	$y = \cos^2(x)$	$y = \cos^2(x) - \sin^2(x)$	$y = \cos^2(x) + \sin^2(x)$

13-92. Obtain the Lesson 13.2.1 Resource Page from your teacher. This resource page will be referred to as your Identity Tool Kit. Record each identity you have discovered along with its **justification**.

13-93.   Use your new identities to help you rewrite and solve the following equations in the given domains.

   a. $2\cos\left(\frac{\pi}{2} - x\right) = 1$ for all x

   b. $\cos^2(x) - \sin^2(x) = \frac{\sqrt{3}}{2}$ for $0 \le x \le 2\pi$

13-94.   One of the identities that you discovered in problem 13-91 is $\cos^2(x) + \sin^2(x) = 1$. This is called the **Pythagorean Identity**, and it is one of the most useful identities you will learn.

   a.   Work with your team to explore the following question: Why is $\cos^2(x) + \sin^2(x) = 1$ called the Pythagorean Identity? Does it have anything to do with the Pythagorean theorem? Be prepared to share your ideas with the class.

   b.   Two more very useful identities can come directly from the Pythagorean Identity. To discover the first related identity, divide both sides of the equation by $\cos^2(x)$. For the second related identity, divide both sides of the equation by $\sin^2(x)$. Add these two new identities to your Identity Tool Kit (Lesson 13.2.1 Resource Page).

13-95.   Rewrite each of the following expressions in a simpler form.

   a. $\cos^2(\theta - \pi) + \sin^2(\theta - \pi)$

   b. $\cos^2(2w) - \sin^2(2w)$

   c. $\frac{\sin\theta}{\cos\theta}$

13-96.   An isosceles triangle has sides with lengths 10, 10, and 5 cm. What are the measures of the angles in the triangle?

13-97.   Solve for x in *degrees*.

   a. $2\sin(x) = 1$

   b. $\cos^2(x) + 4\cos(x) + 4 = 0$

13-98.   Divide $6x^3 - 5x^2 + 5x - 2$ by $(2x - 1)$.

13-99.   Divide $x^4 - 7x^2 + 3x + 18$ by $(x + 2)$.

13-100.   Each labeled point on the graph below is either a maximum or a minimum.

   a.   Find the period and amplitude of the graph.

   b.   Find an equation for the graph.

   c.   Use one of the labeled points to check your equation.

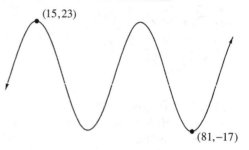

13-101.   Find the equation of an ellipse with center at the midpoint of a segment with endpoints at $(-2,-3)$, $(10,-3)$ and congruent to $x^2 + 36y^2 = 36$.

13-102.   Rewrite the Pythagorean Identity as many ways as you can. One way to change the identity would be to solve the equation for one trigonometric function. Another way is to use factoring. Try several different ways.

13-103.   If $\pi \le \theta \le \frac{3\pi}{2}$ and $\sin\theta = -\frac{3}{5}$, find $\cos\theta$. Use what you know about the Pythagorean Identity and the unit circle to get started.

13-104.   Rewrite each of the following expressions in terms of either $\sin(\theta)$ or $\cos(\theta)$.

   a. $\tan(\theta)$ b. $\csc(\theta)$ c. $\cot(\theta)$ d. $\sec(\theta)$

13-105.   Given the points $(2,9)$ and $(4,324)$:

   a.   Write the equation of a line that passes through them.

   b.   Write the equation of an exponential function with an asymptote at $y = 0$ that passes through them.

13-106.   Without graphing, determine where the graphs of $f(x) = 2x^2 - 3x + 1$ and $g(x) = 4x - 2$ intersect.

13-107.   Simplify each rational expression below.

   a. $\dfrac{\frac{x+1}{2x}}{\frac{x^2-1}{x}}$ b. $\dfrac{\frac{4}{x+3}}{\frac{1}{x}+3}$

13-108.   Hospital records show that 10% of all the cases of a certain disease are fatal. If five patients suffer from this disease, find the probability that:

   a.   All will recover.   b.   At least three will die.

13.2.2 How can I prove it?

Proving Trigonometric Identities

13-109.　Polly Parabola and Carl Conic have a cousin named Thomas Trig. Functions of America, Professional Parabola Productions, and The Courtly Conic Company have enjoyed such huge success that Thomas has decided to open a company called Identity Island. However, to do this, he needs some help and has sent your team the following memo.

> *Dear Study Team,*
>
> *My goal for Identity Island is to be able to offer a wide selection of trigonometric identities to interested customers. I found a list of identities on the Internet, but I know that lots of information on the Internet is false! I cannot afford to be embarrassed in front of my potential customers by offering identities that are not true.*
>
> *I need your help. I need a solid algebraic proof on file for each identity that we offer. Please submit a report by the end of the day that demonstrates each of the identities algebraically.*
>
> *I have the utmost faith in your team's abilities. Thank you for your time!*
>
> *Sincerely,*
>
> *Thomas Trig*

Your task: Work with your team to demonstrate algebraically whether or not each of the identities below is always true, never true or sometimes true. To prove some of the identities you will need to refer to the identities that you developed in Lesson 13.2.1.

a.　$\cot(x) + \tan(x) = \sec(x)\csc(x)$

b.　$(1 - \sin x)(1 + \sin x) = \dfrac{1}{1 + \tan^2(x)}$

c.　$\dfrac{1}{\sec^2(x)} + \dfrac{1}{\csc^2(x)} = 1$

d.　$\sec^2(x) - \csc^2(x) = \tan^2(x) - \cot^2(x)$

e.　$\dfrac{\sec(x)}{\tan(x) + \cot(x)} = \sin(x)$

f.　$\sin^2(x)\cot^2(x) + \cos^2(x)\tan^2(x) = 1$

g.　$\dfrac{\csc^2(x) - 1}{\csc^2(x)} = \cos^2(x)$

h.　$\dfrac{\sin x}{\cos x} + \dfrac{\cos x}{\sin x} = 2$

13-110. A 125-foot redwood tree is leaning 20° off vertical toward the north. How long will its shadow be when the noon sun is 68° above the horizon? (When the sun is 68° above the horizon, the angle the sunlight makes with the ground is 68°.)

13-111. Divide each of the following polynomials, $P(x)$, by $D(x)$ to find the quotient $Q(x)$ and then rewrite the polynomial in the form $P(x) = D(x) \cdot Q(x) + R$, where R is the remainder.

 a. $P(x) = 2x^4 - x^2 + 3x + 5$ b. $P(x) = x^5 - 2x^3 + 1$
     $D(x) = x - 1$ $D(x) = x - 3$

13-112. Without using a calculator, solve each equation below in the domain $0 \le x \le 2\pi$.

 a. $\sin(x) = -1$ b. $2\cos(x) - 1 = 0$

 c. $\tan(x) = 1$ d. $2\sin(x) = 4\sin(x) + 1$

13-113. Solve for x.

 a.   b.

13-114. If two dice are thrown and the numbers that come up are added to calculate a total number of points, what is the probability that each of the following events will occur?

 a. Five points.   b. Seven points.

 c. Five points before seven points.

13-115. Simplify each expression.

 a. $\dfrac{2x^2 - x - 3}{3x^2 - 11x + 6}$ b. $\dfrac{x^3 - 8}{4x^3 - 3x^2 - 10x}$

13-116. Solve.

 a. $\log_7(3x - 2) = 2$ b. $2^x \cdot 2^{x-2} - 16^2 = 0$

13-117. Graph each of following relations. Some of the equations may need to be changed to a more useful form.

a. $\dfrac{(x-2)^2}{9} - \dfrac{(y+3)^2}{4} = 1$ b. $\dfrac{y^2 - 2y + 1}{4} - \dfrac{x^2 + 6x + 9}{25} = 1$

c. $4(x^2 - 10x + 25) - 16(y^2 + 6y + 9) = 64$

13-118. Prove that each of the following equations is an identity. In other words, prove that they are each true for all values for which the functions are defined.

a. $(\sin\theta + \cos\theta)^2 = 1 + 2\sin\theta\cos\theta$ b. $\tan\theta + \cot\theta = \sec\theta\csc\theta$

c. $(\tan\theta\cos\theta)(\sin^2\theta + \frac{1}{\sec^2\theta}) = \sin\theta$

13-119. Solve $\frac{2+\sin^2\theta}{3} = \frac{3}{4}$ in the domain $0 \le \theta \le 2\pi$. Show your solutions on a unit circle.

13-120. If the side lengths of $\triangle ABC$ are $a = 9$, $b = 10$, and $c = 5$, calculate the measure of the largest angle.

13-121. Write an equation for the curve shown at right. Is it a function? **Justify** your answer.

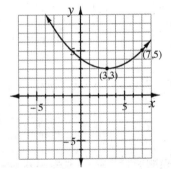

13-122. Solve for x, correct to three decimal places.

a $27 = 6^x$ b. $27 = \dfrac{1}{6^x}$

c. $27 = \dfrac{1}{(\frac{1}{6})^x}$ d.   Show that $\dfrac{1}{(\frac{1}{6})^x} = 6^x$.

13-123. Solve each system of equations. Explain the graphical implications of your answer.

a. $3x - 2y = -10$ b. $7x - 2y = 11$
     $4x + y = 49$ $14x - 4y = 3$

13-124. Find a polynomial function of degree three with roots $x = 3, 1 \pm i$. Express your answer in standard form.

13-125. For each of the following equations, identify the curve, write the equation in graphing form, and list the following information: center, focus or foci, and asymptotes. Refer to the Math Notes boxes in Lessons 11.2.2, 11.2.4, and 11.2.6 for definitions

a. $2x^2 + y^2 - 4x + 6y - 7 = 0$ b. $3y^2 - x^2 + 12y = 0$

c. $12x^2 + 8y^2 + 48x - 48y + 24 = 0$

13.2.3 What about sums and differences?

Angle Sum and Difference Identities

In this lesson you will use your knowledge of relationships in the unit circle to develop four new identities called the Angle Sum and Difference Identities.

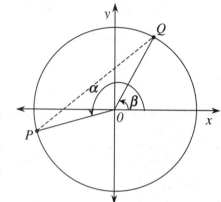

13-126. Danny and Damian were working on finding identities. They thought it would be useful to look at the sums and differences of angles. They started with a unit circle and created the angles α and β as shown at right. They recognized that they had formed a triangle, $\triangle POQ$.

a. Write the measure of the obtuse angle in $\triangle POQ$ in terms of α and β.

b. Danny and Damian each realized that they can calculate the length of side PQ of their triangle, but they wanted to use two different methods. What are the two methods they could be thinking of?

c. Danny wanted to use the idea of distance between points P and Q to calculate the length. In order to do that, he needs to label the coordinates of points P and Q. Based on angles α and β, represent the coordinates of each point using trigonometric functions.

d. Use your answer from part (c) to write an expression for the distance between points P and Q.

e. Damian realized that since this is a unit circle, the lengths of OP and OQ are both one unit, so he wanted to use the Law of Cosines. Use the Law of Cosines to write an expression for the length of side PQ.

f. Since the expressions you wrote for parts (c) and (d) both represent the length of PQ, what equation can you write? Simplify your equation to write a formula for $\cos(\alpha - \beta)$. This is called the **Angle Difference Identity** for cosine. Add this to your Identity Tool Kit (Lesson 13.2.1 Resource Page).

13-127. Danny and Damian were so pleased with this result that they wanted to keep going. They wanted to know how they could rewrite $\cos(\alpha + \beta)$. As they were thinking about this, Damian had a realization. *"I know how we could figure it out!"* he exclaimed. *"We could use the identity we already found to rewrite $\cos(\alpha - (-\beta))$, since that's the same thing as $\cos(\alpha + \beta)$."* Work with your team to use this idea to find the **Angle Sum Identity** for cosine.

13-128. *"So now we have the sum and difference formulas for cosine, but what about for sine?"* Damian asked. Danny pondered this for a while and then remembered an identity he thought they could use to figure these out. *"Don't we have an identity that relates sine to cosine?"* he asked.

a.   Which identity is Danny thinking of?

b.   Danny and Damian realized that they could use this to rewrite $\sin(\alpha + \beta)$. Work with your team to rewrite $\sin(\alpha + \beta)$ and find the **Angle Sum Identity** for sine.

c.   Now work with your team to develop the **Angle Difference Identity** for the sine. Be prepared to share your **strategies** with the class.

㉯ETHODS AND MEANINGS

Trigonometric Identities

Identities are equations that are true for all values for which the functions are defined.

$$\cos(-x) = \cos(x) \qquad \sin(-x) = -\sin(x)$$

Reciprocal Trigonometric Functions:

$$\csc(x) = \frac{1}{\sin(x)} \qquad \sec(x) = \frac{1}{\cos(x)} \qquad \cot(x) = \frac{1}{\tan(x)}$$

Pythagorean Identities:

$$\sin^2(x) + \cos^2(x) = 1 \qquad \tan^2(x) + 1 = \sec^2 x \qquad 1 + \cot^2(x) = \csc^2(x)$$

Co-function Identities:

$$\sin(x) = \cos\left(\frac{\pi}{2} - x\right) \qquad \cos(x) = \sin\left(\frac{\pi}{2} - x\right) \qquad \sec(x) = \csc\left(\frac{\pi}{2} - x\right)$$

$$\csc(x) = \sec\left(\frac{\pi}{2} - x\right) \qquad \tan(x) = \cot\left(\frac{\pi}{2} - x\right) \qquad \cot(x) = \tan\left(\frac{\pi}{2} - x\right)$$

Angle Sum and Difference Identities:

$$\sin(x+y) = \sin(x)\cos(y) + \cos(x)\sin(y)$$

$$\sin(x-y) = \sin(x)\cos(y) - \cos(x)\sin(y)$$

$$\cos(x+y) = \cos(x)\cos(y) - \sin(x)\sin(y)$$

$$\cos(x-y) = \cos(x)\cos(y) + \sin(x)\sin(y)$$

Double Angle Identities:

$$\sin(2x) = 2\sin(x)\cos(x)$$

$$\cos(2x) = \cos^2(x) - \sin^2(x)$$

13-129. Write $\frac{\pi}{12}$ as the difference of two special angles. Then use the appropriate angle difference formula to find the exact sine and cosine of $\frac{\pi}{12}$.

13-130. Write each angle as the sum or difference of two special angles and then find the exact sine or cosine.

    a. $\sin\frac{7\pi}{12}$
                        b. $\cos\frac{11\pi}{12}$

13-131. Show how to derive the double angle formulas for $\sin(2x)$ and $\cos(2x)$ by substituting x for both α and β in the formulas for $\sin(\alpha+\beta)$ and $\cos(\alpha+\beta)$, then simplifying.

13-132. Consider the function $f(x)=\cos(x+\frac{\pi}{2})$.

    a.   Make a complete graph of $f(x)$.

    b.   Write a simpler trig function that is represented by the same graph.

    c.   Now use the angle sum identity to expand and simplify $\cos(x+\frac{\pi}{2})$.

    d.   Does your work in part (c) agree with your graphical results from parts (a) and (b)? Explain.

13-133. Express $\frac{\cos x}{1-\tan x}-\frac{\sin x}{\cot x-1}$ in terms of $\sin x$ and $\cos x$ and then simplify.

13-134. Latisha had graphed the polynomial $y=x^3-5x^2+8x-6$ during class and remembered that it had one real root at $x=3$. Explain how you could use division to find the other roots, and then find them.

13-135. Each of the following sums is the beginning of an arithmetic series. Find the nth term of each series, for the specified value of n.

    a. $(-2)+(-5)+(-8)+...,\ n=12$
             b. $9+15+21+...,\ n=20$

13-136. Without using a calculator, solve these two problems from a college entrance exam.

    a.   If $x^{-4/3}+1=17$, find $x^{-1/3}$.
          b.   If $\log(A)=a$, find $\log(\frac{A}{100})$.

13-137. In a certain family, the probability of any one child having dark hair is $\frac{3}{4}$. If the family has three children, what is the probability that exactly one has dark hair?

13-138. Graph the following equations. Some of them will need to be changed into a more useful form.

a. $\dfrac{(x+2)^2}{9} + \dfrac{(y-3)^2}{4} = 1$

b. $\dfrac{x^2 + 2x + 1}{16} + \dfrac{y^2 + 6y + 9}{25} = 1$

c. $4(x^2 - 10x + 25) + 9(y^2 - 8y + 16) = 36$

Chapter 13 Closure What have I learned?

Reflection and Synthesis

The activities below offer you a chance to reflect on what you have learned in this chapter. As you work, look for concepts that you feel very comfortable with, ideas that you would like to learn more about, and topics you need more help with. Look for connections between ideas as well as connections with material you learned previously.

①   TEAM BRAINSTORM

With your team, brainstorm a list for each of the following categories. Be as detailed as you can. How long can you make your list? Challenge yourselves. Be prepared to share your team's ideas with the class.

Topics: What have you studied in this chapter? What ideas and words were important in what you learned? Remember to be as detailed as you can.

Connections: How are the topics, ideas, and words that you learned in previous courses connected to the new ideas in this chapter? Again, make your list as long as you can.

② MAKING CONNECTIONS

Below is a list of the vocabulary used in this chapter. Make sure that you are familiar with all of these words and know what they mean. Refer to the glossary or index for any words that you do not yet understand.

$\cos^{-1}$	cosecant	cotangent
identity	reciprocal	secant
$\sin^{-1}$	solution	$\tan^{-1}$

Make a concept map showing all of the connections you can find among the key words and ideas listed above. To show a connection between two words, draw a line between them and explain the connection, as shown in the example below. A word can be connected to any other word as long as you can **justify** the connection. For each key word or idea, provide a sketch of an example.

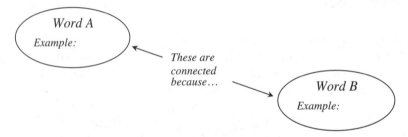

Your teacher may provide you with vocabulary cards to help you get started. If you use the cards to plan your concept map, be sure either to re-draw your concept map on your paper or to glue the vocabulary cards to a poster with all of the connections explained for others to see and understand.

While you are making your map, your team may think of related words or ideas that are not listed above. Be sure to include these ideas on your concept map.

③ SUMMARIZING MY UNDERSTANDING

This section gives you an opportunity to show what you know about certain math topics or ideas.

With your team, make a list of the **big ideas** of this chapter. Discuss the important ideas of the chapter and try to agree on a short list of no more than five big ideas. Be prepared to share your list in a whole class discussion. When the class has reached agreement on a list, continue with parts (a) and (b) below.

a. Write your own description of each big idea.

b. For each big idea, provide one or two representative example problems. Solve each problem completely, using multiple representations, if applicable.

④ WHAT HAVE I LEARNED?

This section will help you evaluate which types of problems you feel comfortable with and which you need more help with. This section will appear at the end of every chapter to help you check your understanding. Even if your teacher does not assign this section, it is a good idea to try these problems and find out for yourself what you know and what you need to work on.

Solve each problem as completely as you can. The table at the end of this closure section has answers to these problems. It also tells you where you can find additional help and practice on similar problems.

CL 13-139. Decide whether each of the following statements is sometimes true, always true, or never true. If it is sometimes true, give the values for x that make it true; if it is always true or never true, **justify** how you know.

a. $\cos(x) = \frac{3}{4}$

b. $2\tan(x) = 0$

c. $\sin(x) = \frac{5}{2}$

d. $\sin(x) = \cos(\frac{\pi}{2} - x)$

CL 13-140. Solve each of the following equations in the domain $0 \le x < 2\pi$.

a. $2\cos(x) = 1$

b. $4\tan(x) + 4 = 0$

c. $2\sin^2(x) - \sin(x) - 1 = 0$

d. $\csc(x) = -2$

CL 13-141. Explain why the graph of $y = \sec(x)$ has asymptotes.

CL 13-142. Solve each of the following equations in the domain $0 \le x \le 2\pi$.

a. $\cot(x) = 1.2$

b. $\cos(x) = -1$

c. $\frac{1}{4}\csc(x) = \sin(x)$

d. $\cos(2x) = \frac{1}{2}$

CL 13-143. Rewrite each expression as an equivalent expression that has only one trigonometric function.

a. $\sin(x) \cdot \csc(x) - \sin^2(x)$

b. $\frac{1 - \sin^2(x)}{\cot^2(x)}$

c. $\tan(x) \cdot \cot(x) - \cos^2(x)$

d. $\sin^2(x) \cdot (1 + \tan^2 x)$

CL 13-144. Show that the identity $\frac{1}{\cos(x)} - \cos(x) = \tan(x)\sin(x)$ is true.

CL 13-145. Using radian measure, represent all possible solutions to each equation.

    a. $\tan(x) = \sqrt{3}$ b. $\cos(x) = -\frac{\sqrt{2}}{2}$

    c. $\sin(x) = \frac{\sqrt{3}}{2}$ d. $\cot(x) = -1$

CL 13-146. Start with the expression $\sin(x + \frac{\pi}{2})$.

    a. Use the angle sum identity to expand and simplify.

    b. What other equation has a graph that is the same as the graph of $y = \sin(x + \frac{\pi}{2})$?

CL 13-147. Graph each of the following functions.

    a. $y = 3\sin 2(x - \frac{\pi}{4}) + 1$ b. $f(x) = -2\cos(x + \frac{\pi}{12}) - 1$

CL 13-148. Find the roots of the function $f(x) = x^4 + x^3 + 2x - 4$.

CL 13-149. Check your answers using the table at the end of this section. Which problems do you feel confident about? Which problems were hard? Have you worked on problems like these in math classes you have taken before? Use the table to make a list of topics you need help on and a list of topics you need to practice more.

⑤   HOW AM I THINKING?

This course focuses on five different **Ways of Thinking**: justifying, generalizing, choosing a strategy, investigating, and reversing thinking. These are some of the ways in which you think while trying to make sense of a concept or attempting to solve a problem (even outside of math class). During this chapter, you have probably used each Way of Thinking multiple times without even realizing it!

Review each of the five Ways of Thinking described in the closure sections of Chapters 1 through 5. Then choose three of these Ways of Thinking that you remember using while working on this chapter. Show and explain where and how you used each one. Describe why thinking in this way helped you solve a particular problem or understand something new. Be sure to include examples to demonstrate your thinking.

Answers and Support for Closure Activity #4
What Have I Learned?

Problem	Solutions	Need Help?	More Practice
CL 13-139.	a. True when $x \approx 0.72 + 2\pi n$ radians or when $x \approx 5.56 + 2\pi n$ radians. b. True for $x = \pi n$ radians. c. Never true. The range of sine is $-1 \le y \le 1$. d. Always true.	Lesson 13.1.1	Problems 13-2, 13-5, 13-15, 13-25, and 13-69
CL 13-140.	a. $\frac{\pi}{3}, \frac{5\pi}{3}$ b. $\frac{3\pi}{4}, \frac{7\pi}{4}$ c. $\frac{7\pi}{6}, \frac{11\pi}{6}, \frac{\pi}{2}$ d. $\frac{7\pi}{6}, \frac{11\pi}{6}$	Lessons 13.1.2, 13.1.4 and 13.2.1	Problems 13-31, 13-46, 13-56, 13-66, 13-71, 13-72, 13-82, 13-112, and 13-119
CL 13-141.	$y = \sec(x)$ is the same as $y = \frac{1}{\cos(x)}$, so whenever cosine is 0, secant will be undefined.	Lesson 13.1.4	Problems 13-64, and 13-65
CL 13-142.	a. $x \approx 0.69$ radians or $x \approx 3.84$ radians b. $x = \pi$ c. $x = \frac{\pi}{6}, \frac{5\pi}{6}, \frac{7\pi}{6}, \frac{11\pi}{6}$ d. $x = \frac{\pi}{6}, \frac{5\pi}{6}, \frac{7\pi}{6}, \frac{11\pi}{6}$	Lessons 13.1.2 and 13.1.4 Math Notes box in Leson 13.2.3	Problems 13-66, 13-67, 13-71, 13-72, 13-82, 13-112, and 13-119
CL 13-143.	a. $\cos^2(x)$ b. $\sin^2(x)$ c. $\sin^2(x)$ d. $\tan^2(x)$	Lessons 13.2.1 and 13.2.2 Math Notes box in Leson 13.2.3	Problems 13-95, 13-104, 13-109, 13-133
CL 13-144.	$\frac{1}{\cos(x)} - \cos(x) = \frac{1}{\cos(x)} - \frac{\cos^2(x)}{\cos(x)}$ $= \frac{1-\cos^2(x)}{\cos(x)} = \frac{\sin^2(x)}{\cos(x)} = \frac{\sin(x)}{\cos(x)} \cdot \sin(x)$ $= \tan(x)\sin(x)$	Lessons 13.2.1 and 13.2.2 Math Notes box in Leson 13.2.3	Problems 13-109, and 13-118

Problem	Solutions	Need Help?	More Practice
CL 13-145.	a. $\frac{\pi}{3} + \pi n$ b. $\frac{3\pi}{4} + 2\pi n, \frac{5\pi}{4} + 2\pi n$ c. $\frac{\pi}{3} + 2\pi n, \frac{2\pi}{3} + 2\pi n$ d. $-\frac{\pi}{4} + \pi n$ or $\frac{3\pi}{4} + \pi n$	Lesson 13.1.2	Problems 13-29, 13-31, 13-43, 13-45, 13-46, 13-56, 13-66, 13-71, and 13-112
CL 13-146.	a. $\sin(x)\cos(\frac{\pi}{2}) + \cos(x)\sin(\frac{\pi}{2})$ $= \cos(x)$ b. $y = \cos(x)$	Lesson 13.2.3 Math Notes box in Leson 13.2.3	Problems 13-128, 13-129, and 13-130
CL 13-147.	a. b.	Lessons 8.1.2, 8.1.7, 8.2.1, 8.2.3, and 8.2.4	Problems 8-115, 8-127, 8-140, 8-143, 8-145, 8-146 8-153, 8-159, 8-161, and 13-10
CL 13-148.	$x = 1, -2, \pm\sqrt{2}i$	Lesson 9.3.2 Math Notes Box in Lesson 9.3.2	Problems, 9-140, 9-149, CL 9-185, 10-50, 11-93, 11-123, 12-166

Algebra 2 Checkpoint Materials

Notes to Students (and their Teachers)

Students master different skills at different speeds. No two students learn exactly the same way at the same time. At some point you will be expected to perform certain skills accurately. Most of the Checkpoint problems incorporate skills that you should have been developing in Algebra 1 and geometry. If you have not mastered these skills yet it does not mean that you will not be successful in this class. However, you may need to do some work outside of class to get caught up on them.

Starting in Chapter 2 and finishing in Chapter 9, there are eighteen problems designed as Checkpoint problems. Each one is marked with an icon like the one above. After you do each of the Checkpoint problems, check your answers by referring to this section. If your answers are incorrect, you may need some extra practice to develop that skill. The practice sets are keyed to each of the Checkpoint problems in the textbook. Each has the topic clearly labeled, followed by the answers to the corresponding Checkpoint problem and then some completed examples. Next, the complete solution to the Checkpoint problem from the text is given, and there are more problems for you to practice with answers included.

Remember, looking is not the same as doing! You will never become good at any sport by just watching it, and in the same way, reading through the worked examples and understanding the steps is not the same as being able to do the problems yourself. How many of the extra practice problems do you need to try? That is really up to you. Remember that your goal is to be able to do similar problems on your own confidently and accurately. This is your responsibility. You should not expect your teacher to spend time in class going over the solutions to the Checkpoint problem sets. If you are not confident after reading the examples and trying the problems, you should get help outside of class time or talk to your teacher about working with a tutor.

Two other sources for help with the Checkpoint problems and the other new topics in Algebra 2 are the *Parent's Guide with Review (Algebra 1)* and the *Parent's Guide with Review (Algebra 2)*. These resources are available free of charge from the Internet at www.cpm.org.

Checkpoint Topics
(Volume 1 contains numbers 1 through 13 and Volume 2 contains numbers 11 through 18)

1. Using the Slope-Intercept Form of a Line to Solve a System of Equations
2. Solving Systems of Linear Equations in Two Variables
3. Multiplying Polynomials
4. Simplifying Expressions with Positive Exponents
5. Factoring Quadratic Expressions
6. Writing the Equation of a Line Given Two Points
7. Finding the x- and y-intercepts of a Quadratic Function
8. Finding the Slope of a Line through Two Points and the Distance Between the Points
9. Using Function Notation and Identifying the Domain and Range
10. Solving for One Variable in an Equation with Two or More Variables
11. Integral and Rational Exponents
12. Graphing Linear Inequalities
13. Solving Rational Equations
14. Completing the Square and Finding the Vertex for a Parabola
15. Writing and Solving Exponential Equations
16. Solving Absolute Value Equations and Inequalities
17. Finding an Equation for the Inverse of a Function.
18. Solving a System of Equations in Three Variables

Checkpoint Number 11

Problem 6-48

Integral and Rational Exponents

Answers to problem 6-48:

a. $x^{1/5}$ b. x^{-3} c. $x^{2/3}$ d. $x^{-1/2}$

The following properties are useful for simplifying expressions with integral (positive or negative whole numbers) or rational (fractional) exponents.

$x^0 = 1$ Examples: $2^0 = 1$, $(-3)^0 = 1$, $(\tfrac{1}{4})^0 = 1$

(Note that 0^0 is undefined.)

$x^{-n} = \dfrac{1}{x^n}$ Examples: $x^{-3} = \dfrac{1}{x^3}$, $y^{-4} = \dfrac{1}{y^4}$, $4^{-2} = \dfrac{1}{4^2} = \dfrac{1}{16}$

$\dfrac{1}{x^{-n}} = x^n$ Examples: $\dfrac{1}{x^{-5}} = x^5$, $\dfrac{1}{x^{-2}} = x^2$, $\dfrac{1}{3^{-2}} = 3^2 = 9$

$x^{a/b} = (x^a)^{1/b} = (\sqrt[b]{x})^a$ Examples: $5^{1/2} = \sqrt{5}$

or : $16^{3/4} = (\sqrt[4]{16})^3 = 2^3 = 8$

$x^{a/b} = (x^{1/b})^a = (\sqrt[b]{x})^a$ $4^{2/3} = \sqrt[3]{4^2} = \sqrt[3]{16} = 2\sqrt[3]{2}$

We can apply these patterns to problem 6-48, which asked us to rewrite each of the following expressions as a power of x.

a. Using the fourth property above, $\sqrt[5]{x} = x^{1/5}$.

b. Using the second property above, $\dfrac{1}{x^3} = x^{-3}$.

c. Using the fourth property above, $\sqrt[3]{x^2} = x^{2/3}$.

d. Using the second and fourth properties above, $\dfrac{1}{\sqrt{x}} = \dfrac{1}{x^{1/2}} = x^{-1/2}$.

Here are some exercises to try. Use integral or rational exponents to rewrite each expression without negative or fractional exponents and simplify. You should not need a calculator for any of these.

a. x^{-5} b. m^0 c. 4^{-1} d. y^{-3}

e. 5^{-2} f. 5^0 g. y^{-7} h. $(x^3y^4)^{-2}$

i. $x^{-1}y^{-8}$ j. $x^{-4}y^{-2}(x^{-3}y^{-6})^0$ k. $25^{1/2}$

l. $25^{-1/2}$ m. $2^{1/2}$ n. $(\frac{1}{27})^{-1/3}$ o. $x^{3/2}$

p. $9^{3/2}$ q. $(x^3y^6)^{1/3}$ r. $16^{-3/4}$ s. $(m^2)^{-3/2}$

t. $(x^3y^6)^{1/2}$ u. $(9x^3y^6)^{-2}$

Answers:

a. $\frac{1}{x^5}$ b. 1 c. $\frac{1}{4}$ d. $\frac{1}{y^3}$

e. $\frac{1}{25}$ f. 1 g. $\frac{1}{y^7}$ h. $\frac{1}{x^6y^8}$

i. $\frac{1}{xy^8}$ j. $\frac{1}{x^4y^2}$ k. 5 l. $\frac{1}{5}$

m. $\sqrt{2}$ n. 3 o. $\sqrt{x^3} = x\sqrt{x}$ p. 27

q. xy^2 r. $\frac{1}{8}$ s. $\frac{1}{m^3}$ t. $xy^3\sqrt{x}$

u. $\frac{1}{81x^6y^{12}}$

Checkpoint Number 12
Problem 7-73
Graphing Linear Inequalities

Answer graph to problem 7-73, part (a):

Graphing inequalities is very similar to graphing equations. First you graph the line that you would graph if the inequality were an equation. You must determine if the line is solid (included) or dashed (not included) and which side of the line should be shaded. Here are two examples of graphing a system of inequalities.

Example 1: On graph paper, graph and shade the solution region for the $y \le \frac{2}{5}x$
              systems of inequalities at right. $y > 5 - x$

Solution: We will address the inequality $y \le \frac{2}{5}x$ first. We start by graphing the equation
            $y = \frac{2}{5}x$. We can graph it using the slope, $\frac{2}{5}$, and y-intercept, (0, 0). Since the
            inequality contains the solutions to the equation (the symbol is $\le$, not $<$), we draw the
            graph as a solid, rather than dashed, line.

Once it is graphed, we notice that the line divides the grid into two regions. We must determine which region contains the solutions to the inequality $y \le \frac{2}{5}x$. We choose a point in either region and test whether or not it makes the original inequality true. Using (0, 1) as the test point:

Test point: (0, 1)

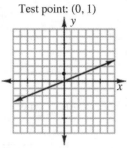

$1 \overset{?}{\le} \frac{2}{5}(0)$ FALSE!

Since (0, 1) makes the inequality false, we can assume that all points above the line make the inequality false, and that the points below the line must make it true. Therefore, we shade the area below the line to show that all points in this region are solutions.

Next we do the same thing for the second inequality. First we graph the equation on the same set of axes. The slope is -1 and the y-intercept is (0, 5). This inequality does not contain the solutions to the equation (the symbol is $>$, and not $\ge$). We show this by drawing a dashed, rather than solid, line. This line has also divided the grid into two regions and we must choose a point as to test to determine which region contains the solutions. Again, using (0, 1) as the test point:

Test point: (0, 1)

$1 \overset{?}{>} 5 - 0$ FALSE!

Example continues on next page. →

Checkpoint Materials

Continued from previous page.

Since our test point made the inequality false, we can conclude that point on the opposite side of this line would make the inequality true. So for the second inequality we shade above the line and to the right.

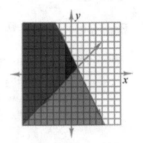

Answer: The region where the shading overlaps contains solutions to both inequalities in this system. We indicate this by shading this region more darkly, as in the graph at right.

Now we can return to problem 7-73.

Example 2: **Graph the system of inequalities** $y \le -2x + 3$, $y \ge x$, **and** $x \ge -1$.

Solution: Start by looking at the equation of the line that marks the edge of each inequality. The first has slope -2 and y-intercept $(0, 3)$. Checking $(0, 1)$ gives a true statement so we shade below the solid line. The second line has slope 1 and y-intercept $(0, 0)$. Again checking $(0, 1)$ gives a true statement, so we shade above the solid line. The third is a vertical line at $x = -1$. Checking a point tells us to shade the right side. The overlapping shading is a triangle with vertices $(-1, 5)$, $(1, 1)$, and $(-1, -1)$.

Here are a few more to try. Graph and shade the solution region for each system of inequalities below.

a. $y \le -x + 2$
$y \le 3x - 6$

b. $y \ge \frac{2}{3}x + 4$
$y \le \frac{7}{12}x + 5$

c. $x < 3$
$y \ge -2$

d. $y \le 4x + 16$
$y \ge -\frac{4}{3}x - 4$

Answers:

a.

b.

c.

d.

Checkpoint Number 13
Problem 7-145
Solving Rational Equations

Answers to problem 7-145:

a. $x = \pm 2\sqrt{3}$

b. $x = 2$

c. $x = \frac{2}{9}$

d. $x = \frac{-1 \pm \sqrt{13}}{6} \approx 0.434$ or -0.768

To solve rational equations (equations with fractions) it is usually best to first multiply everything by the common denominator to remove the fractions, a method known as **fraction busters**. After you have done this, you can solve the equation using your usual strategies. Following are a few examples.

Example 1: Solve $\frac{24}{x+1} = \frac{16}{1}$.

Solution: The common denominator in this case is $(x+1)$.
Multiplying both sides of the equation by $(x+1)$ removes all fractions from the equation. You can then simplify and solve for x. This process is demonstrated at right.

$$(x+1)(\frac{24}{x+1}) = (x+1)(\frac{16}{1})$$
$$24 = 16(x+1)$$
$$24 = 16x + 16$$
$$8 = 16x$$
$$x = \frac{1}{2}$$

Answer: $x = \frac{1}{2}$

Example 2: Solve $\frac{5}{2x} + \frac{1}{6} = 8$.

Solution: Again, we multiply both sides of the equation by the common denominator, which, in this case, is $6x$. We must be careful to remember to distribute so that we multiply each term on both sides of the equation by $6x$. Then we simplify and solve, as shown at right.

$$6x(\frac{5}{2x} + \frac{1}{6}) = 6x(8)$$
$$6x \cdot \frac{5}{2x} + 6x \cdot \frac{1}{6} = 48x$$
$$15 + x = 48x$$
$$15 = 47x$$
$$x = \frac{15}{47}$$

Answer: $x = \frac{15}{47}$

Now we can return to problem 7-145. Solve each of the following rational equations.

Example 3: $\frac{x}{3} = \frac{4}{x}$

$$3x(\frac{x}{3}) = 3x(\frac{4}{x})$$
$$x^2 = 12$$
$$x = \pm\sqrt{12} = \pm 2\sqrt{3}$$
$$x \approx \pm 3.46$$

Example 4: $\frac{x}{x-1} = \frac{4}{x}$

$$x(x-1)(\frac{x}{x-1}) = x(x-1)(\frac{4}{x})$$
$$x^2 = 4(x-1)$$
$$x^2 - 4x + 4 = 0$$
$$(x-2)(x-2) = 0$$
$$x = 2$$

Example 5: $\frac{1}{x} + \frac{1}{3x} = 6$

$$3x(\frac{1}{x} + \frac{1}{3x}) = 3x(6)$$

$$3x(\frac{1}{x}) + 3x(\frac{1}{3x}) = 18x$$

$$3 + 1 = 18x$$

$$x = \frac{2}{9}$$

Example 6: $\frac{1}{x} + \frac{1}{x+1} = 3$

$$x(x+1)(\frac{1}{x} + \frac{1}{x+1}) = x(x+1)(3)$$

$$x(x+1)(\frac{1}{x}) + x(x+1)(\frac{1}{x+1}) = x(x+1)(3)$$

$$x + 1 + x = 3x^2 + 3x$$

$$0 = 3x^2 + x - 1$$

Using the Quadratic Formula,
$$x \approx -0.434, \, -0.768$$

Here are some more to try. Solve each of the following rational equations.

a. $\frac{3x}{5} = \frac{x-2}{4}$

b. $\frac{4x-1}{x} = 3x$

c. $\frac{2x}{5} - \frac{1}{3} = \frac{137}{3}$

d. $\frac{4x-1}{x+1} = x - 1$

e. $\frac{x}{3} = x + 4$

f. $\frac{x-1}{5} = \frac{3}{x+1}$

g. $\frac{x+6}{3} = x$

h. $\frac{2x+3}{6} + \frac{1}{2} = \frac{x}{2}$

i. $\frac{3}{x} + \frac{5}{x-7} = -2$

j. $\frac{2x+3}{4} - \frac{x-7}{6} = \frac{2x-3}{12}$

Answers:

a. $x = -\frac{10}{7}$

b. $x = \frac{1}{3}, 1$

c. $x = 115$

d. $x = 0, 4$

e. $x = -6$

f. $x = \pm 4$

g. $x = 3$

h. $x = 6$

i. $x = \frac{3 \pm \sqrt{51}}{2}$

j. $x = -13$

Checkpoint Number 14
Problem 8-17
Completing the Square and Finding the Vertex for a Parabola.

Answers to problem 8-17:

Graphing form: $y = 2(x-1)^2 + 3$ $\qquad$ Vertex: $(1, 3)$

If a parabola is in graphing form then the vertex can be found easily and a sketch of the graph can be made quickly. If the equation of the parabola is not in graphing form the equation can be rearranged. One way to rearrange the equation is by completing the square.

Following are three examples:

Note that the first two examples are the same as problems 4-123 and 4-125, which are shown in Chapter 4 with algebra tiles. Refer back to the pictures and explanations for those problems if they seem useful to you.

First, recall that $y = x^2$ is the parent equation for parabolas and the general equation for parabolic functions can be written in graphing form as $y = a(x-h)^2 + k$ where (h, k) is the vertex, and relative to the parent graph the function has been:

- Vertically stretched, if the absolute value of a is greater than 1
- Vertically compressed, if the absolute value of a is less than 1
- Reflected across the x-axis, if a is less than 0.

Example 1: Complete the square to change $y = x^2 + 8x + 10$ into graphing form and name the vertex.

Solution: We need to make $x^2 + 8x$ into a perfect square. To do this, take half of the coefficient of the x-term and square it. This is the number that would make a perfect square. As you can see from the calculations at right, for this example, this number is 16.

$y = x^2 + 8x + 10$
$y = (x^2 + 8x + ?) + 10$
$? = (\frac{8}{2})^2 = 16$

In order to create a perfect square, we add that number. But in order to make sure our new equation is equivalent to the original, we have to subtract 16 as well. Thus, our new form of the equation would look like $y = (x^2 + 8x + 16) + 10 - 16$, which can be rewritten as $y = (x+4)^2 - 6$. Now we can see that the vertex is $(-4, -6)$.

Example 2: **Complete the square to change** $y = x^2 + 5x + 2$ **into graphing form and name the vertex.**

Solution: We need to make $x^2 + 5x$ into a perfect square. Again, we take half of the coefficient of x and square it, as shown at right. In this case, we find that we should add $\frac{25}{4}$ to the expression in parentheses, but then we must subtract $\frac{25}{4}$ again to preserve the equality. This can be written as $y = (x^2 + 5x + \frac{25}{4}) + 2 - \frac{25}{4}$, which can be simplified to $y = (x + \frac{5}{2})^2 - \frac{17}{4}$ or $y = (x + 2.5)^2 - 4.25$. The vertex is $(-2.5, -4.25)$,

$$y = x^2 + 5x + 2$$
$$y = (x^2 + 5x + ?) + 2$$
$$? = \left(\tfrac{5}{2}\right)^2 = \tfrac{25}{4}$$

Example 3: **Complete the square to change** $y = 2x^2 - 6x + 2$ **into graphing form and name the vertex.**

Solution: This problem is a little different because we have $2x^2$. First we must factor the 2 out of the x-terms. Then we make $x^2 + 3x$ into a perfect square as before.

Since $\frac{9}{4}$ is needed to make $x^2 + 3x$ into a perfect square, we add that inside the parentheses. Since all of the amounts in the parentheses are being multiplied by 2, we have really added $2(\frac{9}{4}) = \frac{9}{2}$, so we must subtract $\frac{9}{2}$, to keep the equation equivalent. This process is shown at right.

$$y = 2x^2 - 6x + 2$$
$$y = 2(x^2 - 3x) + 2$$
$$y = 2(x^2 - 3x + \tfrac{9}{4}) + 2 - 2 \cdot \tfrac{9}{4}$$
$$y = 2(x - \tfrac{3}{2})^2 - \tfrac{5}{2}$$

Answer: Graphing form: $y = 2(x - \frac{3}{2})^2 - \frac{5}{2}$ or $y = 2(x - 1.5)^2 - 2.5$; Vertex: $(1.5, -2.5)$.

We can now go back to problem 8-17:

Example 4: **Complete the square to change the equation** $y = 2x^2 - 4x + 5$ **to graphing form, identify the vertex of the parabola, and sketch its graph.**

Solution: First we must factor the 2 out from the x-terms. Then we make the $x^2 - 2x$ into a perfect square as before. The coefficient of x in this case is -2, half of which is -1. Since $(-1)^2 = 1$, we see that a 1 is needed to make the expression in parentheses into a perfect square. Again, since everything inside the parentheses is being multiplied by 2, we must subtract $2(1) = 2$ to keep the value the same. See this process at right.

$$y = 2x^2 - 4x + 5$$
$$y = 2(x^2 - 2x) + 5$$
$$y = 2(x^2 - 2x + 1) + 5 - 2(1)$$
$$y = 2(x - 1)^2 + 3$$

To sketch the graph, we start by plotting the vertex, (1, 3). Then we can plot the next few points by recognizing that the shape of this parabola is the shape of $y = x^2$ stretched by a factor of 2. Therefore, the points one unit to the left and right of the vertex will be 2 units higher than the vertex, which gives the points (0, 5) and (2, 5). The points two units to the left and right of the vertex will be 8 units higher, which gives the points (−1, 11) and (3, 11). Thus we get the graph at right.

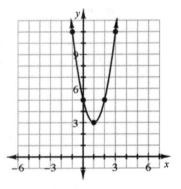

Answer: Graphing form: $y = 2(x - 1)^2 + 3$; Vertex: $(1, 3)$; See graph above right.

Here are some more to try. Complete the square to write each equation in graphing form. Then state the vertex and the stretch factor and sketch a graph.

a. $y = x^2 - 6x + 9$

b. $y = x^2 + 3$

c. $y = x^2 - 4x$

d. $y = x^2 + 2x - 3$

e. $y = x^2 + 5x + 1$

f. $y = x^2 - \frac{1}{3}x$

g. $y = 3x^2 - 6x + 1$

h. $y = 5x^2 + 20x - 16$

i. $y = -x^2 - 6x + 10$

Answers:

a. $(3, 0)$; $a = 1$

b. $(0, 3)$; $a = 1$

c. $(2, -4)$; $a = 1$

d. $(-1, -4)$; $a = 1$

e. $\left(-\frac{5}{2}, -5\frac{1}{4}\right)$; $a = 1$

f. $\left(\frac{1}{6}, -\frac{1}{36}\right)$; $a = 1$

g. $(1, -2)$; $a = 3$

h. $(-2, -36)$; $a = 5$

i. $(-3, 19)$; $a = -1$

Checkpoint Number 15

Problem 8-68

Writing and Solving Exponential Equations

Answers to problem 8-68:

a. The more rabbits you have, the more new ones you get, a linear model would grow by the same number each year. A sine function would be better if the population rises and falls, but more data would be needed to apply this model.

b. $R = 80,000(5.4772...)^t$ c. ≈ 394 million

d. 1859, it seems okay that they grew to 80,000 in 7 years, *if* they are growing exponentially.

e. No, since it would predict a huge number of rabbits now. The population probably leveled off at some point or dropped drastically and rebuilt periodically.

Exponential functions are equations of the form $y = ab^x + c$ where a represents the initial value, b represents the multiplier, c represents the horizontal asymptote. x often represents the time. Some problems just involve substituting in the given information and doing calculations. If you are trying to solve for the time (x), then you will usually need to use logarithms. If you need to find the multiplier (m), then you will need roots. Note that we often assume that $c = 0$, unless we are told otherwise.

Example 1: Lunch at out favorite fast food stands cost $6.50. The price has steadily increased 4% per year for many years.

Question 1: What will lunch cost in 10 years?

Solution: In this case, we can use $6.50 as the initial value, the multiplier is 1.04, so the equation for the situation is $y = 6.50(1.04)^x$. The time we are interested in here is 10 years. Substituting into the equation, $y = 6.50(1.04)^{10} = \$9.62$

Question 2: What did it cost 10 years ago?

Solution: Using the same equation, only using -10 for the years, $y = 6.50(1.04)^{-10} = \$4.39$

Question 3: How long before lunch costs $10?

Solution: Again, we use the same equation, only this time we know the y-value, but not the value of x. To solve for x, we use logarithms, as shown in the work at right.

Answer: About 11 years.

$$\$10 = 6.50(1.04)^x$$
$$1.04^x = \tfrac{10}{6.5}$$
$$\log 1.04^x = \log(\tfrac{10}{6.5})$$
$$x\log 1.04 = \log(\tfrac{10}{6.5})$$
$$x = \frac{\log(\tfrac{10}{6.5})}{\log 1.04} \approx 11$$

Example 2: Tickets for a big concert first went on sale three weeks ago for $60. This week people are charging $100. Write an equation that represents the cost of the tickets w weeks from the time that they went on sale. Assume that they continue to increase in the same way.

Solution: To find the multiplier, we can use what we are given. The initial value is $60, the time is 3 weeks, and the final value is $100. This gives $100 = 60k^3$. Solving for k gives $k = \sqrt[3]{\frac{100}{60}} \approx 1.186$.

Answer: The equation is approximately $y = 60(1.186)^w$.

We now solve parts (b), (c), and (d) of problem 8-68.

Example 3: When rabbits were first brought to Australia, they had no natural enemies. There were about 80,000 rabbits in 1866. Two years later, in 1868, the population had grown to over 2,400,000!

   b.   Write an exponential equation for the number of rabbits t years after 1866.

Solution: For 1866, 80000 would be the initial value, time would be 2 years, and the final amount would be 2400000, which gives the equation $2400000 = 80000m^2$. Solving for m, we get $30 = m^2$ so $m = \sqrt{30} \approx 5.477$. Thus the equation is approximately $R = 80,000(5.477)^t$

   c.   How many rabbits do you predict would have been present in 1871?

Solution: The initial value is still 80,000, the multiplier ≈ 5.477, and now the time is 5 years. This gives $80,000(5.477)^5 \approx 394$ million.

   d.   According to your model, in what year was the first pair of rabbits introduced into Australia?

Solution: In this situation, we use 2 as the initial value, 80000 as the final value, and the multiplier is still 5.477 but the time is not known. Using these values, we get $80000 = 2(5.477)^x$, which is solved at right. The answer 6.23 tells us that approximately 6.23 years had passed between the time of the first pair of rabbits, and the time when there were 80000. Thus, rabbits would have been introduced sometime in 1859.

$$80000 = 2(5.477)^x$$

$$40000 = (5.477)^x$$

$$\log(5.477)^x = \log 40000$$

$$x\log(5.477) = \log 40000$$

$$x = \frac{\log(40000)}{\log(5.477)} \approx 6.23$$

Here are some more to try:

a. A video tape loses 60% of its value every year it is in the store. The video costs $80 new. Write a function that represents its value in t years. What is it worth after 4 years?

b. Inflation is at a rate of 7% per year. Janelle's favorite bread now costs $1.79. What did it cost 10 years ago? How long before the cost of the bread doubles?

c. A bond that appreciates 4% per year will be worth $146 in five years. Find the current value.

d. Sixty years ago, when Sam's grandfather was a kid, he could buy his friend dinner for $1.50. If that same dinner now costs $25.25 and inflation was consistent, write an equation that will give you the costs at different times.

e. A two-bedroom house in Omaha is now worth $110,000. If it appreciates at a rate of 2.5% per year, how long will it take to be worth $200,000?

f. A car valued at $14,000 depreciates 18% per year. After how many years will the value have depreciated to $1000?

Answers:

a. $y = 80(0.4)^t$, **$2.05**   b. **$91, 10.2 years**

c. **$120**   d. $y = 1.50(1.048)^x$

e. **24.2 years**   f. **13.3 years**

Checkpoint Number 16

Problem 8-129

Solving Absolute Value Equations and Inequalities

Answers to problem 8-129:

    a. $x = 1$ or $x = -4$ b. $-\infty < x < \infty$

Absolute value can be defined as a distance from a reference point. The patterns shown below can help solve absolute value equations and inequalities.

Patterns: Examples:

$|x| = k$ means: $x = k$ or $x = -k$ $|x| = 5$ means $x = 5$ or $x = -5$.

                                            (5 and −5 are both 5 units from zero.)

$|x| < k$ means: $-k < x < k$ $|x| < 5$ means $-5 < x < 5$.

                                            (The numbers between −5 and 5 are fewer than 5 units from zero)

$|x| > k$ means: $x > k$ or $x < -k$ $|x| > 5$ means $x > 5$ or $x < -5$.

                                            (The numbers greater than 5 and less than −5 are more than 5 units from zero.)

If the expression inside the absolute value is more complicated, you can still use one of the three basic patterns above, as you can see in the examples below. (Note that ≤ and ≥ follow the same patterns as the pure inequality.)

Example 1: Solve $|2x + 3| = 7$.

Solution: If $|2x + 3| = 7$, then the quantity $(2x + 3)$ must be equal to either 7 or −7, as can be seen in the first pattern above. Therefore, we can set up and solve the two equations show at right to find that $x = 2$ or $x = -5$.

$$2x + 3 = 7 \text{ or } 2x + 3 = -7$$
$$2x = 4 \qquad\qquad 2x = -10$$
$$x = 2 \qquad\qquad\quad x = -5$$

Example 2: Solve $|2x + 3| \leq 7$.

Solution: If $|2x + 3| \leq 7$, then the quantity $(2x + 3)$ must be less than 7 and greater than −7, as can be seen in the second pattern above. Therefore, we can set up and solve the inequalities shown at right to find that $-5 \leq x \leq 2$.

$$-7 \leq 2x + 3 \leq 7$$
$$-10 \leq 2x \leq 4$$
$$-5 \leq x \leq 2$$

Now we can go back and try problem 8-129.

Example 3: Solve $2|2x+3| = 10$.

Solution: Start by isolating the absolute value to get $|2x+3| = 5$. Using the first pattern, this can be rewritten as $2x+3 = 5$ or $2x+3 = -5$. Solving each of these equations yields $x = 1$ or $x = -4$.

Example 4: Solve $-|x+3| < 10$.

Solution: Again, we want to start by isolating the absolute value. Here it is important to know that dividing by a negative changes the inequality sign. Therefore, dividing both sides of this inequality by -1, we get $|x+3| > -10$. Since an absolute value is always positive, this inequality will be true for any real value of x. Therefore $-\infty < x < \infty$.

Here are some more to try. Solve each absolute value equation or inequality.

a. $|x-2|+10 = 8$ b. $15-|x+1| = 3$

c. $-3|x+6|+12 = 0$ d. $|2x+7| = 0$

e. $|x+4| \geq 7$ f. $|x|-5 \leq 8$

g. $|4r-2| > 8$ h. $-2|x-3|+6 < -4$

i. $|4-d| \leq 7$

Answers:

a. **no solution**   b. $x = 11$ or $x = -13$

c. $x = -2$ or $x = -10$ d. $x = -\frac{7}{2}$

e. $x \geq 3$ or $x \leq -11$ f $-13 \leq x \leq 13$

g. $r < -\frac{3}{2}$ or $r > \frac{5}{2}$ h. $x > 8$ or $x < -2$

i. $-3 \leq d \leq 11$

Checkpoint Number 17
Problem 9-23
Finding an Equation for the Inverse of a Function

Answers to problem 9-23:

a. $f^{-1}(x) = \frac{1}{3}(\frac{x-5}{2})^2 + 1 = \frac{1}{12}(x-5)^2 + 1$ for $x \geq 5$

b. See graph at right.

To find the equation for the inverse of a function, you can interchange the x and y variables and then solve for y. This also means that the coordinates of points that are on the graph of the function will be reversed on the graph of the inverse. Here are some examples:

Example 1: Write the equation for the inverse of $y = 2(x + 3)$.

Solution: We can interchange the x and the y to get $x = 2(y + 3)$ as the equation of the inverse. To get our final answer, we solve for y, as shown at right.

$$(y + 3) = \frac{x}{2}$$
$$y = \frac{x}{2} - 3$$

Answer: $y = \frac{x}{2} - 3$

Example 2: Write the equation for the inverse of $y = \frac{1}{2}(x + 4)^2 + 1$.

Solution: Again, we can interchange the x and the y to get the equation of the inverse and then solve for y to get our answer in y-form, as shown at right.

$$x = \frac{1}{2}(y + 4)^2 + 1$$
$$\frac{1}{2}(y + 4)^2 = x - 1$$
$$(y + 4)^2 = 2x - 2$$
$$y + 4 = \pm\sqrt{2x - 2}$$
$$y = \pm\sqrt{2x - 2} - 4$$

Answer: $y = \pm\sqrt{2x - 2} - 4$. Note that because of the $\pm$, this inverse is not a function.

Example 3: Write the equation for the inverse of $y = -\frac{2}{3}x + 6$.

Solution: Interchanging the x and the y, we get $x = -\frac{2}{3}y + 6$. Solving for y gives
$y = -\frac{3}{2}(x - 6) = -\frac{3}{2}x + 9$.

Answer: $y = -\frac{3}{2}x + 9$

Example 4: Write the equation for the inverse of $y = \sqrt{x - 2} + 3$.

Solution: Again, we exchange x and y and then solve for y, as shown at right.

The original function is half of a sleeping parabola, so the inverse is only half of a parabola as well. Thus the domain of the inverse is restricted to $x \geq 3$.

$$x = \sqrt{y - 2} + 3$$
$$\sqrt{y - 2} = x - 3$$
$$y - 2 = (x - 3)^2$$
$$y = (x - 3)^2 + 2$$

Answer: $y = (x - 3)^2 + 2$ in the domain $x \geq 3$.

We can now return to problem 9-23:

Example 5: Find the equation for the inverse of the function $y = 2\sqrt{3(x-1)} + 5$. Then sketch the graph of both the original and the inverse.

Interchanging x and y we get $x = 2\sqrt{3(y-1)} + 5$. We then solve for y, as shown at right. This equation can then be simplified to get $y = \frac{(x-5)^2}{12} + 1$.

$$x = 2\sqrt{3(y-1)} + 5$$
$$2\sqrt{3(y-1)} = x - 5$$
$$\sqrt{3(y-1)} = \frac{x-5}{2}$$
$$3(y-1) = \left(\frac{x-5}{2}\right)^2$$
$$y - 1 = \frac{1}{3}\left(\frac{x-5}{2}\right)^2$$
$$y = \frac{1}{3}\left(\frac{x-5}{2}\right)^2 + 1$$

Note that the domain and range of the inverse are the interchanged domain and range of the original function. In other words, the original function has a domain of $x \geq 1$ and range of $y \geq 5$. The domain of the inverse, then, is $x \geq 5$ and the range is $y \geq 1$.

As you can see by the graph at right, the points on the inverse graph, have interchanged coordinates from the points on the graph of the original function. For example, two points on the original graph are (1, 5) and (4, 11). The corresponding points on the graph of the inverse are (5, 1) and (11, 4).

Answer: $y = \frac{(x-5)^2}{12} + 1$ in the domain $x \geq 5$.

Here are some more to try. Find the equation for the inverse of each function.

a. $y = 3x - 2$

b. $y = \frac{x+1}{4}$

c. $y = \frac{1}{3}x + 2$

d. $y = x^3 + 1$

e. $y = 1 + \sqrt{x+5}$

f. $y = 3(x+2)^2 - 7$

g. $y = 2\sqrt{x-1} + 3$

h. $y = \frac{1}{2+x}$

i. $y = \log_3(x+2)$

Answers:

a. $y = \frac{x+2}{3}$

b. $y = 4x - 1$

c. $y = 3x - 6$

d. $y = \sqrt[3]{x-1}$

e. $y = (x-1)^2 - 5$

f. $y = \sqrt{\frac{x+7}{3}} - 2$

g. $y = \left(\frac{x-3}{2}\right)^2 + 1$

h. $y = \frac{1}{x} - 2$

i. $y = 3^x + 2$

Checkpoint Number 18

Problem 9-127

Solving a System of Equations in Three Variables

Answer to problem 9-127: $(6, -2, -8)$

To solve a system of equations in three variables using elimination you can use the same basic process as you would with two variables. Choose any variable to eliminate and then you are left with two equations in two variables. Continue to solve in the usual way. To solve using matrix multiplication you need to change the system into matrices and then isolate the variable matrix by using the inverse matrix on the graphing calculator. Here is an example of each method.

Example 1: Solve for (x, y, z)

$$5x - 4y - 6z = -19$$
$$-2x + 2y + z = 5$$
$$3x - 6y - 5z = -16$$

Method One—Elimination

Choose a variable to eliminate. We choose z and decide to use the first two equations. We multiply the second equation by 6 to get $-12x + 12y + 6z = 30$ and add it to the first, as shown at right.

$$-12x + 12y + 6z = 30$$
$$\underline{5x - 4y - 6z = -19}$$
$$(A) \quad -7x + 8y = 11$$

Then we must also eliminate z using a different combination of two equations. We choose to multiply the second by 5 to get $-10x + 10y + 5z = 25$ and add it to the third.

$$-10x + 10y + 5z = 25$$
$$\underline{3x - 6y - 5z = -16}$$
$$(B) \quad -7x + 4y = 9$$

Now we have two equations with two variables. We can subtract line (B) from line (A) to eliminate x and find y.

$$(A) \quad -7x + 8y = 11$$
$$(B) \quad \underline{-(-7x + 4y = 9)}$$
$$4y = 2$$
$$y = \tfrac{1}{2}$$

We substitute the value we got for y into equation (A) to get $-7x + 8(\tfrac{1}{2}) = 11$. This gives $-7x = 7$ and $x = -1$.

Then we go back to any of the original equations and substitute the values for x and y to find z. Using the first one:

$$5(-1) - 4(\tfrac{1}{2}) - 6z = -19$$
$$-7 - 6z = -19$$
$$-6z = -12$$
$$z = 2$$

The solution is $(-1, \tfrac{1}{2}, 2)$.

Method Two–Matrices

First we write the problem as a matrix equation.

$$\begin{bmatrix} 5 & -4 & -6 \\ -2 & 2 & 1 \\ 3 & -6 & -5 \end{bmatrix} \cdot \begin{bmatrix} x \\ y \\ z \end{bmatrix} = \begin{bmatrix} -19 \\ 5 \\ -16 \end{bmatrix}$$

We use a graphing calculator to left-multiply both sides of the equation by the inverse of the coefficient matrix. (For help with how to do this with your calculator, refer to the Lesson 7.3.3 Resource Page or consult the manual for your calculator.)

$$\begin{bmatrix} x \\ y \\ z \end{bmatrix} = \begin{bmatrix} 5 & -4 & -6 \\ -2 & 2 & 1 \\ 3 & -6 & -5 \end{bmatrix}^{-1} \cdot \begin{bmatrix} -19 \\ 5 \\ -16 \end{bmatrix}$$

This gives:

$$\begin{bmatrix} x \\ y \\ z \end{bmatrix} = \begin{bmatrix} -1 \\ 0.5 \\ 2 \end{bmatrix}$$

The solution is $(-1, \frac{1}{2}, 2)$.

We can now go back and solve problem 9-127.

Example 2: Use elimination or matrix multiplication to solve this system of equations:

$$x + y - z = 12$$
$$3x + 2y + z = 6$$
$$2x + 5y - z = 10$$

Method One

To eliminate z, we add the first two equations:

$$x + y - z = 12$$
$$+(3x + 2y + z = 6)$$
$$\overline{4x + 3y = 18} \ (A)$$

We can eliminate z again by adding the second and the third:

$$3x + 2y + z = 6$$
$$2x + 5y - z = 10$$
$$\overline{5x + 7y = 16} \ (B)$$

Now we can multiply equation (A) by 5 to get
$5(4x + 3y = 18) \Rightarrow 20x + 15y = 90$ and (B) by -4 to get
$-4(5x + 7y = 16) \Rightarrow -20x - 28y = -64$ and add the results to eliminate x:

$$20x + 15y = 90$$
$$-20x - 28y = -64$$
$$\overline{ -13y = 26}$$
$$y = -2$$

Substituting $y = -2$ into (A) gives $x = 6$. Substituting $y = -2$ and $x = 6$ in any of the original equations gives $z = -8$.

Method Two

We rewrite the system as the matrix equation at right.

$$\begin{bmatrix} 1 & 1 & -1 \\ 3 & 2 & 1 \\ 2 & 5 & -1 \end{bmatrix} \cdot \begin{bmatrix} x \\ y \\ z \end{bmatrix} = \begin{bmatrix} 12 \\ 6 \\ 10 \end{bmatrix}$$

We isolate the variable matrix:

$$\begin{bmatrix} x \\ y \\ z \end{bmatrix} = \begin{bmatrix} 1 & 1 & -1 \\ 3 & 2 & 1 \\ 2 & 5 & -1 \end{bmatrix}^{-1} \cdot \begin{bmatrix} 12 \\ 6 \\ 10 \end{bmatrix}$$

We use the graphing calculator to calculate the inverse and multiply to get

$$\begin{bmatrix} x \\ y \\ z \end{bmatrix} = \begin{bmatrix} 6 \\ -2 \\ -8 \end{bmatrix}$$

The solution is $x = 6$, $y = -2$, $z = -8$.

Here are some more to try. Solve these systems of equations.

a. $x + y + z = 34$
$3x + 2y + 4z = 95$
$x + 2y + 3z = 56$

b. $x - 2y + 3z = 8$
$2x + y + z = 6$
$x + y + 2z = 12$

c. $5x + y + 2z = 6$
$3x - 6y - 9z = -48$
$x - 2y + z = 12$

d. $4x - y + z = -5$
$2x + 2y + 3z = 10$
$5x - 2y + 6z = 1$

e. $x + y = 2 - z$
$-y + 1 = -z - 2x$
$3x - 2y + 5z = 16$

f. $a - b + 2c = 2$
$a + 2b - c = 1$
$2a + b + c = 4$

g. $-4x = z - 2y + 12$
$y + z = 12 - x$
$8x - 3y + 4z = 1$

h. $3x + y - 2z = 6$
$x + 2y + z = 7$
$6x + 2y - 4z = 12$

i. $4x + 4y - 5z = -2$
$2x - 4y + 10z = 6$
$x + 2y + 5z = 0$

Answers:

a. **(17, 12, 5)**

b. **(−1, 3, 5)**

c. **(−1, −3, 7)**

d. **(−1, 3, 2)**

e. **(−3, 0, 5)**

f. **no solution**

g. **(−3, 5, 10)**

h. **infinite solutions**

i. $(\frac{1}{2}, -\frac{3}{4}, \frac{1}{5})$

Glossary

3-dimensional coordinate system   In three dimensions the *z*-axis is perpendicular to the *x*-*y* plane at (0, 0). Points in 3-dimensions are represented with coordinates (*x*, *y*, *z*). The first octant where *x,-y,* and-*z* are positive is shown at right with the point (2, 3, 1). (p. 307)

absolute value   The absolute value of a number is the distance of the number from zero. Since the absolute value represents a distance without regard to direction, it is always a positive real number. For example, $|-7| = 7$, and $|7| = 7$. The absolute value of a complex number is its distance from zero in the complex plane. For a complex number $a + bi$, $|a + bi| = \sqrt{a^2 + b^2}$. For example, $|3 - 2i| = \sqrt{3^2 + (-2)^2} = \sqrt{13}$. (pp. 193, 464, 466)

additive identity   The number 0 is called the additive identity because adding 0 to any number does not change the number. An additive identity matrix or 0 matrix is a matrix of all 0's. (pp. 352, 362)

additive inverse   The additive inverse of a number is the number we can add to that number to get the additive identity, 0. So, for the number 5, the additive inverse is -5; for the number -13, the additive inverse is 13. For any number *x*, the additive inverse is $-x$. (p. 352)

algebraic representation   Algebraic representation generally means representing the mathematical relationships using numbers, a variable or variables, and operation symbols in equations, or inequalities.

algebraic strategies   Using algebraic strategies means to write an algebraic representation of the problem and then to rewrite those expressions to get equivalent, but more useful results that lead to a solution for the problem or that reveal more information to help solve it. (pp. 221, 224)

amplitude   The amplitude of a cyclic graph is one-half the distance between the highest and lowest points. In the graph at right, *a* is the amplitude. (pp. 421, 423)

angle   An angle is formed by two rays joined at a common endpoint (the vertex). In geometric figures, angles are usually formed by two segments with a common endpoint.

angles of rotation.   Angles with one vertex at the origin and formed by counter-clockwise rotation from the positive *x*-axis, are referred to as angles of rotation in standard position. For an angle θ, in standard position, the positive *x*-axis is the initial ray and the terminal ray may point in any direction. The measure of such an angle may have any real value. (p. 403)

appreciation   An increase in value. (p. 151)

arccosine of *x*   See "cosine inverse ($\cos^{-1} x$)." (pp. 675, 679)

arcsine of x See "sine inverse ($\sin^{-1} x$)." (p. 678)

arctangent of x See "tangent inverse ($\tan^{-1} x$)." (p. 679)

area   For a 2-dimensional region, the number of non-overlapping square units needed to cover the region. Also see "surface area."

area model   An area model or diagram is one way to represent the probabilities of the outcomes for a sequence of two events. The total area is one, and the probabilities are represented by proportional parts. In the example, P(S) and P(not S) are the dimensions of the right side. The probabilities that A will occur or not occur depending on when S occurs are the top and bottom of the rectangle. The area of each part is the probability of each possible sequence of two events. (p. 502)

argument   Used with sigma notation for sequences to describe the nth term. In the expression, $\sum_{k=1}^{10} (2k+1)$ the expression $2k+1$ is the argument. (p. 627)

arithmetic sequence   In an arithmetic sequence the difference between sequential terms is constant. Each term of an arithmetic sequence can be generated by adding the common difference to the previous term. For example in the sequence, 4, 7, 10, 13, ..., the common difference is 3. (pp. 71, 75, 83)

arithmetic series   An arithmetic series is the sum of the terms of an arithmetic sequence. Given the arithmetic sequence $3, 7, 11, ..., 43$, the corresponding arithmetic series is $3 + 7 + 11 + ... + 43$. (pp. 610, 618, 622)

arrange, arrangement   We arrange a set of objects or make an arrangement when we put them in a particular order, in a line, in a row, around a circle, on a shelf, in a stack, around a table... (pp. 523, 525, 530)

asymptote   A line that the graph of a curve approaches so that the distance between the graph and the line gets as small as you wish. We often graph functions, which have vertical and/or horizontal asymptotes. For example the asymptotes for the graph of $f(x) = \frac{1}{x+25}$ are $x = -25$ and $y = 0$. (Asymptotes are more completely defined in later courses.) (pp. 116, 118, 181, 183, 289)

axes   In a coordinate plane, the two perpendicular number lines that intersect at the origin (0, 0). The x-axis is horizontal and the y-axis is vertical. In 3-dimensions a third number line, the z-axis is perpendicular to the x-y plane at the origin (0, 0, 0). (p. 307) See "coordinate axes" and "3-dimensional axes" for illustration.

The Binomial Theorem   The formula for the expansion of $(x+y)^n$ is called the Binomial Theorem. (p. 655)

$$(x+y)^n = {_nC_n}x^n + {_nC_{n-1}}x^{n-1}y + {_nC_{n-2}}x^{n-2}y^2 + \ldots + {_nC_1}xy^{n-1} + {_nC_0}y^n$$

For example, $(x+y)^3 = {_3C_3}x^3 + {_3C_2}x^2y + {_3C_1}xy^2 + {_3C_0}y^3 = 1x^3 + 3x^2y + 3xy^2 + 1y^3$

boundary curve   A curve that marks the "edge" of the graph of an inequality. For a strict inequality ($<$ or $>$) the curve is dotted to show that points on the curve are not included in the graph; for $\leq$ or $\geq$ the curve is solid to show that the points on the curve are included. The graph of intersection of $y < x^2 + 4x + 3$ and $y \geq 2x^2 + 5x - 3$ is shown at right. (p. 247)

boundary line   The line that marks the "edge" of the graph of a linear inequality. For a strict inequality ($<$ or $>$) the line is dotted to show that points on the line are not included in the graph; for $\leq$ or $\geq$ the line is solid to show that the points on the line are included. The graph of $y > \frac{2}{3}x - 3$ is at right. (p. 247)

boundary point   On a number line graph, a point that represents the largest or smallest value in the set of real numbers or the largest or smallest number that is not in the set. When the boundary point is in the set to be represented it marked with a solid dot; when it is not in the set we use a "hollow dot." Examples for $-1.5 < x < 4$ and $x \geq -4$ are shown at right. (pp. 236, 238)

circle   In a plane, the set of all points equidistant from a single point. The general equation of a circle is $(x-h)^2 + (y-k)^2 = r^2$ where the point (h, k) is the center of the circle of radius r. (pp. 198, 206, 566, 567, 576)

circular functions   The periodic functions based on the unit circle, including $y = \sin x$, $y = \cos x$, and $y = \tan x$. See "sine function," "cosine function," and "tangent function."

coefficient   When variable(s) are multiplied by a number, the number is called a coefficient of that term. The numbers that are multiplied by the variables in the terms of a polynomial are called the coefficients of the polynomial. For example, 3 is the coefficient of $3x^2$. (p. 440)

combination   A combination is the number of ways we can select items from a larger set without regard to order. For instance, choosing a committee of 3 students from a group of 5 volunteers is a combination since the order in which committee members are selected does not matter. We write $_nC_r$ to represent the number of combinations of n things taken r at a time (or n choose r). For instance, the number of ways to select a committee of 3 students from a group of 5 is $_5C_3$. You can use Pascal's Triangle to find $_5C_3$ or use permutations and divided by the number of arrangements $\frac{_5P_3}{_3P_3} = \frac{5!}{3!2!}$. Formulas for combinations include: $_nC_r = \frac{_nP_r}{r!} = \frac{n!}{r!(n-r)!}$. (pp. 523, 530)

common difference   The difference between consecutive terms of an arithmetic sequence or the *generator* of the sequence. When the common difference is positive the sequence increases; when it is negative the sequence decreases. In the sequence $3, 7, 11, \ldots, 43$, the common difference is 4. (pp. 75, 83)

common ratio   Common ratio is another name for the multiplier or *generator* of a geometric sequence. It is the number to multiply one term by to get the next one. In the sequence: 96, 48, 24, ... the common ratio is $\frac{1}{2}$. (p. 83)

complete graph   A complete graph is one that includes everything that is important about the graph (such as intercepts and other key points, asymptotes, or limitations on the domain or range), and that makes the rest of the graph predictable based on what is shown. For example, a complete graph of the equation $y = \frac{1}{3}(x-2)^2(x+3)$ is shown at right. (p. 9)

completing the square   A standard procedure for rewriting a quadratic equation from standard form to graphing (or vertex) form is called completing the square. Completing the square is also used to solve quadratic equations in one variable. For example, the expression $x^2 - 6x + 4$ starts with the first two terms of $(x-3)^2$. To "complete the square" we need to add 9 to $x^2 - 6x$. Since the original expression only adds 4, completing the square would increase the expression by 5, so $(x-3)^2 - 5$ is an equivalent form that is useful for solving or graphing. (pp. 202, 206, 387)

complex conjugates   The complex number $a + bi$ has a complex conjugate $a - bi$. Similarly, the conjugate of $c - di$ is $c + di$. What is noteworthy about complex numbers conjugates is that both their product $(a+bi)(a-bi) = a^2 - b^2i^2 = a^2 + b^2$ and their sum $(a+bi) + (a-bi) = 2a$ are real numbers. If a complex number is a zero (or root) of a real polynomial function, then its complex conjugate is also a zero (or root). (p. 460)

complex numbers   Numbers written in the form $a + bi$ where a and b are real numbers, are called complex numbers. Each complex number has a real part, a, and an imaginary part, bi. Note that real numbers are also complex numbers with $b = 0$, and imaginary numbers are complex numbers where $a = 0$. (pp. 455, 456)

complex plane   A set of coordinate axes with all the real numbers on the horizontal axis (the real axis) and all the imaginary numbers on the vertical axis (the imaginary axis) defines the complex plane. Complex numbers are graphed in the complex plane using the same method we use to graph coordinate points. Thus, the complex number $1 + 3i$ is located at the point $(1, 3)$ in the complex plane. (p. 466)

composite function   A function that is created as the result of using the outputs of one function as the inputs of another can be seen as a composite function. For example the function $h(x) = |\log x|$ can be seen as the composite function $f(g(x))$ where $f(x) = |x|$ and $g(x) = \log x$. See "composition." (p. 292)

composition   When the output of one function is used as the input for a second function, a new function is created which is a composition of the two original functions. If the first function is $g(x)$ and the second is $f(x)$, the composition can be written as $f(g(x))$ or $f \circ g(x)$. Note that the order in which we perform the functions matters and $g(f(x))$ will usually be a different function. (p. 274)

compound interest   Interest that is paid on both the principal and the previously accrued interest. (pp. 125, 658, 661)

compress   A term used informally to describe the relationship of a graph to its parent graph when the graph increases or decreases more slowly than the parent. For example, the solid parabola shown at right is a compressed version of its parent, shown as a dashed curve. (pp. 170, 175)

conditional probability   The probability of outcome B occurring, given that outcome A has already happened is called the conditional probability of B, given A (the usual notation is $P(B|A)$). One way to calculate the conditional probability of B given A, is to divide the probability of both outcomes A and B by the probability of outcome A alone, or $P(B|A) = \frac{P(A \text{ and } B)}{P(A)}$. In many situations it is possible to calculate the conditional probability directly from the data by counting the number of possibilities for outcome B once outcome A has occurred. (pp. 506, 516)

cone   If you have a circle in a plane and a point P, not in that plane, the solid obtained by joining all of the points inside or on the circle to P is a circular cone. P is called the *apex* of the cone. A *standard* cone is a circular cone with its apex P directly over the center of the circle. For the purpose of defining the conic sections visualize two standard cones, one upside down on top of the other, touching at their apexes and both extending infinitely, one upwards and one downwards. (p. 554)

conic section   Circles, ellipses, hyperbolas and parabolas are known as conic sections. They are given this name because each curve can be found by taking a section or slice of a cone. (pp. 554, 561)

conjugate   Every complex number $a + bi$ has a conjugate, $a - bi$, and both the sum and product of the conjugates are real. Similarly, an irrational number that can be written $a + \sqrt{b}$ where a and b are rational, has a conjugate, $a - \sqrt{b}$, and the product and sum of these conjugates are rational. (p. 460)

conjugate axis   The axis of a hyperbola that does not contain the vertices. It is perpendicular to the transverse axis at the center of the hyperbola. The distance from the center to the end of the conjugate axis is represented as b in the general equation. (p. 585) See "hyperbola."

continuous   For this course, when the points on a graph are connected and it makes sense to connect them, we say the graph is continuous. Such a graph will have no holes or breaks in it. This term will be more completely defined in a later course. (pp. 62, 86)

coordinate axes   For two dimensions, two perpendicular number lines, the x- and y-axes, that intersect where both are zero and that provide the scale(s) for labeling each point in a plane with its horizontal and vertical distance and direction from the origin (0, 0). In three dimensions, a third number line, the z-axis, is perpendicular to a plane and intersects it at origin (0, 0, 0). The z-axis provides the scale for the height of a point above or below the plane. See "3-dimensional coordinate system." (p. 307)

coordinates   The numbers in an ordered pair (a, b) or triple (a, b, c) used to locate a point in the plane or in space in relation to a set of coordinate axes. (pp. 22, 307)

cosecant   The cosecant is the reciprocal of the sine. (p. 682)

cosine   In a right triangle (as shown at right) the ratio $\frac{adjacent\ side}{hypotenuse}$ is known as the cosine of the acute angle. At right, $\cos B = \frac{a}{c}$ since the side length a is adjacent to angle B. On a unit circle the cosine of an angle is the x-coordinate of the point the where the terminal ray of an angle in standard position intersects the unit circle. (pp. 392, 407)

cosine function   The cosine of angle θ, denoted $\cos\theta$, is the x-coordinate of the point on the unit circle reached by a rotation angle of θ radians in standard position. The general equation for the cosine function is $y = a\cos b(x-h)+k$. This function has amplitude a, period $\frac{2\pi}{b}$, horizontal shift h, and vertical shift k. (p. 409)

cosine inverse ($\cos^{-1} x$)   Read as the inverse of cosine x, $\cos^{-1} x$ is the measure of the angle with cosine x. We can also write $y = \arccos x$. Note that the notation refers to the inverse of the cosine function, *not* $\frac{1}{\cos x}$. Because $y = \cos^{-1} x$ is equivalent to $x = \cos y$ and there are infinitely many angles y such that $\cos y = x$, the inverse *function* is restricted to select the *principal* value of y such that $0 \le y \le \pi$. The graph of the inverse cosine function is at right. (p. 684)

cotangent   The cotangent is the reciprocal of the tangent. The graph of the cotangent function is at right. (p. 683)

cubic   A cubic polynomial is a polynomial with degree 3. (pp. 182, 207)

cycle   One cycle of a graph of a trigonometric function is the shortest piece that represents all possible outputs. The length of one cycle is the distance along the x-axis needed to generate all possible output values or the distance around the unit circle needed to generate all possible outcomes. (p. 379)

cyclic function   The term cyclic function is sometimes used to describe trigonometric functions, but it also includes any function that sequentially repeats its outputs at regular intervals. (p. 412)

decision chart   A decision chart is a method for organizing a counting problem that could be represented by a symmetric tree diagram. Begin by asking how many decisions need to be made, and then mark a space for each decision. Fill in each space with the number of possibilities for that decision. For example a child has a set of 26 blocks, each with a different letter of the alphabet on it. How many three-letter arrangements could he make by lining up any three of his blocks? There are three decisions, with 26 choices for the first letter, 25 for the second, and 24 for the third. To calculate the total number of possibilities the numbers in the decision chart must be multiplied.

$$26 \cdot 25 \cdot 24$$

The decision chart is a short way to represent a tree with 26 branches at stage one, 25 at stage two, and 24 at stage three. (pp. 514, 521)

Algebra 2 Connections

degree   One degree is an angle measure that is $\frac{1}{360}$ of a full circle or $\frac{\pi}{180}$ radians. (p. 399)

degree of a polynomial   The degree of a monomial is the sum of the exponents of its variables. For example, the degree of $3x^2y^5z$ is 8. For a polynomial the degree is the degree of the monomial term with the highest degree. Example: for the polynomial $2x^5y^2 - 4x^4z^6 + x^7z$ the degree is 10. (p. 440)

degree of a polynomial in one variable   The highest power of the variable. The degree of a polynomial function also indicates the maximum number of factors of the polynomial and provides information for predicting the number of "turns" the graph can take. (p. 440)

dependent variable   The variable whose value is determined by the value of another variable. For a given value of the independent variable, or input, the value of the dependent variable is the output. In an ordered pair, the variable occurring second is the dependent variable. The dependent variable is usually graphed in relation to the vertical axis. (pp. 6, 13, 199)

depreciation   A decrease in value possibly because of normal wear and tear, age, decay, decrease in price. (p. 151)

directrix   A line used to define a conic section. A parabola can be defined as the locus of points equidistant from a line, which is its directrix and a point, which is its focus. (p. 556)

discrete graph   A graph that is made up of separate points. (p. 62)

discriminant   For any quadratic equation $ax^2 + bx + c = 0$, $b^2 - 4ac$ is called the discriminant. If $b^2 - 4ac \geq 0$, the roots of the quadratic are real. If the discriminant is less than 0, the roots are imaginary or complex. (p. 460)

distance formula   An application of the Pythagorean Theorem to find the distance between two points in a plane. The distance between any two points (x_1, y_1) and (x_2, y_2) is $\sqrt{(x_2 - x_1)^2 + (y_2 - y_1)^2}$. In the example at right the distance is $\sqrt{4^2 + 5^2}$. (p. 200)

Distributive Property   The basis for rewriting products as sums and sums as products. For numbers or algebraic expressions A, B, and C, $A(B + C) = AB + AC$. (pp. 94, 99)

domain   The domain of a function is the set of possible values for the independent variable or the set of possible input values. It consists of every number that x can represent for the function, in other words every number that has an output. (pp. 16, 18, 199)

double root   A root of a function that occurs exactly twice. If an expression of the form $(x - a)^2$ is a factor of a polynomial, then the polynomial has a double root at $x = a$. The graph of the polynomial does not pass through the x-axis at $x = a$ but is tangent to the axis at $x = a$. (p. 446)

double root

eccentricity The eccentricity of an ellipse is a measurement reflecting its "roundness." The eccentricity, e, is found with the formula $e = \frac{c}{a}$, where $c^2 = a^2 - b^2$, and a and b are the lengths of the semi-major and semi-minor axes. For a hyperbola, the eccentricity is a measure of the shape of the curve; the larger the eccentricity the more quickly the branches spread apart. The formula is also $e = \frac{c}{a}$. Note that since $c > a$, the eccentricity of a hyperbola is always greater than 1; ellipses have eccentricity less than 1. Parabolas have eccentricity equal to 1, and circles have eccentricity equal to 0. (pp. 576, 585)

elimination to solve a system of equations The key step in the elimination method of solving equations is to add or subtract both sides of the equations to eliminate one of the variables. For example in the equations at right the variable, y, is eliminated when the two equations are added to get $13x = -13$. (p. 66)

$$5x - 3y = 1$$
$$8x + 3y = -14$$

ellipse The set of all points for which the sum of their distances from two fixed points, the foci, remains constant. You can visualize an ellipse as a circle that has been stretched vertically or horizontally. The general form of the equation of an ellipse (with a horizontal major axis) is $\frac{(x-h)^2}{a^2} + \frac{(y-k)^2}{b^2} = 1$. The line through the two vertices of the ellipse in the long direction is called the major axis of the ellipse, and the distance from the center of the ellipse to one end of the major axis is called the semi-major axis. The shortest length across the center of the ellipse is the minor axis, and half this length is the semi-minor axis. If a is the length of the semi-major axis, b the semi minor axis, c the distance from the center to either focus, and (h, k) is the center, then the equation of the ellipse can be written

$$\frac{(x-h)^2}{a^2} + \frac{(y-k)^2}{b^2} = 1, \text{ if the major axis is horizontal or}$$

$$\frac{(x-h)^2}{b^2} + \frac{(y-k)^2}{a^2} = 1, \text{ if the major axis is vertical.}$$

In either case, b is defined by $c^2 = a^2 - b^2$, and the eccentricity is $e = \frac{c}{a}$. (pp. 570, 571, 575, 576)

equally likely Outcomes or events are considered to be equally likely when they have the same probability. (pp. 497, 502, 510)

equation A mathematical sentence in which two expressions have an equal sign between them. (linear pp. 11, 173, exponential p. 123, quadratic p. 177, square root p. 154)

equidistant The same distance or length. For example, all the points on a circle are equidistant from its center and that distance is the length of the radius. (p. 566)

equilateral A polygon is equilateral if all its sides have equal length. The example at right is an equilateral hexagon.

equivalent Two algebraic expressions are equivalent if they have the same value for any legitimate substitution for their variables. Two equations are equivalent if they have the same solutions. (pp. 94, 98, 119)

evaluate   To evaluate an expression with variables, substitute the value(s) given for the variable(s) and perform the operations according the order of operations. For example, to evaluate the expression $x^3 - x^2$ for $x = -3$, substitute -3 for x, $(-3)^3 - (-3)^2 = -27 - 9 = -36$.

event   Used in relation to calculating probabilities, an event is a set of outcomes or an outcome of some action that has alternative possibilities. (pp. 510, 515)

expected value   The expected value for an outcome is the product of the probability of the outcome and the value placed on that outcome. The expected value of an event is the sum of the expected values for its possible outcomes. For example, in a lottery where 7 numbers are drawn from 77 and you have to have chosen all seven to win, the probability that your ticket is the $1,000,000 winner is $\frac{1}{2404808340}$ and the expected value is $0.000416. (pp. 497, 499, 510)

experimental probability   A data-based probability arrived at by conducting trials and recording the results. When a die is rolled 20 times the experimental probability of getting a 6 is the number of times 6 comes up over the total number or rolls 20. (p. 537)

exponential function   An exponential function has an equation of the form $y = ab^x$ for the domain of all real numbers and range positive real numbers , where a is the initial value and b is the multiplier or base. The general form for an exponential function is $f(x) = ab^{x+h} + k$. An example of an exponential function is graphed at right. (pp. 55, 125, 151)

expression   An algebraic representation that contains one or more numbers and/or variables and may include operations and grouping symbols. Some examples of algebraic expressions are $x^5 - 4x^2 + 8$, $\sqrt{a^2 + b^2}$, $\frac{x-9}{2} - 10 + \frac{1}{y}$, x. (pp. 101, 102, 103)

extraneous solution   Sometimes in the process of solving equations, multiplying or squaring expressions involving a variable will lead to a numerical result that does not make the original equation true. This false result is called an extraneous solution. For example, in the process of solving the equation $\sqrt{x+3} = 9 - x$ both sides of the equation are squared to get $x + 3 = x^2 - 19x + 81$ which has solutions 6 and 13. 6 is a solution of the original equation, but 13 is extraneous, because $\sqrt{13+3} \neq 9 - 13$. (pp. 224, 360)

$f^{-1}(x)$ Read this as "f inverse of x," the inverse function for $f(x)$. (p. 231)

factor   A factor is part of a product. A polynomial expression $p(x)$ is a factor of another polynomial expression $P(x)$ when there is a polynomial $q(x)$ such that $p(x)q(x) = P(x)$. In the equation $3x^2 - 9x + 6 = 3(x - 2)(x - 1)$, the expressions $(x - 2)$, $(x - 1)$, and 3 are factors. (pp. 23, 149, 475)

Factor Theorem   States that if a is a root of a polynomial then $x - a$ is a factor, and if $x - a$ is a factor then a is a root. For example, the polynomial $x^2 - 5x - 6 = (x - 6)(x + 1)$ and the roots are 6 and –1.

factorial   A shorthand notation for the product of a list of consecutive positive integers from the given number down to $1: n! = n(n - 1)(n - 2)(n - 3) \cdot \ldots \cdot 3 \cdot 2 \cdot 1$. For example, $5! = 5 \cdot 4 \cdot 3 \cdot 2 \cdot 1 = 120$. (pp. 515, 521)

fair game A game in which the expected values for each player are equal. If you pay to play a game then the game is fair if the cost to play equals the expected value. For example, player A and player B are rolling a die to see how far to move in a board game. If the die comes up 1, 2, 3, or 4, player A moves that many spaces. If the die comes up 5 or 6 player B gets to move that many spaces. Player A has an expected value of moving $\frac{1}{6}+\frac{2}{6}+\frac{3}{6}+\frac{4}{6}=\frac{10}{6}$ spaces on each turn. Player B has an expected value of moving $\frac{5}{6}+\frac{6}{6}=\frac{11}{6}$ spaces per turn, so this game is not fair. (pp. 497, 510)

family of functions A group of functions that have at least one common characteristic. For example we describe all cubic functions, $y = a(x-h)^3 + k$ as the family of functions with parent graph $y = x^3$. All are cubic polynomials and all of the graphs are similar in shape. The set of all equations $y = mx + 7$ describes the family of linear functions with y-intercept 7. (pp. 189, 207)

feasible region Used to describe the intersection of the graphs of a set of inequalities that represent the constraints or parameters of a problem situation. The feasible region represents the points with coordinates that satisfy the given conditions. (pp. 241, 245)

focal length The distance c from the vertex to the focus of a parabola is called the focal length. In a hyperbola or an ellipse focal length is the distance c, from the center to one focus. See "focus of a parabola," "foci of an ellipse," and "foci of a hyperbola." (p. 568)

foci of an ellipse Every ellipse has two points on its major axis called the foci of the ellipse. For any point (x, y) on the ellipse, the sum of the distances from each focus to (x, y) is a constant. An ellipse with its center at the origin, x-intercepts of $(\pm a, 0)$ and y-intercepts $(0, \pm b)$, where $a > b$, has its foci at $(\pm c, 0)$, with $c^2 = a^2 - b^2$. When the center is $(0, 0)$ and the major axis is on the y-axis the foci are $(0, \pm c)$. (pp. 570, 571) See "ellipse. "

foci of a hyperbola Each hyperbola has two points on its transverse axis called the foci of the hyperbola. For any point (x, y) on the hyperbola, the difference between the distances from each focus to (x, y) is constant. A hyperbola with it center at the origin, x-intercepts $(\pm a, 0)$ and asymptotes $y = \pm \frac{b}{a} x$ has its foci at $(\pm c, 0)$, with $c^2 = a^2 + b^2$. When the center is $(0, 0)$ and the transverse axis is on the y-axis the foci are $(0, \pm c)$. (p. 585) See "hyperbola."

focus of a parabola A parabola is defined to be the set of points in the plane, each of which is the same distance from a fixed point (the focus) as it is from a fixed straight line (the directrix). Also, if rays parallel to the line of symmetry enter into the interior of the parabola to intersect the parabola and reflect so that the angle of incidence equals the angle of reflection, then all such rays intersect at the focus of the parabola. (pp. 556, 568) See "parabola."

fractional exponents Raising a number to a fractional exponent indicates a power as well as a root. $x^{a/b} = \sqrt[b]{x^a} = (\sqrt[b]{x})^a$. (pp. 143, 144, 148)

function A relationship in which for each input there is exactly one output. For example, $y = x^2$ is a function because each input for x determines one output. $x^2 + y^2 = 25$ is not a function, because, for example, when $x = 4$, y could be either 3 or –3. (pp. 6, 197, 199)

function notation   A convenient way to represent a function or to write a rule to show what a function machine does is to name the function with a letter and put the variable that represents the inputs in parentheses, for example $f(\ )$.   When the variable is x, this will be $f(x)$. Read it "f of x" to mean the output of the function when the operations of f are performed on the input x. (p. 231)

general equation   If $y = f(x)$ is a parent equation, then the general equation for that function is given by $y = af(x-h)+k$ where (h, k) is the point corresponding to $(0, 0)$ in the parent graph and, relative to the parent graph, the function has been: 1) vertically stretched if the absolute value of a is greater than 1; 2) vertically compressed if the absolute value of a is less than 1; and/or 3) reflected across the x-axis if a is less than 0. (pp. 189, 207)

general quadratic equation for conic sections   The equation $ax^2 + by^2 + cx + dy + e = 0$, in which a and b are not *both* equal to zero is a general equation that could represent a parabola, an ellipse, a hyperbola, a circle, or a pair of lines depending on the values of the coefficients. This equation represents conic sections with axes parallel to the x- or y-axes. The general equation $ax^2 + bxy + cy^2 + dx + ey + f = 0$ includes conics with axes that are not parallel to the x- or y-axes. (p. 593)

generalize   Based on several specific examples describe common characteristics, patterns, or relationships and make a conjecture that can be tested on other examples. Use variables to represent a situation or relationship. (pp. 2, 26, 214)

generator   The generator of a sequence tells what you do to each term to get the next term. Note that this is different from the function for the nth term of the sequence. The generator only tells you how to find the following term, when you already know one term. In an arithmetic sequence the generator is the common difference; in a geometric sequence it is the multiplier or common ratio. (p. 69)

geometric sequence   A geometric sequence is a sequence that is generated by a multiplier. This means that each term of a geometric sequence can be found by multiplying the previous term by a constant. For example: 5, 15, 45... is the beginning of a geometric sequence with generator (common ratio) 3. In general a geometric sequence can be represented $a,\ ar,\ ar^2, ... + ar^{n-1}$. (pp. 71, 79, 80, 81)

geometric series (sum)   The sum of a geometric sequence is a geometric series, for example: $5 + 15 + 45 + ...$ The sum of the first n terms of a geometric sequence, $a + ar + ar^2 + ar^3 + ... + ar^{n-1}$ is given by the formula at right. (pp. 618, 636, 641, 647)

$$S = \frac{a(r^n - 1)}{r - 1}$$

graph   The graph of an equation is the set of points representing the coordinates that make the equation true. The direction to "graph an equation" or "draw a graph" means use graph paper, scale your axes appropriately, label key points, and plot points accurately. This is different from *sketching* a graph. The equation $y = \frac{1}{3}(x-2)^2(x+3)$ is graphed at right. (p. 9)

graphing form   A form of the equation of a function or relation that clearly shows key information about the graph. For example: the graphing form for the general equation of a quadratic function (also called vertex form) is $y = a(x-h)^2 + k$. The vertex (h, k), orientation (whether a is positive or negative) and amount of stretch or compression based on $|a| > 1$ or $|a| < 1$ can be appear in the equation. (pp. 176, 177)

growth factor   One way to analyze how the output value in a mathematical relation changes as the input value increases. Growth can be represented by constant addition, as the slope of a linear function or the constant difference in an arithmetic sequence, or by multiplication as the base of an exponential function or the multiplier in a geometric sequence. (p. 11)

(h, k) In this course h and k are used as parameters in general equations for families of functions $f(x) = af(x-h) + k$ and families of relations to represent the horizontal and vertical shifts of the parent graph. The point (h, k) represents location of a point that corresponds to $(0, 0)$ for parent graphs where $(0, 0)$ is on the graph. For circles, ellipses, and hyperbolas, (h, k) represents the center of the shifted graph. (pp. 190, 207, 576, 585)

half-life   When material decays, the half-life is the time it takes until only half the material remains. (p. 131)

horizontal shift   Used with parent graphs and general equations for functions and relations such as $y = a(x-h)^2 + k$. It is the amount a graph is moved left or right in relation to its parent graph, in this case $y = x^2$. The horizontal shift will be h units to the right if h is positive, to the left if h is negative. (p. 175)

hyperbola   A hyperbola has relationships corresponding to those of an ellipse. $\quad \frac{x^2}{a^2} - \frac{y^2}{b^2} = 1$
A hyperbola is made up of two branches. The line connecting the vertices of the two branches is called the transverse axis, and the letter a is used to represent the distance from the center to either vertex. For the equation at top right the center of $\quad \frac{y^2}{a^2} - \frac{x^2}{b^2} = 1$
the hyperbola is at the origin. The vertices are $(\pm a, 0)$ and the asymptotes have the equations $y = \pm \frac{b}{a}x$. The foci are on the transverse axis, in this case the x-axis, at $(\pm c, 0)$ with c given by the equation $c^2 = a^2 + b^2$. For a hyperbola, the eccentricity is a measure of the shape of the curve; the larger the eccentricity the more quickly the branches spread apart. Eccentricity is given by the formula $e = \frac{c}{a}$. Note that since $c > a$, the eccentricity of a hyperbola is always greater than 1. If the vertices are on the y-axis the foci are on the y-axis at $(0, \pm c)$, and the equation is written as shown in the lower equation at right. Everything else is the same *except* the asymptotes have slopes $\pm \frac{a}{b}$. b is also known as the length of the semi-conjugate axis. (pp. 579, 583)

hypotenuse   The longest side of a right triangle, the side opposite the right angle.

identity (trigonometric)   Equations that are true for all values for which the functions are defined. For example $\sin^2 x + \cos^2 x = 1$ which is true for all values of x, or $\cot x = \frac{1}{\tan x}$ which is true whenever the tangent and cotangent are defined. (p. 688)

identity element   The identity element for addition is the number we can add to any number and not change that number's "identity" or value. For addition, the identity element is 0; $a + 0 = a$ for any number, a. For multiplication, the identity element is 1, because $1 \cdot x = x$ for any number x. (p. 362)

identity matrix   An m by m matrix, often labeled I, with zero in every entry except those on the upper-left to lower-right diagonal. On that diagonal, each entry $m_{ij} = 1$. For any m by m matrix, M, $MI = IM = M$. The identity matrix for a 2 by 2 matrix is shown at right. (p. 362)

$$\begin{bmatrix} 1 & 0 \\ 0 & 1 \end{bmatrix}$$

imaginary numbers   The set of numbers that are solutions of equations of the form $x^2 =$ (a negative number) are called imaginary numbers. They are not positive, negative, or zero. The imaginary number i is a solution of the equation $x^2 = -1$, so $i^2 = -1$. In general, imaginary numbers follow the rules of real number arithmetic (e.g. $i + i = 2i$). Multiplying the imaginary number i by every possible real number yields all possible imaginary numbers. (pp. 454, 456)

independent events   When the probability of two events happening equals the product of their probabilities, the events are said to be independent. For example, the probability of landing on red on two consecutive spins of a roulette wheel is $\frac{9}{19} \cdot \frac{9}{19} = \frac{81}{361}$. (pp. 506, 516)

independent variable   In a function, the independent variable is the input variable. The variable occurring first in an ordered pair. (pp. 6, 13, 199)

index (plural indices)   In summation notation, the indices are the numbers below and above the sigma that indicate which term to start with and which to end with. For a series they show the first and last replacement values for n. When the symbol above sigma is ∞ the series continues without ending. Example: $\sum_{n=1}^{8} 5n - 7 = -2 + 3 + 8 + ... + 33$. (pp. 626, 627)

inequality   A mathematical statement that shows a relationship between two values or expressions where one is greater than (>) the other, or less than (<) the other, or just not equal ($\neq$) to the other. (p. 243)

inequalities with absolute value   If k is any positive number, an inequality of the form: $|f(x)| > k$ is equivalent to the statement $f(x) > k$ or $f(x) < -k$; and $|f(x)| < k$ is equivalent to the statement $-k < f(x) < k$. For example, you can solve the inequality, $|5x - 6| > 4$ by solving the two inequalities $5x - 6 > 4$ or $5x - 6 < -4$. (p. 243)

infinite geometric series   An infinite geometric series is a geometric series which never ends. The sum of such a series with an initial value a and common ratio r, with $-1 < r < 1$, is given by the formula at right. (p. 647)

$$S = \frac{a}{1 - r}$$

inflection point   A point at which a graph changes concavity. Concavity refers to whether the graph opens upward or downward. So an inflection point is a point at which a graph changes from opening upward to opening downward, or vice versa. The graph of $y = x^3$ has an inflection point, otherwise known as a point of inflection, at $x = 0$.

Inflection point

initial ray   When an angle of rotation is drawn in standard position, the positive *x*-axis is called the initial ray. (p. 403) See "angle and angle of rotation."

initial value   The initial value of a sequence is the first term of the sequence. (pp. 69, 86)

input   A replacement value for a variable in a function or relation. The first number in an ordered pair. The set of all possible input values is the domain of a function. (p. 6)

integer   Any whole number or the opposite of a whole number: $\dots -3, -2, -1, 0, 1, 2, 3, \dots$ (p. 475)

integral roots   Roots (or zeros) of functions that are integers. (p. 475)

intercepts   Points where a graph crosses the axes. *x*-intercepts are points at which the graph crosses the *x* axis and *y*-intercepts are points at which the graph crosses the *y* axis. On the graph at right the *x*-intercept is $(3, 0)$ and the *y*-intercept is $(0, 6)$. (p. 11)

interest   An amount paid which is a percentage of the principal. For example, a savings account may offer 4% annual interest rate, which means they will pay $4.00 in interest for a principal of $100 kept in the account for one year. (p. 125)

intersection   A point of intersection is a point that the graphs of two or more equations have in common. Graphs may intersect in one, two, several, many or no points. The set of coordinates of a point of intersection are a solution to the equation for each graph. (pp. 17, 21, 222, 223, 224)

inverse circular functions   See "inverse trigonometric functions." (p. 684)

inverse function   A function that "undoes" what the original function does. It can also be seen as the *x-y* interchange of the function. The inverse of a function performs in reverse order the inverse operation for each operation of the function. The graph of an inverse function is a reflection of the original function across the line $y = x$. For example, $y = x^3 + 2$ is equivalent to $x = \sqrt[3]{y - 2}$, its inverse function is written $y = \sqrt[3]{x - 2}$. (p. 268)

inverse operations   Subtraction is the inverse operation for addition and vice versa, division for multiplication, square root for squaring, and more generally taking the nth root for raising to the nth power.

inverse trigonometric functions   For each trigonometric function $\sin(x)$, $\cos(x)$, and $\tan(x)$, there is an inverse function written $\sin^{-1}(x)$, $\cos^{-1}(x)$, and $\tan^{-1}(x)$. Note: this symbol does not mean $\frac{1}{\sin(x)}$. It is a new function that "undoes" the original trig function, thus giving a specific angle measure when the input is $\sin x$, $\cos x$, or $\tan x$. For example: $\sin^{-1}(-\frac{1}{2}) = -\frac{\pi}{6}$. Note that the range of the inverse function is restricted to outputs for *y* such that $-\frac{\pi}{2} \le y \le \frac{\pi}{2}$ for $\sin x$, $-\frac{\pi}{2} < y < \frac{\pi}{2}$ for $\tan x$ and $0 \le y \le \pi$ for $\cos x$. (p. 684) Also see "cosine inverse," "sine inverse," and "tangent inverse."

investigating a function   To investigate a function means to make a complete graph of the function and to write down everything you know about the function. Some things to consider are: domain, range, intercepts, asymptotes, inverse, and symmetry. (p. 32, 34)

isosceles triangle   A triangle with two sides of equal length.

isometric dot paper   Useful for graphing three dimensional figures. The pattern of dots on the paper enhances the 3-dimensional appearance of the x-, y-, and z-axes. (p. 308)

justify   To give a logical reason supporting a statement or step in a proof. More generally to use facts, definitions, rules, and/or previously proven conjectures in an organized sequence to convincingly demonstrate that your claim is valid. (p. 109)

key point   An important point on a graph. Often an x- or y-intercept, a starting or ending point, a maximum or minimum point. Sometimes a point not on the graph that serves to locate an asymptote. (p. 9)

Law of Cosines   For any $\triangle ABC$, $a^2 = b^2 + c^2 - 2bc\cos A$ (pp. 28, 276)

Law of Sines   For any $\triangle ABC$, $\frac{\sin A}{a} = \frac{\sin B}{b} = \frac{\sin C}{c}$ (pp. 28, 276)

left-multiply   Since multiplication of matrices is not commutative the product AB may not equal BA. If we start with matrix A and we want the product BA we must left-multiply matrix A by matrix B. The order of the multiplication matters; therefore, we specify whether we are multiplying on the left side of the matrix or on the right, which would be right-multiplying. (p. 366)

line   Graphed, a line is made up of an infinite number of points, is one-dimensional and extends without end in two directions. In two dimensions a line is the graph of an equation of the form $ax + by = c$. (pp. 11, 167, 190)

line of best fit   The line that best approximates several data points. For this course we place the line by visually approximating its position. An example is shown in the graph at right.

line of symmetry   A line that divides a figure into two congruent shapes which are reflections of each other across the line. (p. 167)

linear equation   An equation with at least one variable of degree one and no variables of degree greater than one. The graph of a linear equation of two variables is a line in the plane. $ax + by = c$ is the standard form of a linear equation. (p. 11)

linear function   A polynomial function of degree one or zero, with general equation $f(x) = a(x - h) + k$. The graph of a linear function is a line. (p. 38)

linear inequality   An inequality with a boundary line represented by a linear equation. (pp. 247, 326)

linear programming   A method for solving a problem with several conditions or constraints that can be represented as linear equations or inequalities. (pp. 241, 245)

locator point   A locator point is a point which gives the position of a graph with respect to the axes. For a parabola, the vertex is a locator point. (p. 181)

locus   The location of a set of points that fit a given description. For example: A circle with center $(5, -2)$ and radius 3 is described as the locus of points that are a distance of three units from the point $(5, -2)$. (p. 566)

Log-Power Property   (p. 330) See "Power Property of Logs."

Log-Product Property   (pp. 334, 335) See "Product Property of Logs."

Log-Quotient Property   (pp. 334, 335) See "Quotient Property of Logs."

logarithm   An exponent. In the equation $y = 2^x$, x is the logarithm, base 2, of y, or $\log_2 y = x$. (pp. 282, 283)

logarithmic and exponential notation $m = \log_b(n)$ is the logarithmic form of the exponential equation $b^m = n$ ($b > 0$). (p. 283)

logarithmic functions   Inverse exponential functions. The base of the logarithm is the same base as that of the exponential function. For instance $y = \log_2 x$ can be read as "y is the exponent needed for base 2 to get x," and is equivalent to $x = 2^y$. The short version is stated "log, base 2, of x," and written $\log_2 x$. (pp. 281, 285, 286)

major axis   The longer axis of an ellipse. The distance from the center of the ellipse to the end of the major axis is the semi-major axis, represented as a in the general equation. (pp. 574, 576) See "ellipse."

mathematical induction   In this course, a method of proof that can be used to prove that a formula is true for any natural number ($n = 1, 2, 3, ...$) Such a proof consists of the following steps: (*i*) Verify that the formula is true for $n = 1$. (*ii*) Write the general statement of the formula for $n = k+1$. (*iii*) Show and justify the reasoning needed to move from the result for $n = k$ to get to the next case where $n = k+1$. (pp. 629, 632)

matrix   A rectangular array of numbers or algebraic expressions enclosed in square brackets. Usually a matrix is denoted by a capital letter. The plural is "matrices." Each matrix has horizontal rows and vertical columns. The number of rows and columns describe the matrix, so if a matrix has m rows and n columns we say the matrix has dimension m by n. We often write that $m_{i,j}$ is the entry in the ith row and the jth column. In the 3×3 matrix at right, $m_{2,3} = 2$. (p. 351)
$$\begin{bmatrix} 3 & 0 & -1 \\ 12 & 5 & 2 \\ 1 & -2 & 1 \end{bmatrix}$$

maximize   Make as large as possible. (pp. 242, 246)

maximum point   The highest point on a graph. For example, the vertex of a downwardly oriented parabola. (pp. 242, 246)

maximum value   The largest value in the range of a function. For example, the y-coordinate of the vertex of a downwardly oriented parabola. (pp. 242, 246)

mean   The average for a set of data. The mean is found by summing all the numbers and dividing the sum by the number of pieces of data. (p. 94)

median   The middle score of a set of data. The median is found by arranging the numbers from highest to lowest and finding the number in the middle. If the number of values is even, the median is the average (mean) of the two middle numbers. (p. 94)

minimize   Make as small as possible. (pp. 242, 246)

minimum point   The lowest point on a graph. For example, the vertex of an upwardly oriented parabola. (p. 242, 246)

minimum value   The smallest value in the range of a function. For example, the y-coordinate of the vertex of an upwardly oriented parabola. (pp. 242, 246)

minor axis   The shorter axis in an ellipse. The length of the semi-minor axis, the distance from the center to the end of the minor axis, is represented by b in the general equation. (pp. 574, 576) See "ellipse."

multiplicative inverse   The multiplicative inverse for a non-zero number is the number we can multiply by to get the multiplicative identity, 1. For example, for the number 5, the multiplicative inverse is $\frac{1}{5}$; for the number $\frac{2}{3}$ the multiplicative inverse is $\frac{3}{2}$. The multiplicative inverse for a complex number, such as $3-i$, is $\frac{1}{3-i} = \frac{3}{\sqrt{10}} + \frac{1}{\sqrt{10}}i$. The multiplicative inverse for a square matrix is the matrix we can multiply by to get the identity matrix. (pp. 364, 366)

multiplier   In a geometric sequence the number multiplied times each term to get the next term is called the multiplier or the common ratio or generator. The multiplier is also the number you can multiply by in order to increase or decrease an amount by a given percentage in one step. For example, to increase a number by 4%, the multiplier is 1.04. We would multiply the number by 1.04. The multiplier for decreasing by 4% is 0.96. (pp. 79, 80, 83, 86)

negative exponents   Raising a number to a negative exponent is the same as taking the reciprocal of the number. $x^{-a} = \frac{1}{x^a}$ for $x \neq 0$. (pp. 132, 148)

non-function   A relation that has more than one output for one or more of its inputs. (pp. 197, 198)

order   In a counting problem the order in which events occurs is sometimes important. For example, when an outcome ABC is considered to be different from BAC the different arrangements of A, B, and C are being counted as different results and the order of the events is important in determining the number of results. (pp. 523, 530) See "permutations."

ordered pair   A pair of numbers written (x, y) used to represent the coordinates of a point in an xy-plane where x represents the horizontal distance from 0 and y is the vertical. The input and output values of a function or relation can be represented as ordered pairs were x is the input, and y is the output.

ordered triple   Three real numbers written in order (x, y, z) represent a point in space or replacement values for a situation involving three variables. See "3-dimensional coordinate axes." (p. 312)

orientation   Used informally in this course to describe some graphs. For example the direction a parabola opens might be referred to as its orientation. When describing the graph of a polynomial function, a positive orientation would mean the graph eventually continues upward as the value of x increases, as in the example above right. A negative orientation would mean it eventually heads downward as the value of x continues to increase, as in the example below right. (pp. 175, 445)

outcome   Used to describe the result of an event in counting and probability problems. For example, when rolling one six-sided die, the possible outcomes are the numbers 1, 2, 3, 4, 5, and 6. (pp. 497, 502, 510)

output   Used to describe the result of applying a function or relationship rule to an input value. When a function is represented by a function machine the output is the number that comes out of the machine. For the function $f(x) = x^2 - 73$ when the input is 10, the output is 27. Function notation shows how the function operates on the input to produce the output: $f(10) = 10^2 - 73 = 27$. (p. 6)

parabola   The set of all points that are equidistant from a single point (the focus) and a line (the directrix). The general equation for a parabola that is a function (or a quadratic function) in graphing (or vertex) form, is $y = a(x - h)^2 + k$. The general equation of a quadratic function in standard form is $y = ax^2 + bx + c$. A general equation for parabolas that are not functions, "sleeping" parabolas, is $x - h = a(y - k)^2$. (pp. 168, 171, 179, 181-183, 199, 555, 556, 568)

parallel   Two lines in a plane are parallel if they never intersect. Parallel lines have the same slope. Two line segments in a plane are parallel if the lines they lie on lines that never intersect. Two lines in space are parallel if they lie in the same plane and they do not intersect. There is a constant distance between parallel lines.

parameter   In a general equations where x and y represent the inputs and outputs of the function, variables such as a, b, c, m, h, and k are often referred to as parameters, and they are often replaced with specific values. For example: in the equation $y = a(x - h)^2 + k$ representing all parabolas that are functions, the a, h, and k are (variable) parameters that give the shape and location, while x and y are the independent and dependent variables. (pp. 38, 115, 143, 175, 413)

parent graph   The simplest version of a family of graphs. For instance, the graph of $y = x^2$, is considered the parent graph for parabolas that are functions. (p. 182)

Algebra 2 Connections

Pascal's Triangle The array of numbers at right. The triangular pattern continues downward. This array shows all the values of $_nC_r$ where n is the row number when the vertex is $_0C_0$. r is the number of places to the right in row n (when the counting begins with 0). For instance, $_5C_2$ is equal to 10. (p. 649)

```
        1
      1   1
    1   2   1
  1   3   3   1
1   4   6   4   1
1  5  10  10  5  1
```

percentile A percentile ranking indicates the percentage of scores which are below the score in question. For example, if you scored at the 90th percentile on a test, your score was higher than the scores of 90% of the other test takers.

perfect square Usually, a quadratic polynomial $ax^2 + bx + c$ that can be rewritten as the second power of a binomial, $(cx + d)^2$. For example, $x^2 - 6x + 9$ is a perfect square that can be rewritten as $(x - 3)^2$. Also, any polynomial of even degree that can be rewritten as the square of one polynomial factor. For numbers, a whole number that can be written as the second power of another whole number. For example, 1, 4, 9, 16, and 25 are perfect squares.

perimeter The distance around the exterior of a figure on a flat surface. For a polygon the perimeter is the sum of the lengths of its sides. The perimeter of a circle is called its circumference.

period The length of one cycle of a graph, as shown by the dashed line in the graph at right. (pp. 416, 423)

periodic function A function which has a repetitive section or cycle such as the sine, cosine and tangent functions. In a periodic function, the cyclic pattern continues forever both to the left and to the right. (p. 423)

permutation A permutation is an arrangement in which the order of selection matters. For example a batting line-up is a permutation because it is an ordered list of players. If each of five letters, A, B, C, D, E is printed on a card, the number of 3-letter sequences can you make by selecting three of the five cards is a permutation. Permutations can be represented with tree diagrams, decision charts, and their value calculated by using the formula for $_nP_r = \frac{n!}{(n-r)!}$. In the example given above, $_5P_3 = \frac{5!}{2!} = \frac{5 \cdot 4 \cdot 3 \cdot 2 \cdot 1}{2 \cdot 1} = 5 \cdot 4 \cdot 3 = 60$. (pp. 518, 520, 525)

perpendicular Two lines, rays, or line segments that intersect to form a right angle. A line and a plane can also be perpendicular if the line does not lie in the plane, but intersects it and forms a right angle with every line in the plane that passes through the point of intersection.

plane A plane is an undefined term in geometry. It is a two-dimensional flat surface that extends without end. It is made up of points and has no thickness. The part of a plane outlined by its xy-, xz- and yz-traces is often used to represent a plane on a 3-dimensional coordinate system. (pp. 312, 320)

point An undefined term in geometry. A point has no dimensions but can be located by its coordinates on a number line, in a plane, or in space.

point-slope form $y - k = m(x - h)$ is called the point slope form of a linear equation or function because it shows the slope m and a point (h, k) that is on the graph of the line. For example, given a line that has slope $\frac{5}{3}$ and contains the point with coordinates $(3, -4)$ its equation can be written $y + 4 = \frac{5}{3}(x - 3)$. (p. 190)

polynomial   An algebraic expression that involves at most the operations of addition, subtraction, and multiplication. A polynomial in one variable is an expression that can be written as the sum of terms of the form: (any number) $\cdot$ $x^{(\text{whole number})}$. These polynomials are usually arranged with the powers of x in order, starting with the highest, left to right. The numbers that multiply the powers of x are called the coefficients of the polynomial. See "degree of a polynomial" for an example. (pp. 437, 440, 441, 451)

Power Property of Logs $\log_m(a^n) = n \log_m(a)$. For example, $\log_3 625 = 4 \log_3 5$. (pp. 330, 335)

principal   Initial investment or capital. An initial value.

probability   The probability that an event A. with a finite number of equally likely outcomes, will occur is the number of outcomes for event A divided by the total number of equally likely outcomes. This can be written as $\frac{number\ of\ outcomes\ for\ event\ A}{total\ number\ of\ possible\ outcomes}$. A probability p is a ratio, $0 \le p \le 1$. (p. 510)

Product Property of Logs $\log_m(a \cdot b) = \log_m(a) + \log_m(b)$. For example, $\log_3 30 = \log_3 5 + \log_3 6$. (p. 334)

profit   The amount of money after expenses have been accounted for. (pp. 241, 242, 245)

proof by induction   (pp. 629, 632) See "mathematical induction."

proportion   Equal ratios are described as a proportion. For example, the equation $\frac{x-8}{2x+1} = \frac{5}{6}$.

Pythagorean Identity   For trigonometric functions, $\cos^2 x + \sin^2 x = 1$ for any value of x. (pp. 689, 695)

quadratic equation   Any equation where at least one term has degree 2 and no term has degree higher than 2. The standard equation $Ax^2 + By^2 + Cxy + Dx + Ey + F = 0$ represents all quadratic relations in one or two variables. (pp. 23, 171, 177, 188)

quadratic formula   This formula gives you the solutions $x = \frac{-b \pm \sqrt{b^2 - 4ac}}{2a}$, for a quadratic equation in one variable that can be written in the standard form $ax^2 + bx + c = 0$. (p. 23)

quadratic function   A quadratic equation that can be written $y = ax^2 + bx + c$ is also a quadratic function where x is the independent variable and y is the dependent variable. Its graph is a parabola with a vertical orientation. The graphing form of a quadratic function is $f(x) = a(x - h)^2 + k$. (pp. 177, 188)

quadratic relation   The conic sections are quadratic relations. See "general quadratic equation," "quadratic equations," "parabola," "ellipse," and "hyperbola." (p. 593)

Algebra 2 Connections

quotient The result of a division problem is a quotient with a remainder (which could be 0). When a polynomial $p(x)$ is divided by a polynomial $d(x)$ the a polynomial $q(x)$ will be the quotient with a remainder $r(x)$. The product of $q(x)$ and $d(x)$ plus the remainder $r(x)$ will equal the original polynomial. $p(x) = d(x)q(x) + r(x)$. (p. 472)

Quotient Property of Logs $\log_m(\frac{a}{b}) = \log_m(a) - \log_m(b)$. For example, $\log_3 \frac{37}{5} = \log_3 37 - \log_3 5$. (p. 334)

radian measure An arc of a unit circle equal to the length of the radius of the circle is one radian. The central angle for this arc has measure one radian. 1 radian = $\frac{180}{\pi}$ degrees. (p. 399)

range The range of a function is the set of possible outputs for a function. It consists of all the values of the dependent variable, that is every number that y can represent for the function $f(x) = y$. (pp. 18, 199)

ratio The comparison of two quantities or expressions by division. (p. 83)

rational number A number that can be written as a fraction $\frac{a}{b}$ where a and b are integers and $b \neq 0$. (p. 453)

rational equation An equation that includes at least one rational expression. For example, $5 - \frac{x+2}{x} = 7$. (p. 347)

rational expression An expression in the form of a fraction in which the numerator and denominator are polynomials. For example, $\frac{x-7}{x^2+8x-9}$ is a rational expression.

rational function A function that contains at least one rational expression. For example, $f(x) = \frac{5}{x-3}$.

real numbers The set of all rational numbers and irrational numbers is referred to as the set of real numbers. Any real number can be represented by a point on a number line. (pp. 17, 199, 456)

rebound height The height a ball reaches after a bounce. (pp. 60, 64)

rebound ratio The ratio of the height a ball bounces after one bounce to the height from which it dropped. (pp. 60, 64)

reciprocal The multiplicative inverse of a number or an expression. (p. 682)

rectangular numbers The terms of the sequence 0, 2, 6, 12, 20, …. These numbers are called rectangular because they count the number of dots in rectangular arrays with the dimensions $n(n+1)$ where $n = 0, 1, 2, 3, 4, ...$

recursive definition For a sequence, a recursive definition is a rule that gives the first term and then tells us how to get the next term of the sequence from the term or terms that precede it. For example, in the Fibonacci sequence $1, 1, 2, 3, 5, 8, ...$, the next term is the sum of the previous two terms.

reference angle   For every angle of rotation in standard position, the reference angle is the angle in the first quadrant $0 \le \theta \le \frac{\pi}{2}$ whose cosine and sine have the same absolute values as the cosine and sine of the original angle. (p. 403)

reflect vertically   Used here to mean reflect a graph across the x-axis so that every point (x, y) on the original graph becomes $(x, -y)$ on the reflection. The graph of $y = -x^2$ is a vertical reflection of $y = x^2$. (p. 207)

relation   Functions are also relations, but relations are not necessarily functions. The equations for parabolas, ellipses, hyperbolas, and circles are all relations but only the equations that describe vertically oriented parabolas are functions. (pp. 6, 199)

relative maximum (minimum)   A function that has a "peak" (or "valley") at a point P is said to have a relative maximum (minimum) at the point P. This is the point where the function changes direction.

remainder   When dividing polynomials in one variable, the remainder is what is left after the constant term of the quotient has been determined. The degree of the remainder must be less than the degree of the divisor. In the example below the remainder is $3x - 3$.
$$(x^4 + 3x^3 - x^2 + x - 7) \div (x^2 + x + 1) = x^2 + 2x - 4 + \frac{3x-3}{x^2+x+1}.$$ (p. 472) Also see "quotient."

repeated root   A root of a polynomial that occurs more than once. The root r will occur as many times as $(x - r)$ is a factor of the polynomial. (p. 446) See "double root" and "triple root."

repetition   An important criterion to consider when counting outcomes of an event. Whether an outcome can be repeated determines the number of alternatives that would include that outcome. For example: If A, B, and C are letters written on cards, the number of arrangements possible will be $3 \cdot 2 \cdot 1$. But if you ask how many arrangements of A, B, and C could appear on a license plate, the answer will be $3 \cdot 3 \cdot 3$. Arrangements that involve repetition of a letter, such as AAA or CAC are counted when counting possible license plates. (pp. 523, 529)

reversing   To reverse your thinking can be described as "thinking backward." It sometimes means starting at the end of a problem and working backward to the beginning. It is useful to think this way when you want to undo a process or understand a concept from a new direction. Thinking about inverse functions involves reversing your thinking. Writing polynomials, given their zeros is another example. (pp. 263, 286)

rewrite   To rewrite an equation or expression is to write an equivalent equation or expression. Rewriting could involve using the Distributive Property, following the order of operations, using properties of 0 or 1, substitution, inverse operations, Properties of Logarithms, or use of trigonometric identities. We usually rewrite in order to change expressions or equations into more useful forms or sometimes, just simpler forms. (pp. 68, 97, 101, 144, 222, 244)

Algebra 2 Connections

right-multiply   Since multiplication of matrices is not commutative the product *AB* may not equal *BA*. If we want the product *BA* we can right-multiply matrix *B* by matrix *A* or we can left-multiply matrix *A* by matrix *B*. The order of the multiplication matters; therefore, we specify whether we are left-multiplying or right-multiplying. See "left-multiply." (p. 366)

right angle   An angle with measure 90°.

right triangle   A triangle with a right angle.

roots of a function   The number *r* is a root (or zero) of the function $f(x)$ if $f(r) = 0$. A root may be a real or a complex number. Real roots occur where the graph of the function $f(x)$ crosses the *x*-axis. Complex roots must be found algebraically. (pp. 144, 446, 447)

rule   An algebraic representation or a written description of a mathematical relationship. (pp. 123, 135)

sample space   With probability, all the possible outcomes. (pp. 501, 510)

secant   The reciprocal of the cosine. (p. 683)

sequence   A function in which the independent variable is a positive integer (sometimes called the "term number"). The dependent variable is the term value. A sequence is usually written as a list of numbers. For example, the arithmetic sequence 5, 8, 11, ... (pp. 69, 71, 83)

series   The sum of the terms of a sequence. (pp. 610, 618, 636)

sigma   The Greek letter Σ which is used to mean sum. Using Σ provides a way to write a short, compact mathematical representation for a series. (p. 626) See "summation notation."

similar   Two figures are similar if they have the same shape, but are not necessarily the same size. The ratios of the lengths of corresponding sides of similar figures are equivalent.

simple interest   Interest paid on the principal alone. (p. 125)

simplify   To rewrite an expression or equation as an equivalent expression or equation in a form that is considered to be simpler or less cumbersome than the original. (p. 133) See "rewrite."

sine   In a right triangle (as shown at right) the ratio $\frac{opposite\ side}{hypotenuse}$ is known as the sine of the acute angle. **At right,** $\sin B = \frac{b}{c}$ since the side length *b* is opposite angle *B*. (p. 407)

sine function   For any real number θ, the sine of θ, denoted $\sin \theta$, is the *y*-coordinate of the point on the unit circle reached by a rotation angle of θ radians in standard position. The general equation for the sine function is $y = a \sin b(x - h) + k$. This function has amplitude *a*, period $\frac{2\pi}{b}$, horizontal shift *h*, and vertical shift *k*. (pp. 383, 409, 423)

sine inverse ($\sin^{-1} x$)   Read as the inverse of sine x, $\sin^{-1} x$ is the measure of the angle with sine x. We can also write $y = \arcsin x$. Note that the notation refers to the inverse of the sine function, *not* $\frac{1}{\sin x}$. Because $y = \sin^{-1} x$ is equivalent to $x = \sin y$ and there are infinitely many angles y such that $\sin y = x$, the inverse *function* is restricted to select the *principal* value of y such that $-\frac{\pi}{2} \le y \le \frac{\pi}{2}$. The graph of the inverse function, $y = \sin^{-1} x$ with $\frac{\pi}{2} \le y \le \frac{\pi}{2}$ is at right. (p. 684)

sketch   To sketch the graph of an equation means to show the approximate shape of the graph in the correct location with respect to the axes with key points clearly labeled. (p. 8)

"sleeping" parabola   A "sleeping" parabola is a parabola which opens to the left or right, rather than upward or downward. These parabolas are not the graphs of functions. (p. 199)

slope   The ratio of the vertical change to the horizontal change between any two points on a line. For any two points (x_1, y_1) and (x_2, y_2) on a given line, the slope is $\frac{y_2 - y_1}{x_2 - x_1}$. For example, the slope of a line between points with coordinates $(3, -5)$ and $(-7, 2)$ is $\frac{2-(-5)}{-7-3} = -\frac{7}{10}$. (pp. 11, 200)

slope-intercept form   A linear equation written in the form $y = mx + b$ is written in slope-intercept form. In this form, m is the slope of the line and the point $(0, b)$ is the y-intercept. (p. 11)

solution   Of an equation or inequality is a number or expression that makes the equation or inequality true when substituted for the variable. To find the numerical solution means to identify all the numbers that make a mathematical equation or inequality true. There may be any number of solutions for an equation or inequality, from 0 to infinitely many. Solutions to equations and inequalities in one variable are single numbers. For two variables they are ordered pairs, for three variables ordered triples. Equations with no solutions, such as $|x - 5| = -3$, are never true. Equations with one, several, or many solutions, such as $x(x + 3)(x - 7) = 0$ are sometimes true, and equations or identities such as $5(2x - 4) = 10x - 20$ are always true. (pp. 224, 225, 226, 229, 250, 443, 447)

standard form (linear function)   A linear equation written in the form $Ax + By = C$ is written in standard form. For linear functions, $B \ne 0$. (p. 11)

standard form (quadratic function)   The standard form for the equation of a quadratic function is $y = ax^2 + bx + c$ where $a \ne 0$. (p. 177)

standard form (quadratic relations in general)   The standard for parabolas, ellipses, and hyperbolas with axes parallel to the x- or y-axes is $Ax^2 + By^2 + Cx + Dy + E = 0$. (p. 593)

standard window   The graphing window on a calculator set to show the x- and y-axes for values $-10 \le x \le 10$ and $-10 \le y \le 10$.

stretch factor   Used to describe the effect of a in the graphing form of a quadratic, cubic, absolute value, or exponential function. For $a > 1$ or $a < -1$ the outputs increase or decrease faster than the outputs for the parent functions, and the graphs are described as being stretched upwards or downwards in relation to the parent graph. (pp. 170, 175)

subproblems   A large problem can sometimes be separated into smaller or simpler problems called "subproblems" so that the solution of these subproblems leads to the solution of the larger problem. (p. 529)

substitution   Replacing a variable or expression with a number, another variable, or another expression. For example, when evaluating the function $f(x) = 5x - 1$, for $x = 3$, substitute 3 for x to get $f(3) = 5(3) - 1 = 14$. (p. 56)

substitution to solve a system of equations   A method for solving a system of equations by replacing one variable with an expression involving the remaining variable(s). (p. 56)

summation notation   A convenient way to represent a series is to use summation notation. The Greek letter sigma, Σ, indicates a sum. For example, $\sum\limits^{4} 3n = 3(1) + 3(2) + 3(3) + 3(4) = 30$.

The numbers below and above the sigma are called the indices. The index below, $n = 1$, tells us what value to start with for n. The top index tells us how high the value can go. In the example shown above, n starts at 1 and increases to 4. (pp. 626, 627)

surface area   The sum of all the areas of the surfaces of a three-dimensional figure or object.

symmetry   A figure that appears not to change when reflected across a line is said to have reflection symmetry. A figure that appears not to change when rotated through an angle of less than 360° is described as having rotation symmetry. (p. 167)

system of equations   A system of equations is a set of equations with more than one unknown or variable. The systems we solve most often in this course have two or three equations and two or three variables. Systems of equations are often solved using substitution or elimination to reduce the number of variables. A system of quadratic equations is shown at right. (pp. 17, 223, 224, 229, 232, 250)

$$y = x^2 + 8x - 4$$
$$y = 2x^2 + 5x - 8$$

tangent   In a right triangle (at right) the ratio $\frac{opposite\ side}{adjacent\ side}$ is known as the tangent of an acute angle. At right, $\tan B = \frac{b}{a}$ since the side of length b is opposite angle B and the side length a is adjacent to (or next to) angle B. The function $f(\theta) = \tan(\theta) = \frac{y}{x}$ where (x, y) are the coordinates of the point on the unit circle where the radius makes an angle of θ with the positive horizontal axis. (pp. 405, 407)

tangent function   For any real number θ, the tangent of θ, denoted $\tan\theta$, is the slope of the line containing the ray which represents a rotation of θ radians in standard position. The general equation for the tangent function is $y = a\tan b(x - h) + k$. This function has period of $\frac{\pi}{b}$, vertical asymptotes at $\frac{\pi}{2b} + h \pm \frac{n\pi}{b}$ for $n = 1, 2, \ldots$, horizontal shift h, and vertical shift k. (p. 405)

tangent inverse ($\tan^{-1} x$)   Read as the inverse of tangent x, $\tan^{-1} x$ is the measure of the angle that has tangent x. We can also write $y = \arctan x$. Note that the notation refers to the inverse of the tangent function, *not* $\frac{1}{\tan x}$. Because $y = \tan^{-1} x$ is equivalent to $x = \tan y$ and there are infinitely many angles y such that $\tan y = x$, the inverse *function* is restricted to select the *principal* value of y such that $\frac{\pi}{2} < x < \frac{\pi}{2}$. The graph of the inverse tangent function is at right. (p. 679)

term   A single number, variable, or product of numbers and variables. A monomial is a term. Also a component of a sequence. (p. 75)

term number   In a sequence, a number that gives the position of a term in the sequence. A replacement value for the independent variable in a function that determines the sequence. See "sequences." (p. 92)

terminal ray   When an angle of rotation is drawn in standard position, the positive x-axis is called the initial ray and the ray that determines the angle is called the terminal ray. (p. 407) See "angle."

theoretical probability   A probability calculation based on counting possible outcomes. (p. 540)

transverse axis   In a hyperbola, the line connecting the vertices of the two branches. (p. 585) See "hyperbola."

tree diagram (or model)   Tree diagrams are useful for representing possible outcomes of probability experiments. For example, the tree diagram at right represents the possible outcomes when a coin is flipped twice. (pp. 497, 502)

triangular numbers   The terms of the sequence 0, 1, 3, 6, 10, ... are known as the triangular numbers. These numbers are called triangular because they count the number of points in a sequence of triangular patterns. Each number also represents the sum of the first n integers ($n \geq 0$).

trigonometric ratios   (p. 28) See "sine," "cosine," "tangent," "secant," "cosecant," and "cotangent."

triple root   A root of a function that occurs exactly three times. If an expression of the form $(x-a)^3$ is a factor of a polynomial, then the polynomial has a triple root at $x = a$. The graph of the polynomial has an inflection point at $x = a$. (p. 446)

undoing   Using inverse operations and reversing the order of operations to solve an equation in one variable or to "undo" a function rule in order to write its inverse. For example, in the equation $y = x^3 - 7$, add y and write the cube root. (pp. 222, 263, 264)

unit circle   A circle with a radius of one unit is called a unit circle. (pp. 390, 402)

variable   A symbol used to represent one or more numbers. In this course, letters of the English alphabet are used as variables in addition to the Greek letters, θ, α, and β. (p. 38)

vertex   For a parabola that is a function, the vertex of a parabola is the lowest or highest point of the graph of the parabola. The vertex of a parabola locates its position with respect to the axes. It is the lowest or highest point of the graph of the parabola. In general, the vertex is the turning point for a graph. (p. 168) See "parabola," "ellipse," "hyperbola," "absolute value," for other graphs with vertices (the plural of vertex).

vertices

vertex form   The vertex form for the equation of a quadratic function (also called graphing form) is written $y = a(x-h)^2 + k$. (p. 177)

vertical shift   Used to describe the location of a graph in relation to its parent graph, the shift is the vertical distance (up or down) of each point on the graph from the corresponding point on the parent graph. For example, each point on the graph of $y = x^2 + 2$ is two units higher that its corresponding point on $y = x^2$. In a general equation such as $y = a(x-h)^2 + k$ the vertical shift is represented by k. (p. 175)

volume   For a 3-dimensional figure the number of non-overlapping cubic units that will fit inside. (p. 25)

x-intercept   A point where a graph intersects the x-axis. In two dimensions, the coordinates of the x-intercept are $(x, 0)$. In three dimensions they are $(x, 0, 0)$. (pp. 11, 446, 447) See "intercept."

x-y interchange   The result of exchanging the x and y variables and then solving for y. The resulting equation is the inverse of the original function. (pp. 276, 283)

x → y table   A table that represents pairs of related values. The input value x appears in the first row or column, and the output value, y, appears in the second. The $x \to y$ table at right contains input and output pairs for the equation $y = x^2 - 3$. (p. 8)

x	y
−3	6
−2	1
−1	−2
0	−3
1	−2
2	1

y-intercept   A point where a graph intersects the y-axis. In two dimensions the coordinates of the y-intercept are $(0, y)$. In three dimensions, the coordinates are $(0, y, 0)$. (p. 11) See "intercept."

zero factorial   Zero factorial is 1, $0! = 1$. (pp. 522, 526, 543)

zero power   The result of raising any number (except zero) to the zero power is 1. $x^0 = 1$ for any number $x \neq 0$. (pp. 132, 148)

Zero Product Property   When the product of two or more factors is zero, at least one of the factors must equal zero. Used to solve equations in factored form. For example, given the equation $(x-4)(x+5)=0$ you can see that 4 and -5 are solutions and that they are the only possible solutions because there are no other numbers that make either factor zero. (p. 23)

zeros of a function   The roots of a function or the values of x for which the function value $y = 0$. The x-intercepts of the graph of a function in the real plane are zeros. These are also called the roots of the function. A function can have complex zeros. These complex zeros cause $y = 0$, but they are not x-intercepts since they do not exist in the real plane. (p. 447) See "roots of a function."

Index
Student Version and Additional Resources

Many of the pages referenced here contain a definition or an example of the topic listed, often within the body of a Math Notes box. Others contain problems that develop or demonstrate the topic. It may be necessary to read the text on several pages to fully understand the topic. Also, some problems listed here are good examples of the topic and may not offer any explanation. The page numbers below reflect the pages in the Student Version. References to Math Notes boxes are bolded.

PG indicates page numbers from the Parent Guide with Extra Practice.

SSD indicates a web-based resource available at: www.cpm.org/teachers/state_stds_supplements.htm.

An electronic copy of the Parent Guide with Extra Practice is also available for free download at: www.cpm.org/teachers/resources.htm.

Since the time of this printing, additional recourses may have been added. Please check the websites above for the most complete list.

Graphing form (of a quadratic), 176, **177**, 736; PG 46
Growth factor, **11**

H

Half-life, 131; PG 30
Horizontal asymptote, **118**; PG 7
Horizontal compression, 175; PG 44
Horizontal shift, 175; PG 44
Hyperbola, 579, 583; PG 6
    conjugate axis, **585**
    eccentricity, **585**
    foci, **585**
    general equation, **585**
    transverse axis, **585**
    vertices, **585**

I

Identity matrix
    additive, 362
    multiplicative, 362; PG 100
Imaginary
    numbers, 453, **454**, **456**; PG 128
    graphing, 466
    roots, 458; PG 129
Independent events, 506, **516**
Independent variable, **6**, 13, **199**
Index, 626, **627**; PG 160
Induction, 629, **632**; PG 163
    proof by, 629; PG 163
Inequalities
    absolute value, 236, 237, **243**, 742
    graphing, 235, 236, **247**, 732; PG 67
    linear, 236, 247; PG 68
    system, 237
    solving, 235; PG 67
Inequality notation, 18; PG 68
Infinite geometric series
    sum, **647**; PG 167
Infinity, 17
Initial term, **92**
Initial value, 69, **86**; PG 15
Input, **6**; PG 1
Integral root, 475; PG 134
Integral Zero Theorem, **478**; PG 134

Intercepts
    average of, 176, 177; PG 53
    x-intercept, 11, 720; PG 3
    y-intercept, 11, 720; PG 3
Interest
    compound, 125; PG 29
    simple, 125
Intersection, 17, 21, 222, 223, 224; PG 3, 61
Inverse, 267, **269**, 272, **276**, 744; PG 77, 78
    absolute value, 279
    additive, 352
    cosine, 675, 679; PG 173
    equation, 272, 443, 744; PG 77
    exponential, 282; PG 81
    exponential function, 277, 278, 281; PG 81
    function, 268, 744; PG 77
    graphing, 267, 268, **269**, **276**, 744; PG 78
    notation, **269**, **276**; PG 77
    relations, 268
    sine, 678; PG 174
    tangent, 679; PG 174
    trigonometric functions, **684**; PG 173
    variation, SSD
Inverse cosine
    graph, **684**; PG 173
Inverse function, 272; PG 77
Inverse sine
    graph, **684**; PG 174
Inverse tangent
    graph, **684**; PG 174
Investigating, 2, 47
Investigating a function
    introduction, 32, 34; PG 6
Irrational numbers, **453**

J

Joint variation, SSD

L

Law of Cosines, **28**, **276**
Law of Sines, **28**, **276**
Laws of exponents, 132, **148**,713, 730; PG 31
Learning log, 18
Left multiply, **366**
Line, forms
    of symmetry, 167
    parent equation of, 190
    point-slope, 190; PG 13
    slope-intercept, **11**, 704; PG 3
    standard, **11**
Line of symmetry, 265, 268
Linear equation, **11**, 704; PG 3
Linear function, 38
    sequence, 77
Linear inequalities, 247
    graphing, 326, 732; PG 69
Linear programming, 241, 245; PG 69
List, systematic, **502**
Locator point, 181; PG 44
Locus, 566
    definition, 566
Logarithm, 282, **283**; PG 81
    base, **283**; PG 81
    base 10, 288, 329; PG 82
    definition, **335**; PG 81
    general equation, 289
    graphing, 281, 285, 286; PG 81
    introduction, 278; PG 81
    inverse relationship, **335**; PG 81
    notation, **283**; PG 81
    power property, 335; PG 93
    power rule, 330; PG 93
    product property, 334, **335**; PG 94
    quotient property, 334, **335**; PG 94
    solving equations, 329; PG 93
Logarithmic form, 283; PG 81
Looking inside, 222

M

Major axis, 574, **576**
Mathematical induction, 629, **632**; PG 163
Mathematical model
    cubic
        Game Tank Lab, 484
    exponential
        The Bouncing Ball Lab, 60, 64
        Fast Cars Lab, 151
        The Penny Lab, 130
    linear programming
        The Toy Factory Lab, 241
    logarithm
        Case of the Cooling Corpse, 342
    parabola, 179
    probability
        Casino Dice Game, 538
        The Candy Dish Investigation, 537
    trigonometric
        Pendulum Experiment, 379
Matrix, **351**; PG 98
    column, 348, **351**; PG 98
    dimensions, **351**; PG 98
    entry, **351**; PG 98
    introduction, 348; PG 98
    left inverse, **366**
    left-multiply, **366**
    multiplication, 349, **351**, 354, **356**; PG 98
    multiplicative inverse, 364, **366**; PG 100
    right inverse, **366**
    right-multiply, **366**
    row, 348, **351**; PG 98
    zero, 352
Matrix equation, 362, 364, 747; PG 100
Maximize, 242, 246; PG 69
Mean, 94; SSD: Measures of Central Tendency
Measures of Central Tendency, SSD
Median, 94; SSD: Measures of Central Tendency